PROGRESS IN
Nucleic Acid Research and Molecular Biology
Volume 38

PROGRESS IN
Nucleic Acid Research and Molecular Biology

edited by

WALDO E. COHN

Biology Division
Oak Ridge National Laboratory
Oak Ridge, Tennessee

KIVIE MOLDAVE

University of California
Santa Cruz, California

Volume 38

ACADEMIC PRESS, INC.

Harcourt Brace Jovanovich, Publishers

San Diego   New York   Berkeley   Boston
London   Sydney   Tokyo   Toronto

ACADEMIC PRESS, INC.
San Diego, California 92101

United Kingdom Edition published by
ACADEMIC PRESS LIMITED
24-28 Oval Road, London NW1 7DX

LIBRARY OF CONGRESS CATALOG CARD NUMBER: 63-15847

ISBN   0-12-540038-1   (alk. paper)

PRINTED IN THE UNITED STATES OF AMERICA
90 91 92 93   9 8 7 6 5 4 3 2 1

Contents

Control of Prokaryotic Translational Initiation by mRNA Secondary Structure

Maarten H. de Smit and Jan van Duin

Molecular Genetics of Na,K-ATPase

Jerry B. Lingrel, John Orlowski, Marcia M. Shull and Elmer M. Price

Retroviral-Mediated Gene Transfer

Jeanne R. McLachlin, Kenneth Cornetta, Martin A. Eglitis and W. French Anderson

Structure–Function Relationships in *Escherichia coli* Promoter DNA

Marshall S. Z. Horwitz and Lawrence A. Loeb

Gene Expression in Seed Development and Germination

J. Derek Bewley and Abraham Marcus

Transcriptional and Translational Regulation of Gene Expression in the General Control of Amino-Acid Biosynthesis in *Saccharomyces cerevisiae*

Alan G. Hinnebusch

Mechanisms Regulating Transient Expression of Mammalian Cytokine Genes and Cellular Oncogenes

Raymond Reeves and Nancy S. Magnuson

Abbreviations and Symbols

All contributors to this Series are asked to use the terminology (abbreviations and symbols) recommended by the IUPAC-IUB Commission on Biochemical Nomenclature (CBN) and approved by IUPAC and IUB, and the Editors endeavor to assure conformity. These Recommendations have been published in many journals (1, 2) and compendia (3) and are available in reprint form from the Office of Biochemical Nomenclature (OBN); they are therefore considered to be generally known. Those used in nucleic acid work, originally set out in section 5 of the first Recommendations (1) and subsequently revised and expanded (2, 3), are given in condensed form in the frontmatter of Volumes 9–33 of this series. A recent expansion of the one-letter system (5) follows.

SINGLE-LETTER CODE RECOMMENDATIONS[a] (5)

Symbol	Meaning	Origin of symbol
G	G	Guanosine
A	A	Adenosine
T(U)	T(U)	(ribo)Thymidine (Uridine)
C	C	Cytidine
R	G or A	puRine
Y	T(U) or C	pYrimidine
M	A or C	aMino
K	G or T(U)	Keto
S	G or C	Strong interaction (3 H-bonds)
W[b]	A or T(U)	Weak interaction (2 H-bonds)
H	A or C or T(U)	not G; H follows G in the alphabet
B	G or T(U) or C	not A; B follows A
V	G or C or A	not T (not U); V follows U
D[c]	G or A or T(U)	not C; D follows C
N	G or A or T(U) or C	aNy nucleoside (i.e., unspecified)
Q	Q	Queuosine (nucleoside of queuine)

[a]Modified from *Proc. Natl. Acad. Sci. U.S.A.* **83**, 4 (1986).
[b]W has been used for wyosine, the nucleoside of "base Y" (wye).
[c]D has been used for dihydrouridine (hU or H_2 Urd).

Enzymes

In naming enzymes, the 1984 recommendations of the IUB Commission on Biochemical Nomenclature (4) are followed as far as possible. At first mention, each enzyme is described *either* by its systematic name *or* by the equation for the reaction catalyzed *or* by the recommended trivial name, followed by its EC number in parentheses. Thereafter, a trivial name may be used. Enzyme names are not to be abbreviated except when the substrate has an approved abbreviation (e.g., ATPase, but not LDH, is acceptable).

REFERENCES

1. JBC **241**, 527 (1966); *Bchem* **5**, 1445 (1966); *BJ* **101**, 1 (1966); *ABB* **115**, 1 (1966), **129**, 1 (1969); and elsewhere.† General.

2. EJB **15**, 203 (1970); *JBC* **245**, 5171 (1970); *JMB* **55**, 299 (1971); and elsewhere.†

3. "Handbook of Biochemistry" (G. Fasman, ed.), 3rd ed. Chemical Rubber Co., Cleveland, Ohio, 1970, 1975, Nucleic Acids, Vols. I and II, pp. 3–59. Nucleic acids.

4. "Enzyme Nomenclature" [Recommendations (1984) of the Nomenclature Committee of the IUB]. Academic Press, New York, 1984.

5. EJB **150**, 1 (1985). Nucleic Acids (One-letter system).†

Abbreviations of Journal Titles

Journals	*Abbreviations used*
Annu. Rev. Biochem.	ARB
Annu. Rev. Genet.	ARGen
Arch. Biochem. Biophys.	ABB
Biochem. Biophys. Res. Commun.	BBRC
Biochemistry	Bchem
Biochem. J.	BJ
Biochim. Biophys. Acta	BBA
Cold Spring Harbor	CSH
Cold Spring Harbor Lab	CSHLab
Cold Spring Harbor Symp. Quant. Biol.	CSHSQB
Eur. J. Biochem.	EJB
Fed. Proc.	FP
Hoppe-Seyler's Z. Physiol. Chem.	ZpChem
J. Amer. Chem. Soc.	JACS
J. Bacteriol.	J. Bact.
J. Biol. Chem.	JBC
J. Chem. Soc.	JCS
J. Mol. Biol.	JMB
J. Nat. Cancer Inst.	JNCI
Mol. Cell. Biol.	MCBiol
Mol. Cell. Biochem.	MCBchem
Mol. Gen. Genet.	MGG
Nature, New Biology	Nature NB
Nucleic Acid Research	NARes
Proc. Natl. Acad. Sci. U.S.A.	PNAS
Proc. Soc. Exp. Biol. Med.	PSEBM
Progr. Nucl. Acid. Res. Mol. Biol.	This Series

†Reprints available from the Office of Biochemical Nomenclature (W. E. Cohn, Director).

Some Articles Planned for Future Volumes

Protamine Genes and the Histone/Protamine Replacement Reaction
GORDON H. DIXON

RNA Polymerase Sigma Factor: Promoter Recognition and Control of Transcription
ALEX GOLDFARB, DAVID L. FOX AND SOHAIL MALIK

Damage to Chromatin DNA Structure from Ionizing Radiations, and the Radiation Sensitivities of Mammalian Cells
JOHN T. LETT

Enzymes of DNA Repair
STUART LINN

VA RNA and Translational Control in Adenovirus-infected Cells
MICHAEL B. MATHEWS

Genetic Analysis of Ribosomal RNA Synthesis and Function
EDWARD A. MORGAN

Mitochondrial Aminoacyl-tRNA Synthetases
ALEXANDER TZAGOLOFF

The Structure and Expressions of the Insulin-like Growth Factor II Gene
LYDIA VILLA-KOMAROFF AND KENNETH M. ROSEN

Eye Lens Genes and Proteins
HANS BLOEMENDAL AND WILFRIED W. DE JONG

Molecular Evolution of the Vacuolar H^+-ATPase
BARRY BOWMAN AND LINCOLN TAIZ

RNases, tRNA Nucleotidyltransferase and 3'-Processing of tRNA
MURRAY P. DEUTSCHER

Multicopy Single-stranded DNA
MASSAYORI INOUYE, BERT LAMPSON AND SUMIKO INOUYE

A Tale of Two Enzymes—Deoxycytidylate Deaminase and Thymidylate Synthetase
FRANK MALEY AND GLADYS F. MALEY

The Coordinate Control of Ribosome Formation in Yeast
RUDI J. PLANTA

Metabolic Biology and Regulatory Aspects of Glycogen Biosynthesis in Bacteria
JACK PREISS AND TONY ROMEO

DNA Loop Formation: Role in Gene Regulation and Implications for DNA Structure
M. THOMAS RECORD, JR. AND GREGORY BELLOMY

Control of Prokaryotic Translational Initiation by mRNA Secondary Structure

MAARTEN H. DE SMIT AND
JAN VAN DUIN

Department of Biochemistry
Leiden University
Leiden, The Netherlands

The recognition of translational initiation sites by prokaryotic ribosomes has been the subject of many investigations over the last two decades. Although the statistical analysis of hundreds of ribosome binding sites has not resulted in a true consensus sequence, several features functioning in the recognition process have been revealed.

The ribosome binding site, defined as the mRNA region protected against nuclease attack in an initiation complex, usually extends over about 35 nucleotides. The initiation codon is located at about two-thirds of this region and usually consists of an AUG or GUG triplet, but UUG and AUU are also used occasionally. Preceding the initiation codon, a short polypurine stretch can usually be found. This "Shine–Dalgarno" (SD)-sequence base-pairs with the 3' end of 16-S rRNA during initiation site selection. Statistical analyses have further revealed that the choice of nucleotide is biased throughout the binding site. Although some nucleotides may function directly in the site-selection process, we will present evidence that this bias results, at least partially, from the need to minimize the formation of second-

1

Progress in Nucleic Acid Research
and Molecular Biology, Vol. 38

ary structure. [For a general discussion of translational initiation, refer to recent reviews by Gold (1) and Stormo (2).]

Although the sequences and strengths of several hundreds of ribosome binding sites have been determined, it has not been possible to relate translational efficiency to nucleotide sequence. In this review, we present evidence that differences in the secondary structures of RNA are probably the main cause of this unpredictability. By the early 1970's, it appeared that denaturation of bacteriophage RNAs drastically yet reversibly affected the expression of the phage genes (3–5). In later reports, poor expression of cloned genes was often ascribed to base-pairing of the start codon, the SD-sequence, or both. Unfortunately, most of the structures proposed were based solely on theoretical predictions, and the relevance of the conclusions is therefore limited.

However, in recent years, a number of more detailed studies unequivocally established that stable secondary structures inhibit translational initiation. Our results, presented in this review, show that the efficiency of a ribosome binding site is reduced by one order of magnitude when the stability of its secondary structure is increased by 2.3 kcal/mol.

Several sophisticated mechanisms of translational regulation that function through reversible changes in inhibitory secondary structures have been elucidated and are discussed in this review.

I. mRNA Secondary Structure Reduces the Efficiency of Translational Initiation

A number of investigations have indicated that the efficiency of a ribosome binding site is related to the strength of its secondary structure. Hall *et al.* (6) described two mutations, 701 and 708, that reduce the translational efficiency of the *1amB* gene (6). This phenotype is readily explained by a stabilizing effect on a potential hairpin structure (Fig. 1). Genetic recombination of the two mutations into one construct, 701–708, supports this idea. The stability of the hairpin in the double mutant is close to that of the wild type, owing to the juxtaposition of the two mutations in the helix. The finding that the expression in 701–708 was almost restored to the wild-type level strongly indicated that the stability of the structure was indeed the main determinant of translational efficiency. Moreover, the difference observed in the expression of 701 and 708 correlated with the difference in stability. The formation of a G·C base-pair (701) caused a stronger repression of translation than did an U·A pair (708).

Optimizing the expression of the human IFN-γ gene* in *Escherichia coli*

---

* "The Interferon Genes" is the subject of a review by Charles Weissman and Hans Weber in Vol. 33 of this series [Eds.].

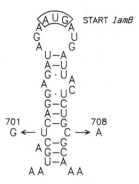

FIG. 1. *lamB* ribosome binding site. Mutations 701 and 708 are indicated. (Modified from 6.) In all figures, hyphens indicate Watson–Crick base-pairs; centered dots, other juxtaposed bases (e.g., U·G).

by changing nucleotides at three codon wobble-positions within the ribosome binding site gave similar results (7). Although not all effects could be explained, a strong relationship between the IFN-γ expression and the stability of a helical structure in the various mutants was observed.

A more elaborate analysis was performed by Buell *et al.* (8), who attempted to optimize the expression in *E. coli* of a synthetic gene, coding for the human growth factor, somatomedin C (SMC). Although all known elements of sequence and codon usage were optimal according to prevailing opinions, only a low level of expression was obtained. To test whether this was due to the formation of the hairpin shown in Fig. 2, the nucleotides at

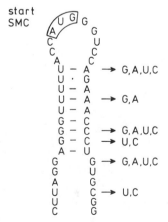

FIG. 2. Ribosome binding site of the synthetic SMC gene. Substitutions are indicated. (Redrawn from 8.)

the six indicated positions were varied. Several mutants with either increased or decreased expression were sequenced. In the ten mutants with increased expression analyzed (24 to 46 times wild type), the helix was found to be significantly destabilized [calculated $\Delta G°$ between -1.4 and $+4.8$ kcal/mol (9), relative to the wild type ($\Delta G°$ -5.6 kcal/mol)]. Conversely, in all four mutants showing decreased expression (6–8% of wild type), the helix was extended by two base-pairs, resulting in an increased stability ($\Delta G°$ -7.0 to -8.2 kcal/mol). In a similar system, expression of the rat interferon IFN-α_1 gene could be manipulated predictably by introducing mutations altering the stability of the local secondary structure (9a). These results demonstrate a relationship between structure and translational efficiency, as well as the impressive effects of a few nucleotide changes in a potentially inhibitory structure.

II. The Efficiency of a Ribosome Binding Site Is Linearly Proportional to the Fraction of Unfolded Molecules

We have recently investigated in a more quantitative manner the relation between the stability of the secondary structure of a ribosome binding site and its efficiency in translational initiation (M. H. de Smit and J. van Duin, unpublished). For several reasons, we chose the initiation region of the coat gene of RNA bacteriophage MS2 as a model system. First, chemical and enzymatic modification studies and phylogenetic sequence comparison had provided evidence that this ribosome binding site adopts the hairpin structure shown in Fig. 3 (9b). The presence of this hairpin enabled us to modulate the stability of the secondary structure by minimal changes in the nucleotide sequence. Second, the coat-gene ribosome binding site is very efficient. MS2 cDNA cloned behind the inducible P_L-promoter (from phage λ)

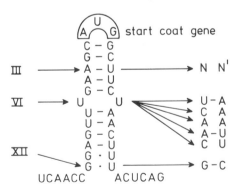

FIG. 3. Ribosome binding site of the MS2 coat gene. Mutated base-pairs are denoted by Roman numerals; substitutions are indicated (cf. Table I).

produces large amounts of coat protein upon induction. Third, antiserum against coat protein is available, allowing quantification of the expression by Western blotting over four orders of magnitude.

As a first exploration of the effects of alterations in the helix on coat-gene translation, mutations were introduced in base-pair III (Fig. 3). [All substitutions discussed in this section leave the SD-region as well as the amino-acid sequence intact.] Site-specific nutagenesis with a mixture of oligonucleotides yielded the 12 mutations shown in Table I as Nos. 2–13. Ten of these mutations destabilized the hairpin, and their effects on coat-protein production proved to be minimal. On the other hand, the two stabilizing mutations

TABLE I
MUTATIONS INTRODUCED IN THE MS2 COAT HAIRPIN

No.	Base-pairs[a]			Calculated $\Delta G°$ [b]	Expression (% of wild type)[c]
	III	VI	XII		
1	(A-U)	(U U)	(G·U)	−2.4	100
2	G G	—	—	+1.0	100
3	G A	—	—	+1.0	100
4	G·U	—	—	−1.8	100
5	G-C	—	—	−4.4	4
6	A A	—	—	+1.0	100
7	A C	—	—	+1.0	100
8	U·G	—	—	−2.0	100
9	U U	—	—	+1.0	100
10	U C	—	—	+1.0	100
11	C-G	—	—	−3.9	20
12	C U	—	—	+1.0	100
13	C C	—	—	+1.0	100
14	G-C	U-A	G-C	−10.7	<0.003
15	G-C	A A	G-C	−7.2	0.1
16	G-C	C A	G-C	−7.2	0.05
17	A C	U-A	G-C	−5.3	3
18	A C	A A	G-C	−1.8	80
19	A C	C A	G-C	−1.8	100
20	—	—	G-C	−5.2	6
21	—	C U	—	−2.4	100
22	—	A-U	—	−6.0	0.2
23	—	U-A	—	−5.9	0.3

[a]Base-pairs are numbered as in Fig. 3. Base-pairs in the wild-type structure (No. 1) are shown in parentheses. Hyphens indicate Watson–Crick base-pairs; centered dots indicate "wobble" base-pairs.

[b]$\Delta G°$ of the hairpin, calculated using the energy parameters of Freier et al. (9).

[c]Relative expression, determined by comparing dilution series of induced cultures on Western blots.

significantly decreased translation (Nos. 5 and 11). This cannot be attributed to the base substitutions per se, since the same substitutions occur separately in destabilized mutants, where they have no effect. Therefore, the most plausible conclusion is that strengthening the secondary structure indeed diminishes the efficiency of the ribosome binding site.

To obtain maximal stabilization, we constructed a mutant in which base-pairs III, VI, and XII were stabilized simultaneously (No. 14). Coat-protein synthesis in this mutant dropped below detection level, i.e., to less than 0.003% of the wild type. Apparently, the efficiently translated coat gene can be completely closed by a secondary structure of sufficient stability. Compensatory mutations confirmed that the stabilized structure was indeed responsible for the decreased expression. Starting from mutant No. 14, base-pair III was opened again by changing G·C to A·C* (No. 17). This mutation indeed partially restored coat-protein production. When in mutants No. 14 and 17 the U·A of base-pair VI was changed to A·A or C·A (Nos. 15, 16, 18, and 19), all four resulting constructs showed a further increase in expression. Low expression in Nos. 14 and 17 must be due to the increased stability rather than to sequence changes per se, since it could be restored by second site destabilizing mutations.

Finally, the effects of single base-pair substitutions at different positions in the helix were analyzed. The terminal G·U pair of the wild-type hairpin (base-pair XII) was changed into G·C (No. 20). The resulting drop in expression confirmed the participation of this base pair in the hairpin structure. The importance of the mismatch in the middle of the helix (base-pair VI) was investigated by changing it from U·U to C·U, A·U and U·A, respectively (Nos. 21–23). As expected, the change to C·U had no effect at all. In contrast, translation was virtually blocked by the A·U and U·A mutations. Apparently, the mismatch plays an important role in determining the stability of the helix and, consequently, the efficiency of coat-protein synthesis. Furthermore, the mutations in base-pairs VI and XII again demonstrate that it is not the *identity* of the bases at these positions that determines the strength of the ribosome binding site, but their *potential* to form base-pairs.

The stability of an RNA secondary structure is usually expressed as its free energy of formation ($\Delta G°$). Since the formation and disruption of helices are in a dynamic equilibrium, the $\Delta G°$ is a measure of the fraction of molecules present in the unfolded state. This is expressed in Eq. (1a):

$$\Delta G° = RT\ln K_c \qquad (1a)$$

---

* Centered dot indicates bases that are juxtaposed in the stem, not necessarily in Watson–Crick base-pairing.

Substitution of R (1.99 cal/mol K) and T (315 K) results in Eq. (1b):

$$\ln K_c = 1.60 \, \Delta G° \qquad (1b)$$

K_c is the equilibrium constant of the helix-coil transition; at low $\Delta G°$ (high stability) it equals the fraction of unfolded molecules. The $\Delta G°$ of the hairpin in each of our mutants can be calculated using the parameters of Freier *et al.* (9). In Fig. 4, the natural logarithm of coat gene expression ($\ln E$) is plotted as a function of this calculated $\Delta G°$, revealing a linear relationship in the high-stability region. Linear regression on the basis of eight points (excluding the ones with maximal expression, which form a plateau) yields the following equation:

$$\ln E = 1.7 \, \Delta G° + 9.7 \qquad (2)$$

The virtual identity of the coefficients of Eqs. (1b) and (2) (compare

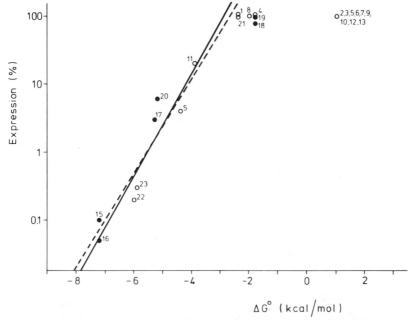

FIG. 4. Relationship between the stability of the coat initiator hairpin and coat protein production. Expression is plotted on a natural logarithmic scale. The solid line is based on linear regression of the lower eight points. The broken line indicates the slope of $1/RT$, expected on theoretical grounds (see text). Open circles indicate mutants with G·U as base-pair XII, filled circles mutants with G·C at this position. Mutant numbers correspond to Table I.

theoretical and measured slope in Fig. 4) constitutes strong evidence that the expression of the coat gene in our mutants is linearly proportional to the fraction of molecules in the open form.

This finding has several implications. First, initiating ribosomes do not recognize secondary structures. The earlier idea that an initiation codon in the loop of a hairpin is preferentially recognized is contradictory to our results. Second, stabilization by only 1.4 kcal/mol is sufficient to reduce the expression to a tenth, and this explains why effects of secondary structure are usually much larger than those of nucleotide sequence. We therefore suggest that the nucleotide bias in ribosome binding sites results mainly from a selective pressure against the formation of strong secondary structures. Third, the parameters used (9) give a reasonably accurate estimate of the $\Delta G°$ values of the various base-pair stacks *in vivo*.

Close examination of Fig. 4 reveals one possible discrepancy. It seems that the stability of all mutant hairpins with a terminal G·U base-pair (open circles in Fig. 4) is slightly underestimated relative to the ones with G·C at this position (closed circles). Maximal correlation can be achieved by attributing an extra −0.7 kcal/mol to the terminal G·U pair. Whereas the Freier rules provide −2.0 kcal/mol for the stacking of G·C onto C·A, no such contribution has been suggested for a terminal G·U pair. Presumably, the stacking of G·U onto C·A can provide most of the missing −0.7 kcal/mol. In addition, the stacking energy of two G·U pairs may be underestimated.

Figure 4 further shows that destabilization of the wild-type structure gives no significant increase in coat-protein synthesis. Theory predicts that expression approaches a plateau corresponding to full accessibility. The height of the plateau is set by a rate-limiting step inherent in the translational machinery (M. H. de Smit and J. van Duin, unpublished). It is intriguing, though, that the wild-type structure is on the verge of becoming inhibitory. Apparently, the evolution of this helix has resulted in the highest stability compatible with maximal expression.

It is conceivable that the stability of a helix is influenced by its natural context and thus differs from the calculated $\Delta G°$. Within a large RNA molecule, the equilibrium between the open and closed forms of a hairpin may be shifted through tertiary interactions such as pseudo-knots and coaxial stacking, or through intramolecular tensions. Such effects would result in a shift along the horizontal axis of Fig. 4, but they would not change the slope. In fact, there is evidence that the coat-gene initiator helix is destabilized by its natural environment in the phage RNA. Removing the 5' MS2 RNA context progressively reduces coat-gene expression (10) (Fig. 5). This reduction can be reversed by destabilizing mutations. For instance, introduction of mutation 6 (A·U to A·A; see Table I) in the construct with the largest deletion (Fig. 5) raised its expression from 3% to an almost wild-type level. These

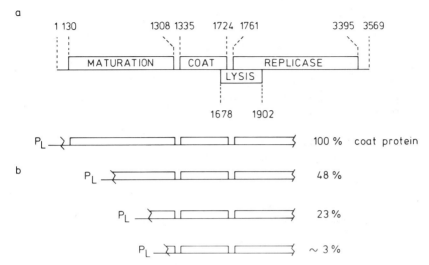

FIG. 5. (a) Genetic map of RNA bacteriophage MS2. (b) Effect of deletions upstream from the MS2 coat gene on coat protein production. Segments of MS2 cDNA starting at nucleotide numbers 103, 869, 1221, and 1305, respectively, were cloned behind the inducible P_L promoter of phage λ.

findings suggest that the natural RNA context has a destabilizing effect on the inhibitor hairpin (M. H. de Smit and J. van Duin, unpublished).

III. Natural Ribosome Binding Sites Have a Low Potential for Secondary Structure Formation

The inhibitory effect of secondary structure on translational initiation is reflected in the fact that natural ribosome binding sites generally display a lower potential than other parts of the messenger to form stable helices. An illustrative example is the transcript of the highly expressed *ompA* gene. Its proposed secondary structure consists of a row of 25 hairpins only interrupted by a single-stranded region 99 nucleotides long that includes the ribosome binding site (*13*). A structure with similar features has been proposed for the *1pp* messenger (*14*). Likewise, enzymatic structure mapping reveals that the 5' part of the *lacI* transcript is completely involved in secondary structure except for the first 50 nucleotides, which again include the ribosome binding site (*15*).

Statistical analysis has shown that the absence of stable helices in natural ribosome binding sites is not restricted to a few specific examples as mentioned above. Using a Tinoco-plot approach, Ganoza *et al.* (*16*) analyzed all possible foldings of a specified minimal length and stability in a set of 123 ribosome binding sites and compared these to an equivalent set of sequences surrounding internal noninitiator AUGs. They found a much higher base-pairing potential around the internal AUGs than around true initiator codons. In part, this difference is a consequence of the low (G+C)-content of ribosome binding sites. The strong preference for A residues at most positions (16a) only allows the formation of relatively weak structures. *In vitro* experiments have demonstrated that the (G+C)-content of the RNA is indeed a major determinant of the efficiency of ribosome binding. Binding of *Bacillus stearothermophilus* ribosomes to synthetic polyribonucleotides with increasing (G+C)-content showed at 37°C an optimum at 10% (G+C). When the temperature was raised to 65°C, the optimum shifted to 30% (G+C), strongly suggesting that the inefficiency of (G+C)-rich sequences at lower temperatures was due to the formation of random structures (17).

However, the increased base-pairing potential around internal AUGs (16) could not be attributed entirely to the base composition. Complementary sequences were found in most of the RNAs analyzed. One of the functions of the encoded hairpin structures is probably the shielding of internal pseudo-initiation sites. The presence of such potential ribosome binding sites in the coding region of natural messengers has been demonstrated in two ways. First, the denaturation of phage RNA by heat or formaldehyde activates at least three previously unrecognized (spurious) initiation sites (3). Secondly, termination at nonsense codons, introduced close to internal pseudo-initiation sites, usually results in reinitiation at these sites (15, 18).

IV. Secondary Structures Upstream of the Shine–Dalgarno Sequence

In an initiation complex the ribosome protects about 35 nucleotides against nuclease attack. This region extends from about 20 nucleotides upstream to about 15 nucleotides downstream from the initiation codon, and almost perfectly coincides with the biased sequence area. It is therefore assumed that this area, by definition the ribosome binding site, closely interacts with the initiating ribosome. However, additional contacts may exist beyond these boundaries (see Section VIII). Surprisingly, there is evidence that stable secondary structures within the ribosome binding site are not always incompatible with efficient initiation. The *rIIB* messenger of phage T4 forms a stable hairpin of five base-pairs, 14 nucleotides upstream from the initiation codon. By stepwise addition, Shinedling *et al.* (19) increased this stem to nine base-pairs with a calculated $\Delta G°$ of -12.7 kcal/mol (9), but found no effect on *rIIB* expression.

Based on these findings, a model for the 30-S ribosomal subunit was suggested, in which the mRNA binding tract forms a trough that allows mRNA helices to protrude into the solvent (1, 19). This model is compatible with the recognition of the structured ribosome binding site of T4 gene 38. This site forms a hairpin containing the strongly stabilizing CUUCGG motif in the loop (20), which brings the AUG and the SD-sequence together in a presumably better spacing (1) (Fig. 6). Furthermore, the model may provide an explanation for the skipping of a "translational intron" in T4 gene 60. There, translating ribosomes skip a part of the messenger, which forms a stable secondary structure and is apparently passed without being unfolded (20a).

The trough model is, however, not generally applicable. Expression of gene IX of bacteriophage f1, for example, is strongly reduced by a hairpin 16 nucleotides upstream from the AUG (21) (Fig. 9). Similarly, a hairpin 24 nucleotides upstream from the start codon of gene 0.3 of phage T7 is believed to prevent expression (22, 23); and in a recently proposed model for the autoregulation of the S10 operon, a small hairpin 19 nucleotides upstream from the AUG is also implicated as an inhibitory element (24) (Fig. 14b).

Finally, expression of the replicase gene of bacteriophage MS2 is shut off by a long-distance interaction, probably involving nucleotides −23 to −17 relative to the AUG (Fig. 11). It is possible that the spatial orientation of the structures, rather than their strength, inhibits the binding of ribosomes. The hairpins of gene IX and gene 0.3 are relatively long (much more than the 9 base-pairs introduced in rIIB), and the S10 hairpin and the replicase helix are both believed to be stabilized by coaxial stacking to other helices. Whatever the precise mechanism, there is no doubt that structures upstream from the SD-sequence can inhibit translational initiation. On the effects of helices downstream from the initiation codon, there are, to our knowledge, no data available.

V. Inducible Ribosome Binding Sites

In the last ten years, regulation of gene expression at the translational level has been found much more often than expected. The mechanisms of

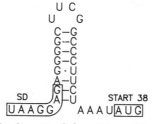

FIG. 6. Ribosome binding site of phage T4 gene 38. (Redrawn from 1.)

translational regulation can be divided into two main classes. In the first class, translational initiation is prevented directly by the binding of a repressor protein [discussed by Gold (1)]. We focus on the second class, which exploits mRNA secondary structures. In what we call "inducible ribosome binding sites," the formation or disruption of inhibitory secondary structures is coupled with the movement of ribosomes over upstream RNA regions. Activation of such translationally coupled genes can be brought about by terminating, elongating, or stalling ribosomes.

A. Activation by Terminating Ribosomes

The most extensively studied example of activation by terminating ribosomes comes from the RNA phages f2 and MS2. These phages contain a reading frame overlapping the coat and replicase genes (Fig. 5a) that encodes a small lysis peptide (25–27). Its expression is tightly coupled to coat-gene translation, deduced from the fact that deletion of the coat "start" as well as coat "ambers" abolish cell lysis (28, 29). The mechanism of coupling poses two main questions: First, why is the initiation site of the lysis gene not recognized in the absence of coat-gene translation, and second, how does translation of the coat gene activate the lysis start.

Since the lysis ribosome binding site of MS2 contains both an AUG codon and a reasonable SD-sequence, attention was focused on the possibility of an inhibitory secondary structure. Deletions introduced just upstream from the start codon, if traversing a certain point, caused lysis gene expression in the absence of upstream translation (uncoupled lysis) (28) (Fig. 7). Details of the inhibitory structure have been resolved by analysis of the RNA with structure-sensitive enzymes and chemical reagents and by phylogenetic sequence comparison with RNA bacteriophage M12 (31) (Fig. 7). The phenotypes of the above-mentioned deletion mutants are fully compatible with the deduced structure.

To assess that this helix indeed prevents ribosome binding, substitutions to alter its stability were introduced. The effects of these mutations, summarized in Fig. 8, were again measured in the absence of coat-gene translation. The only mutations that led to uncoupled lysis expression were those that destabilized the helix (d1, d2, and q1). Conversely, mutations that maintained or increased its stability (d3, d4, and t1) produced no lysis protein (31). These results, together with the observed quantitative relation between stability and expression in mutants d1 and q1, constitute strong evidence that access of ribosomes to the lysis gene is indeed prevented by this hairpin.

The second question concerns the mechanism by which coat-gene translation activates this start site. The activation is not triggered by elongating ribosomes traversing the initiation region but by termination at the coat "stop" codon. A mutation leading to termination 24 nucleotides further

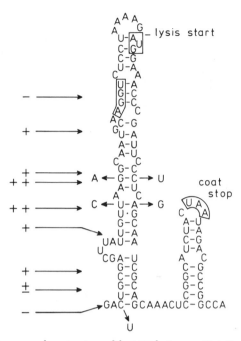

FIG. 7. Regulatory secondary structure of the MS2 lysis gene. Variations in the lysis hairpin of RNA phage M12 are indicated. Arrows mark the endpoints of deletions from the 5′ side. Phenotypes are indicated by plus (lysis) and minus (no lysis) signs.

downstream eliminates lysis activation (32). Moving the stop codon one triplet upstream or downstream has little effect on the lysis gene expression. In addition, destabilization of the lysis "hairpin" by the terminating ribosome seems essential for lysis activation, because mutants d4 and t1, containing a stabilized hairpin, produce no lysis protein even when coat-gene translation terminates at the natural site. Apparently, the destabilization of the helix in these mutants by the terminating ribosome is not sufficient to expose the lysis ribosome binding site (31). However, coupled expression in mutants d4 and t1 is restored by making the ribosomes terminate further upstream, at the indicated stop codons in the rising strand of the helix (33) (Fig. 8). Termination at these sites presumably results in disruption of the hairpin. Thus, the natural coupling mechanism only functions if the stability of the helix is kept within narrow limits. If it becomes too weak, uncoupled expression will occur, but should it get too strong, activation is prevented altogether. These limits are reflected in the nature of the base-pair substitutions in phage M12 (Fig. 7).

Based on these observations, two mechanisms for the activation can be

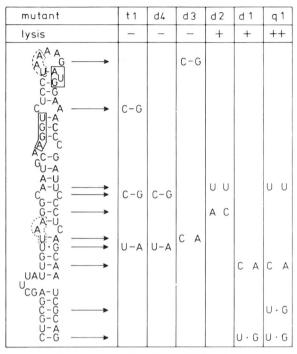

FIG. 8. Substitutions altering the stability of the MS2 lysis hairpin. Phenotypes are indicated by plus (uncoupled lysis) and minus (no lysis) signs. Dashed-line boxes mark two out-of-frame stop codons that were used to activate mutants t1 and d4 (see text).

envisaged. Ribosomes at the coat terminator may, by weakening the helix, expose the lysis start to vacant ribosomes. Alternatively, the terminated ribosome may remain bound to the messenger and reach the lysis start through lateral movement. These mechanisms, referred to as the two- and single-ribosome models, respectively, are now under investigation. Circumstantial evidence is in favor of the single-ribosome model. For instance, in the related RNA phage GA, the coat and lysis genes overlap by only one nucleotide, the gene boundary being UAAUG (34). Here, the involvement of two ribosomes can obviously be excluded. Furthermore, the lysis gene of RNA phage fr starts with a UUG codon that is not shielded by secondary structure. Instead, this UUG has an intrinsically poor activity in primary initiation. Its functionality in coupled expression again argues for the single-ribosome model (34a).

As a last argument we mention our finding that a functional ribosome binding site is silenced when made part of an actively translated sequence. In a construct in which the lysis ribosome binding site is exposed through a deletion in the hairpin and where the termination codon of the coat gene is removed, no lysis protein is produced (35). Expression reappears when an early coat amber is introduced, showing that elongating ribosomes interfere with the process of primary initiation. Therefore, this phenomenon seems to exclude a two-ribosome model for the activation of the lysis gene. Reinitiation by the same ribosome is probably a much faster process and therefore is less sensitive to interference by elongating ribosomes. It may be noted that a similar reinitiation event upstream from the termination codon has been observed in mammalian cells (36, 37).

The analysis of the structure involved in the MS2 lysis gene regulation has revealed some features that may have general validity (31). First, the results of the enzymatic and chemical structure mapping were virtually identical, whether obtained from complete phage RNA or from partial RNAs synthesized with T7 polymerase. Apparently, this specific secondary structure was maintained in various contexts. Furthermore, structure analysis of destabilized mutants revealed hardly any difference from the wild type. Small changes in stability, not apparent from structure probing with chemicals and enzymes, are thus sufficient to expose a ribosome binding site. Moreover, a mutant carrying 13 substitutions in the rising strand of the helix (not shown), which expressed the lysis gene independently, had its SD-sequence fully protected from RNase T1. The fact that protection of bases within the SD-sequence is not necessarily related to inefficient expression has also been pointed out by Rosa (38).

Of the many examples of translational coupling by reinitiation that have been discovered so far (39–43), only a few have been shown unambiguously to involve secondary structures. In the filamentous DNA phages (M13 and f1), nonsense mutations in gene VII are polar on expression of the downstream gene IX (44). The RNA just upstream of the SD-sequence of gene IX folds into the hairpin structure shown in the right part of Fig 9. Deletion of the left side of this helix (indicated in Fig. 9) raises *in vitro* ribosome binding to gene IX tenfold (21). Similar structures have been proposed to function in the coupling of genes 1.1 and 1.2 of phage T7 (Fig. 10a) (45) and in that of genes 44 and 62 of phage T4 (46) (Fig. 10b). These structures also await experimental confirmation.

Translational coupling via termination–reinitiation may not of necessity require the involvement of secondary structure. We have mentioned above that in phage fr it is the UUG initiation codon rather than its surrounding structure that inhibits primary initiation at the lysis gene. In bacteriophage f1, initiation at gene VII fully depends on translation of the upstream gene V. In contrast to what was found for gene IX (see above), this coupling is not based on the presence of an inhibitory structure. Deletions into the postulated hairpin (shown in the left part of Fig. 9) revealed that the ribosome

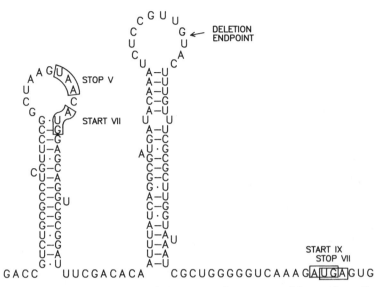

FIG. 9. mRNA section from phage fl, comprising the start sites of the translationally coupled genes VII and IX. The endpoint of a deletion from the 5' side, resulting in uncoupled IX expression is indicated. (Redrawn from 21.)

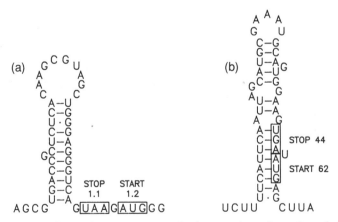

FIG. 10. Proposed secondary structures involved in translational coupling of phage T7 genes 1.1 and 1.2 (a) and phage T4 genes 44 and 62 (b). (Modified from 45 and 46, respectively.)

binding site of gene VII is intrinsically inactive in primary initiation (*44a*). Similarly, no inhibitory structure explaining the coupling of the genes coding for ribosomal proteins L11 and L1 could be found (*47*). Whether a basically different mechanism is operating here awaits further analysis.

B. Activation by Elongating Ribosomes

Translational coupling can also be achieved through base-pairing of the ribosome binding site of the downstream gene to an internal sequence of the upstream one. Elongating ribosomes temporarily disrupt such long-distance interactions and thus activate the hidden ribosome binding site. This mechanism operates in the translational coupling of the coat and replicase genes of the RNA phages, e.g., MS2 and Qβ. Regulation of the replicase genes of these phages is rather sophisticated. First, translation of the coat gene activates the initiation site of the replicase gene. As the concentration of coat protein in the cell rises, however, it binds to the replicase ribosome binding site and represses translation again. The repression by coat protein and the structural elements required for recognition have been the subject of extensive studies (*48*). Here, we focus on the activation of replicase expression by ribosome movement across the coat gene.

The coupling between the coat and replicase genes was deduced in the early days of RNA phage research from the fact that an amber mutation at position 6 of the coat gene is polar on replicase expression, but an amber at position 50 is not (*49*). This suggested that some region of the RNA between these two positions base-pairs with the ribosome binding site of the replicase gene. Support for this idea came from the finding that denaturation by heat or formaldehyde virtually abolishes the polar effect of the amber-6 mutation. A model for this long-distance interaction was proposed (*50*) and is shown in a partially revised form in Fig. 11. The hairpin that contains the ribosome binding site of the replicase gene is weak enough to allow efficient initiation (*51*). Interestingly, a mutation adding an extra A·U base-pair strongly reduces replicase synthesis (*25, 26*).

To assess the inhibitory effect of the putative long-distance interaction, deletions were introduced in the relevant coat-gene portion (Fig. 11). Clones where the start codon of the coat gene was deleted but where the long-distance interaction remained intact showed a low basal level of replicase synthesis (indicated by minus signs in Fig. 11). Removal of the long-distance interaction indeed raised this level tenfold (*52*). The interaction is possibly stabilized by coaxial stacking with the coat terminator hairpin, since replicase expression could be modulated through mutations altering the stability of this hairpin (J. van Duin and B. van Geffen, unpublished). When the long-distance interaction is removed, the effect of the coat terminator hair-

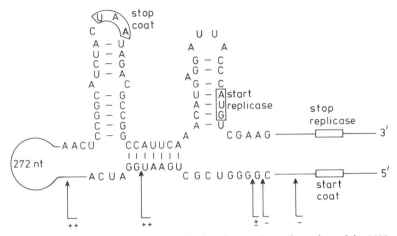

FIG. 11. Long-distance interaction involved in the translational coupling of the MS2 coat and replicase genes. Arrows mark the endpoints of deletions from the 5' side. Phenotypes are indicated by plus (uncoupled replicase expression) and minus (basal level) signs. (Modified from 50.)

pin on replicase expression is lost (51), excluding direct interference of this stem–loop structure with initiation at the replicase start.

Regulatory long-distance interactions are probably relatively rare, since generally the formation of local secondary structures is much more likely than base-pairing with the distant sequences. It has been suggested that translation of the *trp* leader is restricted to the first round through base-pairing of its ribosome binding site to a downstream region (53). Although nuclease sensitivity data are not inconsistent with this interaction (54), no detailed analysis of its function has yet appeared. One more example of a regulatory long-distance interaction is discussed in Section VII.

C. Activation by Stalling Ribosomes

1. Translational Attenuation in the Inducible *erm* Genes

The *erm* genes of Gram-positive bacteria code for methylases that act upon a specific adenosine residue in the 23-S rRNA. Dimethylation of this adenosine confers resistance on the ribosomes to the MLS (macrolide, lincosamide, streptogramin) antibiotics. Many *erm* genes are induced by specific antibiotics, and extensive analysis of the *ermC* gene of *Staphylococcus aureus* reveals that the induction involves changes in the mRNA secondary structure, caused by the antibiotic-dependent stalling of ribosomes in an open reading frame, present in the leader.

A first analysis of the expression of the plasmid-encoded *ermC* gene showed that induction by erythromycin occurs at a posttranscriptional level and involves erythromycin-sensitive ribosomes. When the *ermC* plasmid was transferred to a strain containing mutant ribosomes with a lowered affinity for erythromycin, the inducibility was virtually lost (55). The sequence of the *ermC* transcript, simultaneously determined by two groups (56, 57), provided a molecular explanation for this phenomenon. The *ermC* gene is preceded by a 140-nucleotide leader sequence containing an open reading frame coding for a peptide of 19 amino acids. Further, a number of complementary sequences are present, allowing several alternative secondary structures. Figure 12a shows one of the proposed structures with the complementary regions indicated as A and A' and 1–4. An alternative stable secondary structure consisting of helices 2·3, 1·4, and A·A' may also form (not shown). On the basis of these features, both groups proposed similar models for the induction by antibiotics, stating that, in the absence of antibiotics, the leader peptide is translated, but the ribosome binding site of the *ermC* gene remains closed by either helix 3·4 or helix 1·4 (56, 57). The addition of a sub-inhibitory concentration of erythromycin was suggested to stall ribosomes at a specific position within the leader. This would prevent formation of helix 1·2 or 1·4 and thus lead to the structure shown in Fig. 12c, where the ribosome binding site of the *ermC* gene is free for initiation. Because of its similarity to the attenuation of transcription in the *trp* operon, this mechanism was termed "translational attenuation" (57).

Patterns of sensitivity to structure-specific enzymes and chemical reagents are consistent with the proposed structures (58, 59). However, since the same sequences are base-paired in the structure of Fig. 12a and the previously mentioned alternative structure, this technique can not distinguish between these two possibilities. Helix A·A' is rather weak and may also be formed in Fig. 12a. An interesting finding was that deletion of sequence 1 led to an equilibrium between helices 2·3 and 3·4, consistent with its constitutive phenotype *in vivo*.

The function of the proposed structures in the regulation of *ermC* expression has been assessed in different ways. First, a number of available constitutive mutants were sequenced; three of these involved single point-mutations, as indicated in Fig. 12a (56). The mutation in sequence 1 acts through a destabilization of the 1·2 hairpin and thus favors the formation of helix 2·3, thereby activating *ermC* translation. The other two mutations destabilize the 3·4 hairpin and activate *ermC* in a more direct manner. Later, an extensive deletion analysis (60) fully confirmed the model (Fig. 12b).

Narayanan and Dubnau (59) demonstrated the inhibitory effect of the secondary structure of ribosome binding *in vitro*. Whereas the ribosome binding site of the leader was protected by ribosomes against nuclease attack, the *ermC* start was not. Translation of the leader peptide was visualized

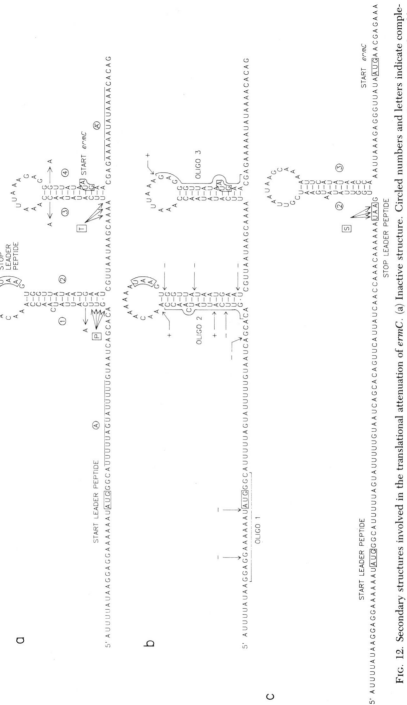

FIG. 12. Secondary structures involved in the translational attenuation of *ermC*. (a) Inactive structure. Circled numbers and letters indicate complementary regions. The three point-mutations resulting in constitutive *ermC* expression are indicated. T and P arrows mark nuclease cleavage sites induced by termination of translation at the leader stop codon (T) or by premature termination at a nonsense codon, introduced at position 2 (P). (b) Inactive structure. Arrows mark the endpoints of deletions from the 5′ side. Phenotypes are indicated by plus (constitutive *ermC* expression) or minus (basal level, noninducible) signs. Lines represent complementary oligonucleotides (see text). (c) Active structure induced by stalled ribosomes. Circled numbers

(58) through a fusion with the E. coli lacZ gene. The amino terminus of the hybrid β-galactosidase protein corresponded to the DNA sequence of the leader. In addition, a nonsense codon introduced at position 2 of the leader abolished induction of the ermC gene (61). Translation of the leader is thus essential for activation of the ermC ribosome binding site.

The translational attenuation model was further supported by the effects of three oligonucleotides on in vitro translation (Fig. 12b). Oligonucleotides 1 and 3, complementary to the ribosome binding sites of the leader and the ermC gene, respectively, both inhibited ermC expression. Conversely, oligonucleotide 2 induced ermC by mimicking the action of a stalled ribosome (62) (Fig. 12b). This in vitro system also provided an opportunity to investigate the effects of the ratio of resistant (methylated) to sensitive (unmethylated) ribosomes on induction. This is an important parameter, since sensitive ribosomes are needed for induction, but the translation of the ermC gene requires resistant ribosomes. Indeed, induction did not occur in the absence of sensitive ribosomes. On the other hand, a low fraction of resistant ribosomes proved to be essential for ermC translation, especially at higher erythromycin concentrations (62). This is provided for in vivo by a low basal level of ermC expression (60).

Finally, the in vitro system allowed the direct demonstration of ribosomes stalled in the leader. The inherent RNase activity of the S-30 extract was used to mark the position of the ribosomes (63). Translation of the leader in the absence of antibiotics induced cleavage 28 to 30 nucleotides downstream from the termination codon of the leader, as indicated in Fig. 12a. The introduction of an amber codon at position 2 of the leader induced cleavage 27 to 29 nucleotides downstream from this UAA. Unlike the authors (63), we conclude that these cleavage sites are determined by the position of termination. This is not unlikely, since termination is a time-consuming process.

When translation was performed in the presence of erythromycin or oleandomycin (both inducers), cleavage was observed around the leader termination codon (Fig. 12c). In analogy to the cleavages elicited by termination, we interpret these findings as an indication that ribosomes are stalled some 28 nucleotides upstream from this region, i.e., around the 10th codon. This interpretation agrees with the observation that erythromycin inhibits transpeptidation only after the nascent peptide has reached a minimal length (57). During the preparation of this review, we learned that mutational analysis indeed shows leader amino-acids 5 through 9 to be critical for induction, although the relation between the nature of these amino-acids and the mode of action of erythromycin is not yet understood (63a). Furthermore, in vivo footprinting has revealed that erythromycin causes specific protection by stalled ribosomes of codons 8 through 10 against dimethylsulfate

(B. Weisblum, personal communication). The effects of several noninducing antibiotics on the cleavage pattern *in vitro* demonstrate the crucial role of the stalling position. Whereas some antibiotics produced the same cleavage pattern as observed in their absence, others appeared to cause stalling in earlier parts of the leader (*63*). These findings explain the high antibiotic specificity of induction.

A somewhat paradoxical aspect of the model of *ermC* induction is the location of hairpin 2·3 in the active conformation (Fig. 12c). Since it lies only 18 nucleotides upstream from the AUG codon, it could conceivably interfere with translational initiation. The situation is reminiscent of the expression of the phage T4 gene *rIIB*, in which initiating ribosomes ignore an engineered hairpin of nine base-pairs, located 14 nucleotides upstream from the initiation codon (*19*).

A number of other inducible *erm* genes have been sequenced. Their leaders have a small open reading frame and contain complementary regions suggestive of translational attenuation. The leaders of *ermA* and *ermG* are highly homologous to *ermC*, but contain an open reading frame coding for a second leader peptide (*64, 65*). Three other genes, *ermAM*, *ermD*, and *ermSF* show no homology in the leader and seem to form more complex secondary structures (*66–68*). Constitutive *erm* genes have also been isolated and they completely lack the regulatory region (*69–71*).

2. INDUCTION OF *cat* EXPRESSION BY CHLORAMPHENICOL

cat genes, coding for chloramphenicol acetyltransferase, which confers resistance to the antibiotic chloramphenicol, are found in many different bacterial species. Whereas in Gram-negative bacteria, their expression is always constitutive, the *cat* genes of Gram-positive bacteria are induced by sub-inhibitory concentrations of chloramphenicol. Analysis of a number of these inducible *cat* genes has revealed a mechanism of induction that displays similarities to the translational attenuation of the *erm* genes.

Figure 13 shows that the mRNAs of at least five of the six inducible *cat* genes analyzed so far (pC194 is discussed later) form a hairpin structure that includes part of the *cat* ribosome binding site. Furthermore, a short reading frame is present, partially overlapping the helix. Together with the fact that induction of the *cat* genes by chloramphenicol takes place at a posttranscriptional level (*72, 73*), these features suggested the following mechanism of induction (*74*). In the absence of antibiotics, the leader sequence is translated, but this results only in a low basal level of *cat* translation, caused by transient unfolding of the hairpin. When chloramphenicol is added, however, ribosomes are stalled at a specific position in the leader and, by disrupting the hairpin, they induce *cat* expression.

For the *cat* gene encoded on the *Staphylococcus aureus* plasmid pUB112,

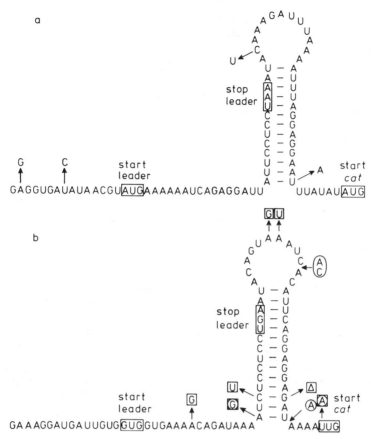

FIG. 13. Secondary structures involved in chloramphenicol induction of several *cat* genes. (a) *cat* gene of pUB112. Variations in the related *cat* gene of pC221 are indicated. (b) *cat*-86. Circled and boxed letters indicate variations in the related genes *cat*-66 and *cat*-57, respectively. (Sequences from 72.)

the involvement of the leader sequence in induction was established by deletion analysis (74). When the start of the leader is deleted, *cat* gene expression drops below detection level. Larger deletions removing part of the hairpin cause a high, constitutive synthesis of Cat protein, as expected from the model. Translation of the leader *in vivo* was subsequently demonstrated by the use of a leader–*lacZ* fusion construct (75). Introduction of a nonsense codon at the second position of the leader sequence abolishes *cat* expression (75).

Much effort has been invested to clarify the detailed induction mechanism of *cat-86*, originally isolated as a chromosomal *cat* gene of *Bacillus pumilus* (72). In a highly refined analysis, Alexieva *et al.* (76) have mimicked the chloramphenicol-induced ribosomal stalling by starvation for specific amino acids encoded in the nine codons long-leader sequence. Starvation-induced stalling at codons 3, 4, 5, 7, and 8 barely increased *cat* expression. Starvation for amino acid 6, on the other hand, activated *cat* translation about seven-fold. Similar results were obtained by replacing the relevant leader codons by nonsense codons. Again, *cat* expression was exclusively induced by termination at position 6 but, interestingly, could still be doubled by the addition of chloramphenicol.

It is surprising that the ribosomes must stall this close to the inhibitory structure to elicit activation. Since ribosomes are thought to unfold at least ten nucleotides downstream from the P-site, pausing at position 5 would presumably disrupt the lower part of the helix. Apparently, this is not sufficient to induce *cat* expression. The fact that ribosomes that are stalled downstream from position 6 do not induce *cat-86* expression, in spite of a complete disruption of the hairpin, is thought to be due to interference of the stalled ribosome itself with the entry of a second ribosome (76).

The induction mechanism of *cat-86* is slightly more complicated than that of the other illustrated *cat* genes, in that this gene is preceded by two consecutive open reading frames (not shown). Deletion studies (77) reveal that the upstream leader hardly affects the induction by chloramphenicol, but is virtually indispensible for induction by a different class of antibiotics, the amicitin family. Not surprisingly, the two related genes *cat-57* and *cat-66* (Fig. 13b), which lack the second (upstream) leader, are only marginally inducible by amicitin. The precise mechanism of such a two-leader system is as yet unknown.

The fact that the *cat* messenger of the S. *aureus* plasmid pC194 can form a similar hairpin structure (not shown) would seem to indicate an identical mechanism of induction. This, however, is contradicted by evidence that transcription of this *cat* gene initiates (at least with RNA polymerase from *E. coli*) at what would be the third codon of the leader (78). Based on these findings, a model was proposed in which the 23-S rRNA of a 50-S subunit base-pairs with a complementary sequence in the leader RNA and thereby disrupts the inhibitory hairpin (79). However, this model was not supported by experimental evidence and it is not yet clear how induction of the pC194 *cat* gene is achieved.

The basic difference between the induction mechanisms of the *erm* and *cat* genes is reflected in the origins of basal expression in both systems. Uninduced synthesis of Cat protein results from translation of the leader, and is presumably caused by temporary disruption of the structure by elongating ribosomes (76). On the other hand, inhibition of translation of the *ermC* leader does not influence the basal expression of this gene (61). Here, ribosomes translating the leader do not reach the inhibitory structure, and uninduced *ermC* translation is solely determined by the stability of this structure.

VI. Regulatory Proteins Functioning through Changes in mRNA Secondary Structure

Translational regulation by proteins usually involves a repressor that binds to the initiation region and thus prevents access of ribosomes. Although secondary structures may participate in the recognition signal for the repressor protein (48), they are not directly involved in the modulation of translational efficiency and are therefore not discussed here. However, some regulatory proteins bind rather far upstream from the initiation site. Presumably, these act through the induction of changes in the secondary structure of the mRNA.

Like most ribosomal protein operons, the S10 operon is autoregulated by one of the proteins for which it codes, viz. L4. Regulation of this operon occurs at the transcriptional, as well as the translational, level (80, 81). Analysis of regulatory mutants has revealed that both types of regulation require an extended region upstream from the S10 gene, the first gene in this operon (82). This suggested that the action of L4 is mediated by changes in the secondary structure of this leader.

Analysis with structure-specific enzymes and chemicals suggests evidence for an equilibrium between the two structures shown in Fig. 14 (24). Earlier mutational analysis had demonstrated the relevance of hairpin HE. Destabilization of this hairpin eliminated translational control by L4, but this could be restored by compensatory mutations on the other side of the helix (82). Based on those findings, it was proposed (24) that the binding of L4 induces a shift in the equilibrium toward structure B (Fig. 14). The single-stranded region between hairpins HE and HG, which is only present in structure a, is allegedly essential for S10 translation. Because the inhibitory hairpin HF is in itself rather weak, it was suggested to be stabilized by coaxial stacking onto hairpin HE. This would also explain the necessity of a stable HE hairpin for translational regulation. Furthermore, this model is compatible with the finding that a deletion of 8 nucleotides in the single-stranded region reduced translational efficiency to a tenth. Deletion of sequences upstream from hairpin HE did not affect translational regulation, whereas a deletion over hairpin HE (and part of HF in structure b) that left the single-stranded region between HE and HG intact resulted in con-

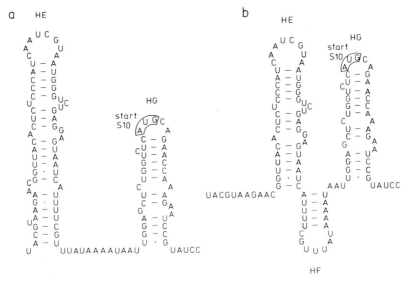

FIG. 14. Active (a) and inactive (b) structures of the S10 operon leader. Hairpins are indicated by HE, HF, and HG. (Redrawn from 24.)

stitutive expression of S10 at the unrepressed level (24). Hairpin HG is apparently too weak to interfere with initiation. Unfortunately, the precise binding site of L4 is not yet known.

A similar model, but involving much more extensive changes in the structure, has been put forward for the autogenous control of the *rif* (β) operon by the L10–L7/L12 complex (83). However, this model has not been supported by direct experimental evidence, and the conversion of one structure to the other is probably too slow to be effective (84).

Positive regulation at the translational level seems very rare. To our knowledge, only one example has been studied in some detail, and this also involves protein-induced changes in mRNA secondary structure. Deletion studies have shown that expression of the CIII gene of bacteriophage λ depends on a region upstream from the ribosome binding site (85). Furthermore, translation of CIII is only a tenth in strains that are deficient in RNase III, an effect that could be reproduced *in vitro* using extracts from wild-type and RNase-III⁻ strains.

As shown in Fig. 15, the CIII mRNA can be folded into two extended hairpins, where the upstream helix contains two RNase-III processing sites, marked E1 and E2. The downstream hairpin is thought to prevent translation of CIII in the absence of RNase III, because three mutations that raised CIII expression weakened this helix (Fig. 15, tor-864, tor-862/s1 and s2). A

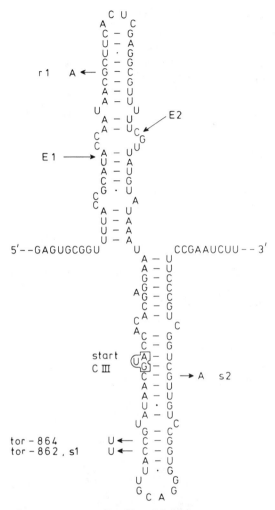

FIG. 15. Secondary structures presumably involved in RNase-III processing and translational regulation of phage λ gene CIII. Processing sites are denoted as E1 and E2. Arrows mark mutations, discussed in the text. (Redrawn from 85.)

mutation (r1) that reduced CIII expression to about a third destabilized the RNase-III hairpin and also caused loss of processing. Although these observations suggested a function for RNase-III cleavage in the activation of CIII, only unprocessed RNA could be translated *in vitro*. Furthermore, mutant r1 that was not processed at all still required the presence of RNase III for CIII synthesis. These findings led the authors (85) to conclude that it is the binding of RNase III, rather than processing, that activates CIII through an as-yet-unspecified change in the secondary structure. Why RNase III should function as a positive regulator remains elusive, but it may be related to the choice of the phage between the lytic and the lysogenic response, which depends on intracellular conditions (85).

VII. Differential Translation from Alternative mRNAs

Alternative RNAs of the same gene can exhibit large differences in expression that have sometimes been associated with the formation of secondary structures. For example, the lysozyme gene of bacteriophage T4 is present on messengers of different lengths synthesized from alternative promoters (86). Early in T4 infection, a transcript starting 47 nucleotides upstream from the lysozyme initiation codon is synthesized. Measurements *in vivo* as well as *in vitro* show that this transcript is not translated. Later in infection, two other promoters are used, producing active transcripts that start at various positions between −23 and −7 (indicated in Fig. 16 as S1 and S2).

Sequence analysis as well as patterns of RNA cleavage suggested the existence of the hairpin shown in Fig. 16, which covers most of the ribosome binding site but can only form in the long (early) transcript. Earlier work (87) had already shown that deletion of all T4-derived upstream sequences strongly increased lysozyme expression from a transcript initiated at an in-

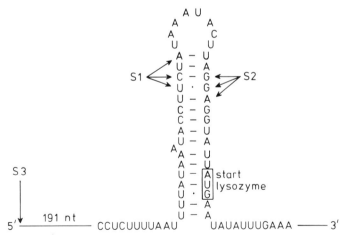

FIG. 16. Translational initiation region of phage T4 lysozyme gene. S1, S2, and S3 mark transcription startpoints from the two late promoters and the early promoter, respectively. (Redrawn from 86.)

troduced *trp* promoter. The same hairpin prevented overproduction of lysozyme when the gene is cloned behind a P22 promoter. Point-mutations that increase expression all acted through destabilization of the structure, even though some also reduced the SD-complementarity (88).

The potential formation of hairpin structures in 5′ extended transcripts has been interpreted as a biological precaution against activation of a gene by aberrant transcription from an unrelated upstream promoter. The *gal* operon of *E. coli* is transcribed mainly from two promoters, P1 and P2 (Fig. 17). These transcripts differ by only 2 to 3 fold in translational efficiency of the *galE* gene, the first gene of the operon (89). However, a much longer transcript that initiates from a weak upstream promoter (P3) is hardly translated. It has been suggested (90) that this is due to the stable hairpin structure shown in Fig. 17. The same structure repressed *galE* translation when the *gal* operon was cloned behind the P_L-promoter (91). Deletions and insertions disrupting this hairpin raised *galE* expression (91). It has been claimed that similar structures cause inefficient translation of 5′ elongated transcripts of the phage φX174 gene A (92) and the *lacZ* gene (93), but this has not been substantiated by experimental evidence.

Alternative mRNAs for the same gene can also originate from specific cleavage by nucleases. The expression of gene 0.3 of bacteriophage T7 depends on RNase-III processing of the transcript (94). The AUG start codon is located only 35 nucleotides downstream from the processing site, suggesting that the same hairpin that is recognized by RNase III prevents access to the

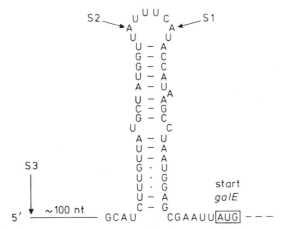

FIG. 17. Translational initiation region of *galE* on 5′ elongated transcripts. S1, S2, and S3 mark transcription startpoints from the two main promoters, P1 and P2, and the minor promoter, P3, respectively. (Modified from 90.)

ribosome binding site in the uncleaved molecule (22). Sequencing of the entire T7 genome later revealed that this hairpin ends at position −24 with respect to the AUG codon (23). Unfortunately, no experimental data confirming its effect on 0.3 translation are available.

A more complicated model has been proposed to explain why expression of the translationally coupled genes 1.1 and 1.2 of bacteriophage T4 is inhibited by incomplete RNase-III cleavage. Here, an RNase-III hairpin containing the two processing sites R5a and R5b is located downstream from the two genes (Fig. 18a). A mutant in which processing at R5a (but not at R5b) was abolished had lost expression of 1.1 and 1.2 (45). Surprisingly, second-site revertants either restored processing at R5a or eliminated processing at both sites. A model was proposed, stating that after processing at R5a the region

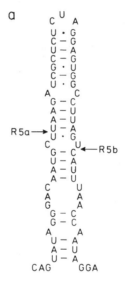

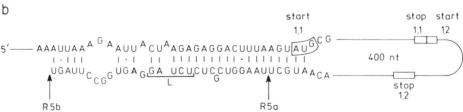

FIG. 18. (a) RNase-III recognition hairpin downstream from phage T4 genes 1.1 and 1.2. Processing sites are indicated by R5a and R5b. (b) Long-distance interaction, closing the ribosome binding site of gene 1.1 after RNase-III cleavage at R5b. L marks the loop of the RNase-III recognition hairpin. (Redrawn from 45.)

between the two sites can base-pair with the ribosome binding site of gene
1.1 and thus prevent its translation (Fig. 18b). As the physiological function
of this interaction, an autoregulatory mechanism that responds to limiting
RNase-III concentrations was suggested.

VIII. Concluding Remarks on the Mechanism of Translational Initiation

Although it has been known for many years that secondary structures of
mRNA can interfere with translational initiation, it is quite surprising to find
a simple, linear relationship between the efficiency of a ribosome binding
site and the fraction of unfolded mRNA molecules (see Section II). In our
view, this relationship implies that ribosomes can bind only to single-
stranded RNA, and have no inherent capacity to recognize and unfold secondary structures. Presumably, a non-sequence-specific interaction of
ribosomes with single-stranded RNA constitutes the first step in the process
of initiation. The existence of such an interaction is supported by several
lines of evidence. For example, the binding of ribosomes to synthetic poly-
cleotides like poly(U) must rely solely on nonspecific contacts, yet results in
efficient polypeptide synthesis. Ribosomes have even been found to bind to
polyxanthylic acid [poly(X)], a polynucleotide that cannot be translated.
Amazingly, the association of 30-S subunits with poly(U) or even poly(X)
promotes the binding of fMet-tRNA (95).

These findings, together with other observations discussed in this review,
suggest the following scenario for the initial steps in initiation-site selection.
First, a 30-S subunit attaches to an unfolded stretch of RNA and this event
triggers the binding of fMet-tRNA. Since the ribosome–mRNA interaction is
mediated by non-sequence-specific contacts, presumably with the phosphate–ribose backbone, random lateral movements along single-stranded
RNA should not encounter large energy barriers. We therefore propose that
such movements occur until the complex either dissociates or establishes
additional contacts through codon–anticodon interaction and/or the SD-
complementarity. In the second step, a 50-S subunit can associate with the
complex and the polymerization process can start. Ribosomal protein S1,
long since implicated in messenger binding, may provide at least part of
these sequence-independent contacts. This protein binds exclusively to single-stranded RNA, lacks sequence specificity, and is only required during
initiation (96). These properties suggest that S1 may extend the period during which a vacant ribosome is attached to the messenger and thus raise the
probability of successful initiation.

Sequence-independent contacts may even exist at the site where the SD-interaction takes place. This conclusion follows from competition experiments between poly(U) and the octanucleotide d(AAGGAGGT), which is fully complementary to the anti-SD-sequence in 16-S RNA. The octamer binds specifically to the anti-SD-sequence in 30-S subunits (97) but can, surprisingly, be displaced by an equal weight of poly(U). Because poly(U) has no complementarity to the 3' end of 16-S rRNA, we suppose that it is held in place at this site by virtue of non-sequence-specific interactions (R. S. Haxo and J. van Duin, unpublished).

The mRNA region that potentially contributes to the association with ribosomes seems larger than the defined ribosome binding site. For example, the oligo(U)-triggered binding of fMet-tRNA or AcPhe-tRNA only reaches maximal efficiency when the chain length approaches 100 nucleotides (98). Similarly, poly(U), with an average length of 80 nucleotides, binds to 30-S subunits a hundred times more tightly than does $(U)_{14}$ (99).

Data on natural initiation sites largely agree with these findings. Using a variety of RNA fragments derived from the replicase-initiation region of phage MS2, Borisova et al. (100) found that 53 nucleotides upstream from the AUG codon were required for maximal activity in the formation of 70-S initiation complexes in vitro. Removal of the nucleotides up to position -35 reduced binding to a third, while no binding could be detected to a fragment starting 21 nucleotides upstream from the initiation codon. Interestingly, nucleotides downstream from the start codon were dispensable.

A similar analysis was performed in vivo by shifting the transcriptional startpoint of the galE gene. Here, 30 nucleotides upstream from the AUG codon were essential for maximal translational efficiency. Further deletions toward the start codon gradually diminished the efficiency, until no expression could be detected when only 11 upstream nucleotides were left (89). It seems, therefore, that the cI messengers of phages λ and 434, which have zero and five nucleotides upstream from the initiation codon, respectively, are not only exceptional in lacking an SD-sequence, but also in not requiring an upstream RNA stretch (101, 102).

Non-sequence-specific contacts between ribosomes and mRNA are also likely to play a role in the process of reinitiation. Here, we assume that a terminated ribosome remains temporarily attached to the messenger and reaches a site suitable for initiation by lateral drift. In our view, this process is identical to primary initiation except that the first step, messenger binding, is bypassed. This difference can explain why ribosome binding sites that are shielded from primary initiation by secondary structures can function efficiently as reinitiation sites. Finally, we suppose that the non-sequence-specific contacts also contribute to the attachment of ribosomes to the mRNA during elongation.

ACKNOWLEDGMENTS

We thank Leen Welmers and Jan Verhoeven for art- and photowork, and Marianne Groothuis for assistance with computer-aided drawings.

REFERENCES

1. L. Gold, *ARB* **57**, 199 (1988).
2. G. D. Stormo, in "Maximizing Gene Expression" (W. Reznikoff and L. Gold, eds.), p. 195. Butterworths, Boston, 1986.
3. H. F. Lodish, *JMB* **50**, 689 (1970).
4. H. F. Lodish, *JMB* **56**, 627 (1971).
5. H. Fukami and K. Imahori, *PNAS* **68**, 570 (1971).
6. M. N. Hall, J. Gabay, M. Debarbouille and M. Schwartz, *Nature* **295**, 616 (1982).
7. L.-H. Tessier, P. Sondermeyer, T. Faure, D. Dreyer, A. Benavente, D. Villeval, M. Courtney and J.-P. Lecocq, *NARes* **12**, 7663 (1984).
8. G. Buell, M.-F. Schulz, G. Selzer, A. Chollet, N. R. Movva, D. Semon, S. Escanez and E. Kawashima, *NARes* **13**, 1923 (1985).
9. S. M. Freier, R. Kierzek, J. A. Jaeger, N. Sugimoto, M. H. Caruthers, T. Neilson and D. H. Turner, *PNAS* **83**, 9373 (1986).
9a. R. A. Spanjaard, M. C. M. van Dijk, A. J. Turion and J. van Duin, *Gene* **80**, 345 (1989).
9b. E. A. Skripkin, M. R. Adhin, M. H. de Smit and J. van Duin, *JMB*, in press.
10. R. A. Kastelein, B. Berkhout, G. P. Overbeek and J. van Duin, *Gene* **23**, 245 (1983).
13. N. R. Movva, K. Nakamura and M. Inouye, *JMB* **143**, 317 (1980).
14. K. Nakamura, R. M. Pirtle, I. L. Pirtle, K. Takeish and M. Inouye, *JBC* **255**, 210 (1980).
15. K. C. Cone and D. A. Steege, *JMB* **186**, 725 (1985).
16. M. C. Ganoza, E. C. Kofoid, P. Marliere and B. G. Louis, *NARes* **15**, 345 (1987).
16a. G. F. E. Scherer, M. D. Walkinshaw, S. Arnott and D. J. Morré, *NARes* **8**, 3895 (1980).
17. C. S. Chen and T. Nakamoto, *PNAS* **75**, 167 (1978).
18. K. C. Cone and D. A. Steege, *JMB* **186**, 733 (1985).
19. S. Shinedling, M. Gayle, D. Pribnow and L. Gold, *MGG* **207**, 224 (1987).
20. C. Tuerk, P. Gauss, C. Thermes, D. R. Groebe, M. Gayle, N. Guild, G. Stormo, Y. d'Aubenton-Carafa, O. C. Uhlenbeck, I. Tinoco, Jr., E. N. Brody and L. Gold, *PNAS* **85**, 1364 (1988).
20a. W. M. Huang, S.-Z. Ao, S. Casjens, R. Orlandi, R. Zeikus, R. Weiss, D. Winge and M. Fang, *Science* **239**, 1005 (1988).
21. K. J. Blumer, M. R. Ivey and D. A. Steege, *JMB* **197**, 439 (1987).
22. J. A. Steitz and R. A. Bryan, *JMB* **114**, 527 (1977).
23. J. J. Dunn and F. W. Studier, *JMB* **166**, 477 (1983).
24. P. Shen, J. M. Zengel and L. Lindahl, *NARes* **16**, 8905 (1988).
25. P. Model, R. E. Webster and N. D. Zinder, *Celi* **18**, 235 (1979).
26. J. F. Atkins, J. A. Steitz, C. W. Anderson and P. Model, *Cell* **18**, 247 (1979).
27. M. N. Beremand and T. Blumenthal, *Cell* **18**, 257 (1979).
28. R. A. Kastelein, B. Berkhout and J. van Duin, *Nature* **305**,741 (1983).
29. N. D. Zinder and L. B. Lyons, *Science* **159**, 84 (1968).
31. B. F. Schmidt, B. Berkhout, G. P. Overbeek, A. van Strien and J. van Duin, *JMB* **195**, 505 (1987).
32. B. Berkhout, B. F. Schmidt, A. van Strien, J. van Boom, J. van Westrenen and J. van Duin, *JMB* **195**, 517 (1987).

33. J. van Duin, B. F. Schmidt, B. Berkhout, A. van Strien, J. van Westrenen and G. P. Overbeek, *in* "Genetics of Translation: New Approaches" (M. F. Tuite, M. Picard and M. Bolotin-Fukuhara, eds.), p. 479. Springer-Verlag, Berlin and New York, 1987.

34. Y. Inokuchi, R. Takahashi, T. Hirose, S. Inayama, A. B. Jacobson and A. Hirashima, *J. Biochem.(Tokyo)* 99, 1169 (1986).

34a. M. R. Adhin and J. van Duin, *MGG* 218, 137 (1989).

35. B. Berkhout, R. A. Kastelein and J. van Duin, *Gene* 37, 171 (1985).

36. D. S. Peabody and P. Berg, *MCBiol* 6, 2695 (1986).

37. D. S. Peabody, S. Subramani and P. Berg, *MCBiol* 6, 2704 (1986).

38. M. D. Rosa, *JMB* 147, 55 (1981).

39. M. Nomura, R. L. Gourse and G. Baughman, *ARB* 53, 75 (1984).

40. D. S. Oppenheim and C. Yanofsky, *Genetics* 95, 785 (1980).

41. A. Das and C. Yanofsky, *NARes* 12, 4757 (1984).

42. S. Aksoy, C. L. Squires and C. Squires, *J. Bact.* 157, 363 (1984).

43. D. Schumperl, K. McKenney, D. A. Sobieski and M. Rosenberg, *Cell* 30, 865 (1982).

44. G. F. M. Simons, G. H. Veeneman, R. N. H. Konings, J. H. van Boom and J. G. G. Schoenmakers, *NARes* 10, 821 (1982).

44a. M. Ivey-Hoyle and D. A. Steege, *JMB* 208, 233 (1989).

45. H. Saito and C. C. Richardson, *Cell* 27, 533 (1981).

46. M. Trojanowska, E. S. Miller, J. Karam, G. Stormo and L. Gold, *NARes* 12, 5979 (1984).

47. F. Sor, M. Bolotin-Fukuhara and M. Nomura, *J. Bact.* 169, 3495 (1987).

48. P. J. Romaniuk, P. Lowary, H.-N. Wu, G. Stormo and O. C. Uhlenbeck, *Bchem* 26, 1563 (1987).

49. J. Tooze and K. Weber, *JMB* 28, 311 (1967).

50. W. Min Jou, G. Haegeman, M. Ysebaert and W. Fiers, *Nature* 237, 82 (1972).

51. B. Berkhout, "Translational Control Mechanisms in RNA Bacteriophage MS2," thesis, Leiden University, Leiden, The Netherlands, 1986.

52. B. Berkhout and J. van Duin, *NARes* 13, 85 (1985).

53. A. Das, J. Urbanowski, H. Weissbach, J. Nestor and C. Yanofsky, *PNAS* 80, 2879 (1983).

54. M. I. Kuroda and C. Yanofsky, *JBC* 259, 12838 (1984).

55. A. G. Shivakumar, J. Hahn, G. Grandi, Y. Kozlov and D. Dubnau, *PNAS* 77, 3903 (1980).

56. S. Horinouchi and B. Weisblum, *PNAS* 77, 7079 (1980).

57. T. J. Gryczan, G. Grandi, J. Hahn, R. Grandi and D. Dubnau, *NARes* 8, 6081 (1980).

58. M. Mayford and B. Weisblum, *JMB* 185, 769 (1985).

59. C. S. Narayanan and D. Dubnau, *NARes* 13, 7307 (1985).

60. J. Hahn, G. Grandi, T. J. Gryczan and D. Dubnau, *MGG* 186, 204 (1982).

61. D. Dubnau, *EMBO J.* 4, 533 (1985).

62. C. S. Narayanan and D. Dubnau, *JBC* 262, 1756 (1987).

63. C. S. Narayanan and D. Dubnau, *JBC* 262, 1766 (1987).

63a. M. Mayford and B. Weisblum, *JMB* 206, 69 (1989).

64. E. Murphy, *J. Bact.* 162, 633 (1985).

65. M. Monod, S. Mohan and D. Dubnau, *J. Bact.* 169, 340 (1987).

66. S. Horinouchi, W.-H. Byeon and B. Weisblum, *J. Bact.* 154, 1252 (1983).

67. T. Gryczan, M. Israeli-Reches, M. Del Bue and D. Dubnau, *MGG* 194, 349 (1984).

68. S. Kamimiya and B. Weisblum, *J. Bact.* 170, 1800 (1988).

69. M. J. Bibb, G. R. Janssen and J. M. Ward, *Gene* 41, 357 (1986).

70. M. Monod, C. Denoya and D. Dubnau, *J. Bact.* 167, 138 (1986).

71. C. J. Smith, *J. Bact.* 169, 4589 (1987).

72. E. J. Duvall, D. M. Williams, P. S. Lovett, C. Rudolph, N. Vasantha and M. Guyer, *Gene* 24, 171 (1983).

73. E. J. Duvall and P. S. Lovett, *PNAS* 83, 3939 (1986).

74. R. Bruckner and H. Matzura, *EMBO J.* **4**, 2295 (1985).
75. R. Bruckner, T. Dick and H. Matzura, *MGG* **207**, 486 (1987).
76. Z. Alexieva, E. J. Duvall, N. P. Ambulos, Jr., U. J. Kim and P. Lovett, *PNAS* **85**, 3057 (1988).
77. N. P. Ambulos, Jr., E. J. Duvall and P. S. Lovett, *J. Bact.* **167**, 842 (1986).
78. N. P. Ambulos, Jr., J. H. Chow, S. Mongkolsuk, L. H. Preis, W. R. Vollmar II and P. S. Lovett, *Gene* **28**, 171 (1984).
79. W.-H. Byeon and B. Weisblum, *J. Bact.* **158**, 543 (1984).
80. J. L. Yates and M. Nomura, *Cell* **21**, 517 (1980).
81. J. M. Zengel, D. Muecki and L. Lindahl, *Cell* **21**, 523 (1980).
82. L. P. Freedman, J. M. Zengel, R. H. Archer and L. Lindahl, *PNAS* **84**, 6515 (1987).
83. T. Christensen, M. Johnsen, N. P. Fiil and J. D. Friesen, *EMBO J.* **3**, 1609 (1984).
84. D. E. Draper, in "Translational Regulation of Gene Expression" (J. Ilan, ed.), p. 1. Plenum, New York, 1987.
85. S. Altuvia, H. Locker-Giladi, S. Koby, O. Ben-Nun and A. B. Oppenheim, *PNAS* **84**, 6511 (1987).
86. D. S. McPheeters, A. Christensen, E. T. Young, G. Stormo and L. Gold, *NARes* **14**, 5813 (1986).
87. L. J. Perry, H. L. Heyneker and R. Wetzel, *Gene* **38**, 259 (1985).
88. J. A. Knight, L. W. Hardy, D. Rennell, D. Herrick and A. R. Poteete, *J. Bact.* **169**, 4630 (1987).
89. A. Bingham, F. Fulford, P. Murray, M. Dreyfus and S. Busby, in "Genetics of Translation: New Approaches" (M. F. Tuite, M. Picard and M. Bolotin-Fukuhara, eds), p. 307. Springer-Verlag, Berlin and New York, 1987.
90. C. Queen and M. Rosenberg, *Cell* **25**, 241 (1981).
91. C. R. Merrill, M. E. Gottesman and S. L. Adhya, *J. Bact.* **147**, 875 (1981).
92. J. A. Steitz, in "Biological Regulation and Development" (R. F. Goldberger, ed.), Vol. 1, p. 349. Plenum, New York, 1979.
93. Y. Xian-Ming, L. M. Munson and W. S. Reznikoff, *JMB* **172**, 355 (1984).
94. J. J. Dunn and F. W. Studier, *JMB* **99**, 487 (1975).
95. K. van der Laken, H. Bakker-Steeneveld and P. van Knippenberg, *FEBS Lett.* **100**, 230 (1979).
96. A.-R. Subramanian, *This Series* **28**, 101 (1983).
97. C. Backendorf, C. J. C. Ravensbergen, J. van der Plas, J. H. van Boom, G. Veeneman and J. van Duin, *NARes* **9**, 1425 (1981).
98. C. J. van der Laken, "Initiation of Protein Synthesis in the Absence of an Initiation Codon," thesis, Leiden University, Leiden, The Netherlands, 1980.
99. R. Linde, N. Q. Khanh, R. Lipecky and H. G. Gassen, *EJB* **93**, 565 (1979).
100. G. P. Borisova, T. M. Volkova, V. Berzin, G. Rosenthal and E. J. Gren, *NARes* **6**, 1761 (1979).
101. M. Ptashne, K. Backman, M. Z. Humayun, A. Jeffrey, R. Mauer, B. Meyer and R. T. Sauer, *Science* **194**, 156 (1976).
102. V. Pirotta, NARes **6**, 1495 (1979).

Molecular Genetics of Na,K-ATPase

JERRY B LINGREL,
JOHN ORLOWSKI,
MARCIA M. SHULL AND
ELMER M. PRICE

*Department of Molecular Genetics,
Biochemistry and Microbiology
University of Cincinnati College of
Medicine
Cincinnati, Ohio 45267*

Molecular genetics is playing an increasingly important role in addressing questions of protein structure and function. This approach allows for exacting studies that complement biochemical, biophysical, physiological, and pharmacological data. In many instances the information is more easily obtained using recombinant DNA techniques, and in some cases it can be obtained by no other means. The power of this approach has clearly been demonstrated by recent advances in understanding Na,K-ATPase.* During the past few years, the primary structure of this oligomeric enzyme (comprised of an α and β subunit) has been determined, a new α-subunit isoform has been reported, tissue-specific and developmental expression of the genes encoding the subunits has been investigated, and structure–function relationships of the protein have been pursued using site-directed muta-

* Na^+/K^+-transporting ATPase (EC 3.6.1.37) [Eds.].

37

genesis coupled with eukaryotic cell-expression systems. The latter studies have been instrumental in identifying the receptor site involved in sensitivity to pharmacologically active cardiac glycosides such as ouabain and digoxin. Continued application of molecular–genetic techniques holds the promise for a fuller understanding of the function of this biologically complex enzyme.

The Na,K-ATPase is an integral membrane enzyme found in all cells of higher organisms and is responsible for the ATP-dependent transport of Na^+ and K^+ across the cell membrane. The ion gradients formed by this enzyme are essential for the Na^+-coupled transport of various nutrients, including glucose and amino acids, into cells (1), movement of such ions as Ca^{2+} (2, 3) and H^+ (4) across the membrane, and osmotic balance and cell-volume regulation (5). Protein synthesis (6) and receptor-mediated endocytosis and recycling (7) also depend on the resulting ion gradients. Because two K^+ ions are pumped into the cell for every three Na^+ ions expelled, an electrochemical gradient is established. This nonequivalent pumping of ions across the cell membrane is essential for maintaining the resting membrane potential of the cell and for the electrical activity of muscle and nerve (8, 9). Na,K-ATPase also appears to play a role in determining the nutrient and ion composition of the cerebrospinal fluid (10, 11) and aqueous humor (12, 13). In addition, the enzyme is responsible for fluid movement across transport epithelia in the gastrointestinal tract, the nasotracheal lining, and the kidney. Fluid reabsorption from the lung at birth also may depend in part on functioning of the Na,K-ATPase (14). The importance of this enzyme cannot be overstated, and it has been estimated that approximately 25% of the ATP catabolized by an individual at rest is used by this enzyme (15).

Na,K-ATPase belongs to a specialized class of ATPases that includes the H,K-ATPase (EC 3.6.1.36) and Ca-ATPase (EC 3.6.1.38). These ATPases have in common the phosphorylation of an aspartate residue as part of their enzymatic cycle. This enzyme class was originally designated as an E_1–E_2 type, referring to two different conformational forms through which the enzyme progresses in going through its catalytic cycle. However, as most ATPases probably undergo such conformational changes, this nomenclature appears inappropriate, and these enzymes are now termed the P-type ATPases (16).

Na,K-ATPase is composed of two subunits in equal molar amounts, an α subunit of M_r 112,000 (9, 17–19), and a smaller glycosylated β subunit of M_r 55,000 (17), the protein portion accounting for 35,000 of the mass of the β subunit (20, 21). It is not known whether the $\alpha\beta$ dimer is the active entity, or whether two of these [$(\alpha\beta)_2$] serve as the catalytic unit (22).

This review emphasizes molecular–genetic approaches to understanding structure–function relationships of the Na,K-ATPase, describes the genes encoding the α and β subunits, and discusses the regulation of their expression. Reviews emphasizing other aspects of Na,K-ATPase have been published (15, 16, 22–29).

I. Na,K-ATPase Structure

A. Primary Structure of the α and β Subunits

The large size of the α subunit of Na,K-ATPase and its hydrophobic character proved a formidable barrier for primary amino-acid sequence determination by conventional techniques. Nevertheless, Collins et al. (32, 33) determined the sequences of several tryptic peptides from the α subunit and the amino terminus of the β subunit of sheep Na,K-ATPase. This sequence information was essential for utilizing molecular–genetic approaches to deduce the amino-acid sequence of the entire α and β chains. Using these approaches, the sequence of the α subunit from sheep (18) and eel (Torpedo californica) (19) was obtained. At the same time, the entire sequence of the slow-twitch sarcoplasmic reticulum Ca-ATPase was also determined, using a similar approach (34). In order to isolate α-subunit cDNAs, a full-length cDNA library was prepared from sheep kidney, as this organ is a rich source of Na,K-ATPase. The library was screened with synthetic oligonucleotides whose sequences were derived from the sequences of the tryptic peptides (32). This approach yielded several clones from which the entire amino-acid sequence could be deduced from the corresponding nucleotide sequence (18). Similar approaches were used for deducing the amino-acid sequences of the α and β subunits from a variety of organisms, including sheep (18, 21), rats (35–39), pigs (40), dogs (31), chickens (41, 42), T. californica (19, 20), frogs (226), and humans (43–45) (Figs. 1 and 2).

An unexpected finding originating from the cDNA cloning studies was the discovery of three isoforms of the rat α subunit. Differences in cardiac glycoside sensitivity in brain (46–50) and other tissues (51–65, 98) and activity and affinity of the enzyme for Na$^+$ in various cells of the brain (51, 57) suggested heterogeneity in the Na,K-ATPase. A possible explanation for this was the existence of isoforms for either the α or β subunit. Evidence for two isoforms of the α subunit came from the isolation (58) of two electrophoretically separable α-subunit proteins from rat brain. These two subunits, which differed in their reactivity to N-ethylmaleimide, trypsin sensitivity, and affinity for the cardiac glycoside strophanthidin, were designated α and α(+). Differential sensitivity of rat brain Na,K-ATPase to pyrithiamine also suggested that this tissue contained two different α isoforms (59). In addition, the presence in adipocytes of two isoforms could be demonstrated by electrophoretic analysis (60). The activity of one of these subunits, α(+), ap-

```
                        1         10        20        30        40        50        60        70        80        90        100       110▼
Sheep   α1   MGKGVGRDKYEPAAVSEHGDKK KAK KERDMDELKKEVSMDDHKLSLDELHRKYGTDLNRGLTTARAAEILARDGPNALTPPPTTPEWVKFCRQLFGGFSMLLWIGAVLCFLAYGIQ▼
Human   α1   ------Q----GK-G---D---                                                             S---S-------------------------------I-------C
Rat     α1   ------------SK---                                                          S---P--------------------------------------I-------R
Rat     α2   --R-A--E-S--TTAENG GGK-KQ  --KEL------A------G---QV--SK--NQ--QD------------------------------I---------------L----------L
Rat     α3   MGDKKDDKSSP-KS--    KER--L-D---A-TE--M-VE-VC--N--CVQ--HSK-Q-------------S---P----------------------------I-----------L
Porcine α1   -----A----T-T---T---  KA-----------------I-----------------S----------T--------------------F-----------L-----SL------T
Avian   α1   --Y-A------T--Q-G--KKGKGKG--K----------------T-E---------F--MQ--------------------------------------------L----L--------T
Xenopus α    --AASE--Q---T--NAKNSKKSKS-TT-L---------L-----N-----Q----TQ---P--k--------------------------------------------I---T--I
Torpedo α

                      120▼      130       140       150       160       170       180       190       200       210       220       230
Sheep   α1   AATEEPQNDNLYLGVVLSAVVIITGCFSYYQEAKSSKIMESFKNMVPQQALVIRNGEKMSINAEEVVVGDLVEVVGDRIPADLRIISANGCKVDNSSLTGESEPQTRSPDFTNENPLE
Rat     α1   S-----P--D-                              --D-----------------D-----------------------V--------SH-----------------E--H---
Rat     α2   --M-D--S---                              --D----E----Q-------------------I----V-----------------H-----------------C--HD--
Rat     α3   -G--DD-SG--    -I--A-                     ------E----QV----------M------------------------------H-----------------S-----
Porcine α1   SVM-G--NS--       -A-                     ----------------------V------G-----------------------H--------------------
Avian   α1   --M-                  -T-                ----------------------S---L------Q----L-D------------V--SH------------------
Xenopus α    V--VDN-A-                                 --D-----------------S---L------Q-----------V--CS----------------S--EYSS----
Torpedo α

                      240       250       260▼      270▼      280       290       300       310       320       330       340       350
Sheep   α1   TRNIAFFSTNCVEGTARGIVVYTGDRTVMGRIATLASGLEGGQTPIAAEIEHFIHIITGVAVFLGVSFFILSLILEYTWLEAVIFLIGIIVANVPEGLLATVVVCLTLTAKRMARKNCLV
Rat     α1   --C-                       --IA-                --E-----L------------QL----V---G-S--------------------------------
Rat     α2   --T-                       -V-A-                -V--M-----QL----------QL------G-----------------------------------
Rat     α3   --T-                       -V-K--I-              -V-----L----------------------------------------------------------
Porcine α1   --V--IS-                    -S-------K---M-----L                 ---Q---------------------------------------------
Avian   α1   -----N--                    -D--R---I-                            ---G---------------------------------------------
Xenopus α    -K-                 -INI--H-             -V-                     ---G---------------------------------------------
Torpedo α

                      360       370       380       390       400       410       420       430       440▼      450       460▼      470
Sheep   α1   KNLEAVETLGSTSTICSDKTGTLTQNRMTVAHMWFDNQIHEADTTENQSGVSFDKTSATWLALSRIAGLCNRAVFQANQDNLPILKRAVAGDASESALLKCIEVCCGSVKEMRERYAKIV
Rat     α1                                                      ------------F---------------K-G-E-ISVS--DT----------LS---RK--D-NP-VA
Rat     α2                                                      -D--AT--R-P--T--   ------------KGG---I-V---D----------LSS----L---NK-VA
Rat     α3                                                      -D--T---S-H--V--H                                          --T----
Porcine α1                                                      --A---S-P--T----V----E-V-----------------------------------P-V-
Avian   α1   --G-                                                 -Q--A----S-P--T---V-----G-E-T----D---------------------RD--KHH-VA
Xenopus α                                                         ---LS-N-----A------G--SV-----S-----------------------------SQ-D-NP--
Torpedo α

                      480       490       500▼      510       520       530       540       550       560       570       580       590
Sheep   α1   EIPFNSTNKYQLSIHKNANAGEPRHLLVMKGAPERILDRCSSILIHGKEQPLDEELKDAFQNAYLELGGLGERVLGFCHLMLPDEQFPEGFQFDTDDVNFPVDNLCFVGLISMIDPPRAA
Rat     α1   -P-TS--S-                                 -L-----------------------F----------------L---------------E-------------M---
Rat     α2   -P-S--K--                                 ------T--VQ---I--K-MQ--------M--------Q-N-SGK--R--K--EL--TEK----------M---
Rat     α3   --EREDSPQS-V--                            ----AT--LQ---M-E---------------YY--E----K--A--C---TT---M------------M---
Porcine α1   --ETEDPNDN-Y-                             --P-TA-------                 ------F---------F-----------T-------------T---
Avian   α1                                            -S-----------D-----V----I---------A--D----D---EK----------M---
Xenopus α    -V----PS-S-Y1-                            -T--ILQ-----                 --A--D---D---EE---TE----------M---
Torpedo α    --E-DKADS-Y-                              -LN-EDK--N--M-E---------------K-STSK----YP--VEEP--ITD------M---
```

40

```
          600        610        620        630        640        650        660        670        680        690        700        710
                                                                                                                                    ▼
Sheep  α1  VPDAVGKCRSAGIKVIMVTGDHPITAKAIAKGVGIISEGNETVEDIAARLNIPVSQVNPRDARACVVHGSDLKDMTPEQLDDILKYHTEIVFARTSPQQKLIIVEGCQRQGAIVAVTGDG
Human  α1  ------------------------------------------------------------------------K-------------S-----------R-------------------
Rat    α1  --------------------------------------------N----------------------E-K-------S-E---R---------------------------------
Rat    α2  ----------------------------------------------------------------K--I---T--S-E-RD-------------------------------------
Rat    α3  ----------------------------------------------------------------K--I-T--F-S--I-E-QN----------------------------------
Porcine α1 ----------------------------------------------------------------K-------S----------------------------------------------
Avian  α1  ---------------------------------------------------------------K--------------S-------LH-------------------------------
Xenopus α  ---------------------D----------------------N--------------------N--K--I--T-----I---RH---------------------------------
Torpedo α  ----------------------------------------N----------------------N--K------T---LSH-N--H----------------------------------

          720        730        740        750        760        770        780        790        800        810        820        830
          ▼
Sheep  α1  VNDSPALKKADIGVAMGIAGSDVSKQAADMILLDDNFASIVTGVEEGRLIFDNLKKSIAYTLTSNIPEITPFLIFIIANIPLPLGTVITLCIDLGTDMVPAISLAYEQAESDIMKRQPRN
Human  α1  -----------A-----------------------------------------------------------------------------------------------------------
Rat    α1  -----------V-----------------------------------------------------------L---------------------------------------------A-
Rat    α2  --------I--S-----------------------------------------------------------L-M---------------------------------------------
Rat    α3  --------------I--------------------------------------------------------------I-----------------------------A-----------
Porcine α1 -----------------------------------------------------------------------------------------------------------------------
Avian  α1  -------------------------------------------------------------------------------------C---------------------------------
Xenopus α  ------------I----------------------------------------------V---V---------------------------------------------------R---
Torpedo α  -----------------------------------------------------------------------------------------------------------------------

          840        850        860        870        880        890        900        910        920        930        940        950
                                                                                                                                    ▼
Sheep  α1  PQTDKLVNERLISMAYGQIGMIQALGGFFTYFVIMAENGFLPNHLLGIRVTHDDRWINDVEDSYGQQWTYEQRKIVEFTCHTAFFVSIVVVQWADLVTCKTRRNSVFQQGMKNKILTFGL
Human  α1  -K------------------------------------L------------I------L--D----------------------------------------------I----------
Rat    α1  -K--------------------------L-----------SR----L---TT--L-------E---------------V---F----------I-----------I--------------
Rat    α2  -R--------------------S-----L------GN-V--LN--TV--L------------------------F--------V---F--------------Y--S--I----------
Rat    α3  -K----Q-----------------S---L-------I--L-N-------------------------F---------------------------------------I----------
Porcine α1 -K--------------------------L-----SG-V--LQ-----------------------------------------------S-I----------------I---------
Avian  α1  -K------------------------WT----N----T-------------------------------------------------------------------------------
Xenopus α  -K-----------------S--------L------ID-I--EK--EL-TQ-L------------------------------------Y--S----I---------I-----------
Torpedo α  -----------------------------------------------------------------------------------------------------------------------

          960        970        980        990       1000       1010
            ▼
Sheep  α1  FEETALAAFLSYCPGMGVALRMYPLKPTWWFCAFPYSLLIFVVDEVRKLIIRRRPGGWVEKETYY
Human  α1  ------------------------------------------------------------------
Rat    α1  -L---------A-----------------I----L-Y------N-R-------------------
Rat    α2  ----------------V----I----I---L-N--S----------------------------
Rat    α3  ------------D---------------S------I---L-N----------------------
Porcine α1 ------------D------------L----I-------N---------------------------
Avian  α1  ------------D------------I-I--S------------------------------------
Xenopus α  ---------T-TDI-----S----------L--A-RF-L--N----Q-----------------
Torpedo α  -----------------------------------------------------------------
```

Fig. 1. Amino-acid sequence comparisons between α subunits of Na,K-ATPase from various species and isoforms. The amino-acid sequence of the sheep α1 subunit (*18*) is shown in its entirety, utilizing the standard one-letter amino-acid code. This sequence is compared pairwise with the α sequence from human (*44*), rat (*35*), porcine (*40*), avian (*41*), *Xenopus laevis* (*226*), and *Torpedo californica* (*19*). Identical amino acids, relative to the sheep α1 sequence, are indicated by a dash, while the identity of amino-acid substitutions are shown by the one-letter amino-acid code. Specific amino acids (Lys-30, Gln-111, Asn-122, Arg-262, Leu-266, Trp-310, Asp-369, Arg-438, Cys-457, Lys-501, Cys-656, Asp-710, Lys-719, and Cys-964) are highlighted (▼) and are discussed further in the text. The putative transmembrane domains are indicated by a double line.

41

Sheep β MARGKAKE EGSWKKFIWNSEKKEFLGRTGGSWFK͟I͟L͟L͟F͟Y͟V͟I͟F͟Y͟G͟C͟L͟A͟G͟I͟F͟I͟G͟T͟T͟G͟T͟T͟Q͟V͟M͟L͟L͟TTSEFKPTYQDRVAPPGLTQIPQIQKTEIAFRPNDPKSYMTYVDNIDNFLKKYRDSAQKD
Human β --S-------EA--L--VR--E--K----R-
Rat β   --S-------EA--L--IR--E--K-----
Porcine β ---L--------S-------Q--ES--VS--VR--E--K--L---
Avian β -----DGD-N----L--------------------------------------S--------V---V---S--TV---DP--K--LEG--N--SAGE--T-
Xenopus β --D---TD-G--R----AD------T----------QV-------------L---------V----E--K------L-------RAV---S--S--SN--QE--KSM---S--NNEK--GS
Torpedo β ---E--STDDG-G---L--D----QV----T---FV--L----------------D--E--K------SHS--YAV---S--SVSN--N--ENH--NGLKEL--N--NE--K--DG

                   10   20   30   40   50   60   70   80   90   100   110

Sheep β DMIFEDCGNVPSELKDRGEFNNEQGERKVCRFKLEWLGNCSGINDETYGYKEGKPCVIIKLNRVLGFKPKPPKNESLETYPV MKYNPVLPVQCTGKRDEDKEKVGSIEYFGLGGYPGFP
Human β ----D----P-E--D--H-R-------------L----------I---------------------N----------D---NV----NS---
Rat β   -----SM---P-E---H-R--------------D---L---S---------M----------------N-----D---N----M--FY---
Porcine β ----E--Y--R-------R-----------L---D-------------------------------H---------------TM---
Avian β NIV-Q---DI-TDY-E--PY-DA--QK---K--R---E---EQ-N-F---D---ILV---II---A-E---PSDLA G-----LI--H-VA----AD-I-MV--Y-M----A
Xenopus β N------TI-GPYHE--AL-KDE-MK-S-V-RR---Q---L--PS-FAD---V----I-A---V--Q-N--PPEMTLN-----I-IH-QA-KE--I--IKEVK-Y-M--FA---
Torpedo β NTP----VI-ADYIT--PIEES--QKR---L-Q--K----D-PS---S----I-A---Y-----GTDLPEALQAN--Q---IH-QA-KE--VRI-T----M--VG---

         120   130   140   150   ▼160   170   180   190 ▼   200   210   220   230

Sheep β LQYYPYYGKLLQPKYLQPLLAVQFTNLTMDTEIRIECKAYGENIGYSEKDRFQGRFDVKIEVKS
Human β ---
Rat β   --------------L--
Porcine β ------M--
Avian β ------R---Q----V-------Y-V-V-------Q--Q--D--------I-FDI--S
Xenopus β -T-----D----I----I-F-A-V------D-HD--------FDI--S
Torpedo β ------R--KN----VGI----HNV-L-V--VF-D--A-----SL---E-----

         240   250   260   ▼ 270   280   290

FIG. 2. Amino-acid sequence comparisons between Na,K-ATPase β subunits from various species. The amino-acid sequence of sheep β (21) is compared to human (43), rat (39), porcine (40), avian (42), Xenopus laevis (42), and Torpedo californica (20) as described in the legend to Fig. 1. The putative transmembrane domain is indicated by a double line and the location of potential glycosylation sites (Asn-157, Asn-192, and Asn-264) are highlighted (▼).

peared to be stimulated in response to insulin (60). The amino-terminal amino-acid sequences of the two isoforms differ (61), which suggests that the subunits are probably the products of two different genes. Alternatively, the two subunits could result from differential processing of a single primary gene transcript.

The existence of multiple α isoforms coded by different genes was discovered by cDNA cloning and sequencing (35). The basic approach was to examine a large number of rat brain cDNA clones that hybridized under reduced stringency to the originally isolated sheep kidney cDNA clone. Restriction endonuclease mapping of these cDNA clones revealed the existence of three distinct classes. Nucleotide sequence analysis showed that one class encodes a large polypeptide of 1023 amino acids and corresponds to that of the kidney form. Kidney contains essentially one form of the α subunit. A second class of cDNA clones encodes a polypeptide of 1020 amino acids and corresponds to α(+), based on the amino-terminal amino-acid sequence (61). A third set of cDNA clones, present in approximately equal abundance to the other cDNA clones, corresponded to an α-like sequence consisting of 1013 amino acids with approximately 86% amino-acid similarity to the other α-subunit isoforms. This latter finding suggested that a third isoform protein exists, but it has yet to be identified *in vivo*. The three isoforms are now called α1, α2, and α3 [formerly α, α(+), and αIII, respectively] (summarized in Table I). The third isoform contains the essential features and general organization of the other two α subunits, including the aspartyl residue that is phosphorylated, the ATP binding site, and similar transmembrane regions (structural features are discussed in Section I,B).

A similar approach was used to search for isoforms of the β subunit. While different-sized cDNAs and mRNAs were observed (39) (Table I), the

TABLE I

SUMMARY OF α-ISOFORM AND β-SUBUNIT PRIMARY STRUCTURE OF RAT Na,K-ATPase

Structural features	α1	α2	α3	β
mRNA length (kb)	~3.7	~5.3, ~3.4	~3.7	~2.7, ~2.35, ~1.7–~1.85, ~1.4
Initiation sites (no.)	1	1	1	2
Potential polyadenylation sites (no.)	1	3	1	5
Deduced amino acids (no.)	1023	1020	1013	304
Processed amino acids (no.)	1018	1015	ND[a]	303
Molecular mass (M_r)	112,573	111,736	111,727	35,052

[a]ND, Not determined.

coding sequence of each of the cDNA clones was identical. The differences in the cDNAs and mRNAs originate from differences in the alternate use of two 5' transcription initiation sites and multiple polyadenylation sites encoded in a single gene (39).

B. Structural Features of Na,K-ATPase

Determination of the primary structures of the α and β subunits of Na,K-ATPase has provided the molecular information necessary for conception of models and design of experiments to investigate structure–function relationships of Na,K-ATPase. Computer-assisted analyses of the hydrophobicity, potential secondary structure, and regional amino-acid conservation of the primary sequence of the α and β subunits among the various species have led to a number of models regarding their respective transmembrane topography. In addition, the relative positions of certain amino acids have been defined by biochemical data.

1. THE α SUBUNIT

a. Transmembrane Domains. It has been suggested that the α subunit has six to ten transmembrane regions, depending upon interpretation of the hydropathy profile data (*18, 19, 35, 40, 41, 44, 226*). One two-dimensional model of the sheep Na,K-ATPase α1 subunit that depicts eight transmembrane regions (*18*) is shown in Fig. 3. (The β subunit has been omitted from this model for clarity.) The uncertainty in the transmembrane passes lies in the carboxyl-terminal end of the molecules. Most of the transmembrane domains are bracketed by charged residues, with the exception of the first and second extracellular membrane boundaries, designated H1 and H2. Interestingly, the rodent α1 subunit possesses charged residues at the H1–H2 extracellular membrane boundaries, and these appear to play a role in the ouabain-resistant character of this subunit (discussed in Section II). The second transmembrane domain also lacks a charged residue on its intracellular boundary. This domain, whose intracellular boundary is not defined by an adjacent charged amino acid, may be involved in conformational changes the enzyme undergoes during catalysis. The absence of a charged residue would allow a more flexible interaction with the plasma membrane. The transmembrane passes are highly conserved among species and isoforms (Fig. 1), including two glutamates in H8 that would be buried in the membrane, if the hydrophobicity analysis is correct. Although speculative, these negatively charged residues may be involved in transmembrane cation transport.

b. Extracellular Domains. Based on the proposed number of transmembrane passes of the α polypeptide, there are four putative extracellular

EXTRACTELLULAR

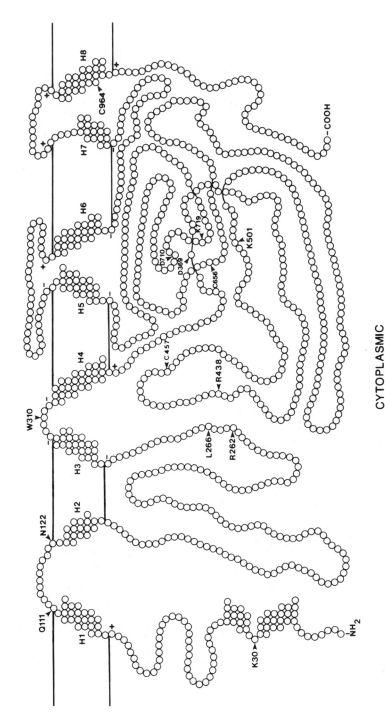

CYTOPLASMIC

FIG. 3. Hypothetical model of the sheep Na,K-ATPase α1 subunit. The extracellular and intracellular sides of the plasma membrane are labeled; the model depicted here shows eight transmembrane domains. Specific amino-acid residues are highlighted and numbered. The significance of these residues is discussed in the text. Certain charged amino acids that define the transmembrane domains are indicated by the appropriate charge.

regions. It is reasonable to assume that these segments play a role in cardiac glycoside binding, as these compounds are known to bind to the extracellular membrane surface. An area of notable sequence variation between the ouabain-resistant rodent $\alpha 1$ and the ouabain-sensitive α subunit of other species lies in the first extracellular domain (Fig. 1, residues 111–122) (35). Some of these amino-acid differences appear to mediate differential sensitivity to cardiac glycoside inhibitors (discussed in Section II), and also may interact with the putative endogenous ouabain-like compound (66). In addition, it has been suggested that part of the cardiac glycoside binding site is polyanionic (94). The presence of several acidic residues between H1 and H2 is consistent with this observation. In comparison to the H1–H2 domain, very few differences occur in the other extracellular regions of the α subunit of the Na,K-ATPase among species. Nevertheless, these regions may also participate in cardiac glycoside binding.

c. *Cytoplasmic Domains.* The region of highest sequence diversity among species occurs at the hydrophilic amino-terminal end of the polypeptide, located on the cytoplasmic side of the membrane. Interestingly, this region (residues 1–30), containing numerous lysine residues, has the distinctive feature of being highly charged. One of the lysine residues (Lys-30) that lies within the lysine-rich sequence appears to correspond to a site highly accessible to trypsin in the E_1Na conformation but much less accessible in the E_2K form (67, 75). Proteolytic cleavage at this site shifts the equilibrium to the E_1 conformation, which binds Na^+. Thus, it appears that the conformational shift that results in Na^+ occlusion involves movement of the lysine-rich sequence. A possible function of this domain may be to serve as an ion-selective gate controlling the passage of Na^+ and K^+ to and from the binding sites occupied during certain stages of the transport process (18, 35). Alternatively, this region may be involved in ion transport via the formation of a salt bridge (75).

Another sequence of the α subunit that exhibits species- and isoform-specific amino-acid variability is the region before Lys-501, the residue labeled with fluorescein 5'-isothiocyanate (FITC) (68). Additional areas of diversity include residues 400–420, 427–440, 461–471, 513–530, 552–585, 646–677, and 873–890. While the functional significance, if any, for these regions is unknown, it is reasonable to speculate that some of these regions may be involved in subtle differences in isozyme activity or regulation. The application of such techniques as site-directed mutagenesis may help to address these questions.

Biochemical characterization of the ATP binding site has identified five amino acids, distantly separated in the primary sequence, that appear to be localized in this region: Asp-369, Lys-501, Cys-656, Asp-710, and Lys-719.

The experimental evidence for implicating these residues is as follows. Asp-369 is the amino acid that is phosphorylated with the γ phosphate of ATP during the catalytic turnover of the enzyme (18). Asp-710 is the residue specifically labeled with the ATP derivative, "γ-[4-(N-2-chlorethyl-N-methylamino)]benzylamide-ATP" (69), where the reactive moiety is at the γ-P position of the nucleotide. Since both of these residues (Asp-369 and Asp-710) are modified by a chemical group at the same relative position of ATP (namely, γ), it is logical to place them in the same vicinity. Labeling studies using an affinity analogue of adenosine, 5'-(p-fluorosulfonyl)benzoyladenosine (FSBA), implicated Cys-656 and Lys-719 as being at or near the ATP binding pocket (70). This analogue has its reactive moiety on the 5' position of the ribose ring. Finally, labeling studies with FITC identified Lys-501 as being involved in ATP binding, perhaps at the site that interacts with the adenine ring of ATP (68). Therefore, based on covalent modification with ATP-binding site-specific reagents, we propose that Asp-710 and Lys-501 are at opposite sides of the ATP binding pocket, Cys-656 and Lys-719 are both located in the center of this pocket, and Asp-369 is between Asp-710 and both Cys-656 and Lys-719.

The model in Fig. 3 also places Cys-457 between the ATP binding site and the first two extracellular regions of the α subunit. This placement is based on distance measurements (73) indicating that Cys-457, labeled with 5-iodoacetamidofluorescein (IAF) (71), is between the FITC binding site (Lys-501) and the ouabain binding site [which is extracellular (103) and probably includes the first (72) and second (18) extracellular domains].

Additional amino acids that have been labeled or otherwise biochemically characterized also are identified in Fig. 3. Three amino acids have been localized that are either accessible or inaccessible to proteolytic cleavage, depending on the conformation of the enzyme (75). Lys-30 and Arg-262 are the tryptic sites exposed when the enzyme is in the E1 conformation. Arg-438 is the tryptic site in the E2 conformation, while Leu-266 is the chymotryptic site cleaved in the E1 conformation. Gln-111, Asn-122, and Trp-310 have been implicated in ouabain binding (18, 72) and Cys-964 is the residue labeled with N-[p-(2-benzimidazolyl)phenyl]maleimide (BIPM) (74).

d. *Sequence Homology with Other P-Type ATPases.* In addition to the Na,K-ATPase, other P-type ATPases have been cloned and their amino-acid sequences determined. Unlike Na,K-ATPase, these ATPases are apparently monomeric. Comparison of sequences reveals a number of highly conserved regions. Figure 4 illustrates such an analysis of the sheep Na,K-ATPase α1 subunit compared to the rat gastric H,K-ATPase (76), the rabbit slow-twitch sarcoplasmic reticulum Ca-ATPase (34), and the rat plasma membrane Ca-

48   JERRY B LINGREL ET AL.

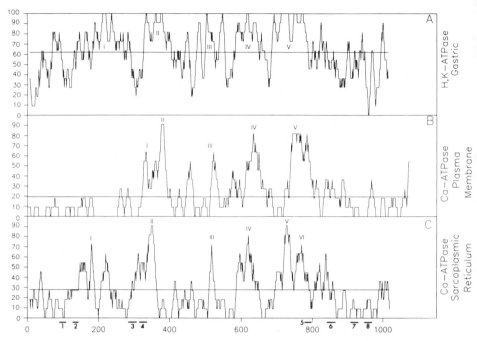

FIG. 4. Sequence homology between the sheep Na,K-ATPase α1 subunit and the H,K- and Ca-ATPases. The amino-acid sequence of sheep α1 (18) is compared to that of (A) rat gastric H,K-ATPase (76), (B) rat plasma membrane Ca-ATPase isoform 1 (78), and (C) rabbit slow-twitch sarcoplasmic reticulum Ca-ATPase (34). The results are presented as the percentage of homology versus amino-acid number. Regions of highest homology are indicated with Roman numerals. Putative transmembrane domains in the sheep sequence are numbered and indicated by a heavy line.

ATPase isoform 1 (78). Of these three enzymes, the H,K-ATPase exhibits the highest overall similarity (62%) to the Na,K-ATPase. The sarcoplasmic reticulum and plasma membrane Ca-ATPase exhibit similarities of 25 and 19%, respectively, compared to the sheep α1 subunit. When conservative amino-acid differences are included in the comparison analysis, the percentage of similarity increases slightly.

Na,K-, H,K-, and Ca-ATPases also contain a number of structural and functional similarities. These enzymes are integral membrane proteins with multiple transmembrane domains. They also bind and hydrolyze ATP, which results in transient phosphorylation of an aspartate residue during the catalytic turnover of the enzyme. Finally, these ATPases actively translocate cations across a membrane against an electrochemical gradient. Thus, it is not surprising that a number of the homologous regions are involved in similar specific structural and/or functional roles. These conserved domains (I–VI) are indicated in Fig. 4 and their sequences are presented in Fig. 5.

Conserved regions II, III, and V have been identified biochemically as domains of the ATPase involved intimately in binding or hydrolysis of ATP. Region II contains the aspartate residue that is modified transiently to aspartyl phosphate via transfer of the terminal phosphate of ATP to the amino acid (Asp-369 in sheep Na,K-ATPase αl, Asp-385 in rat gastric H,K-ATPase, Asp-475 in rat plasma membrane Ca-ATPase isoform 1, and Asp-351 in rabbit slow-twitch sarcoplasmic reticulum Ca-ATPase). The residues adjacent to this aspartate are highly conserved, a fact exploited in the cloning of the H,K-ATPase (76). The importance of this conservation has been verified experimentally by site-specific mutagenesis of the sarcoplasmic reticulum Ca-ATPase (79). Substitution of either the phosphorylated aspartate or the adjacent lysine residue abolishes Ca-ATPase activity. The role of conserved region III was identified utilizing the fluorescent amino-group-specific reagent, FITC (68). This compound covalently modifies a lysine residue of the canine kidney Na,K-ATPase which corresponds to Lys-501 of the sheep αl subunit. Such a chemical modification, prevented by ATP, irreversibly inhibits the enzyme. These findings led to the conclusion that this region of the α subunit is involved in ATP binding.

Region V contains conserved amino acids covalently labeled with two different affinity analogues of ATP. One compound, FSBA, apparently labels a cysteine and lysine residue of the canine kidney enzyme (70). These residues correspond to Cys-656 and Lys-719 of the sheep αl. An aspartate on the porcine kidney enzyme can be labeled with the ATP analogue, ClRATP (69). This residue corresponds to Asp-710 of the sheep αl. Cys-656 is not conserved in the other ATPases, but both Lys-719 and Asp-710 are conserved. Therefore, these data indicate further that these residues, or at least domains that include these residues, are located at or near the ATP binding site.

The role of additional conserved regions in these ATPases in the overall function of the enzyme is unknown. Region I (Fig. 4A) is located in the first cytoplasmic domain of sheep Na,K-ATPase αl (residues 177–248) and rat H,K-ATPase (residues 193–264). The corresponding region in either Ca-ATPase is not conserved to any significant extent, and the significance of the homology between the sheep Na,K-ATPase αl and rat gastric H,K-ATPase is unclear. Region I of Fig. 4C is located in the first cytoplasmic domain of sheep Na,K-ATPase αl (residues 179–215) and rabbit slow-twitch sarcoplasmic reticulum Ca-ATPase. There exists a similar sequence in the H,K-ATPase, but not in the plasma membrane Ca-ATPase. Again, the function of the conserved residues in this region is unknown.

A. Sheep α1 vs. H,K-ATPase

I.
```
sheep alpha1  (177-248)  EVVVGDLVEVKGGDRIPADLRIISANGCKVDNSSLTGESEPQTRSPDFTNENPLETRNIAFFSTNCVEGTAR
H,K-ATPase    (193-264)  QLVVGDLVEMKGGDRVPADIRILSAQGCKVDNSSLTGESEPQTRSPECTHESPLETRNIAFFSTMCLEGTAQ
```

II.
```
sheep alpha1  (320-398)  IIVANVPEGLLATVTVCLTLTAKRMARKNCLVKNLEAVETLGSTSTICSDKTGTLTQNRMTVAHMWFDNQIHEADTTEN
H,K-ATPase    (336-414)  IVVAYVPEGLLATVTVCLSLTAKRLASKNCVVKNLEAVETLGSTSVICSDKTGTLTQNRMTVSHLWFDNHIHTADTTED
```

III.
```
sheep alpha1  (492-526)  GEPRHLLVMKGAPERILDRCSSILIHGKEQPLDEE
H,K-ATPase    (508-542)  RDPRHLLVMKGAPERVLERCSSILIKGQELPLDEQ
```

IV.
```
sheep alpha1  (580-643)  GLISMIDPPRAAVPDAVGKCRSAGIKVIMVTGDHPITAKAIAKGVGIISEGNETVEDIAARLNI
H,K-ATPase    (596-659)  GLVSMIDPPRATVPDAVLKCRTAGIRVIMVTGDHPITAKAIAASVGIISEGSETVEDIAARLRM
```

V.
```
sheep alpha1  (679-774)  TEIVFARTSPQQKLIIVEGCQRQGAIVAVTGDGVNDSPALKKADIGVAMGIAGSDVSKQAADMILLDDNFASIVTGVEEGRLIFDNLKKSIAYTLT
H,K-ATPase    (695-790)  PEMVFARTSPQQKLVIVESCQRLGAIVAVTGDGVNDSPALKKADIGVAMGIAGSDAAKNAADMILLDDNFASIVTGVEQGRLIFDNLKKSIAYTLT
```

B. Sheep α1 vs. PM Ca-ATPase

I.
```
sheep alpha1  (315-349)  IFLIGIIVANVPEGLLATVTVCLTLTAKRMARKNC
PM-Ca-ATPase  (421-455)  IIGVTVLVVAVPEGLPLAVTISLAYSVKKMMKDNN
```

II.
```
sheep alpha1  (363-383)  TSTICSDKTGTLTQNRMTVAH
PM-Ca-ATPase  (469-489)  ATAICSDKTGTLTMNRMTVVQ
```

III.
```
sheep alpha1  (500-516)  MKGAPERILDRCSSILI
PM-Ca-ATPase  (600-616)  SKGASEIILKKCFKILS
```

```
IV.   sheep alpha1 (585-631)    IDPPRAAVPDAVGKCRSAGIKVIMVTGDHPITAKAIAKGVGIISEGN
      PM-Ca-ATPase (683-729)    EDPVRPEVPEAIKKCQRAGITVRMVTGDNINTARAIATKCGILHPGE
                                                      3

V.    sheep alpha1 (704-764)    IVAVTGDGVNDSPALKKADIGVAMGIAGSDVSKQAADMILLDDNFASIVTGVEEGRLIFDN
      PM-Ca-ATPase (791-851)    VVAVTGDGTNDGPALKKADVGFAMGIAGTDVAKEASDIILTDDNFTSIVKAVMWGRNVYDS
```

C. Sheep α1 vs. SR Ca-ATPase

```
I.    sheep alpha1 (179-215)    VVGDLVEVKGGDRIPADLRIISANGC--KVDNSSLTGES
      SR-Ca-ATPase (146-184)    VPGDIVEIAVGDKVPADIRLTSIKSTTLRVDQSILTGES
                                                                      1

II.   sheep alpha1 (322-384)    VANVPEGLLATVTVCLTLTAKRMARKNCLVKNLEAVETLGSTSTICSDKTGTLTQNRMTVAHM
      SR-Ca-ATPase (304-366)    VAAIPEGLPAVITTCLALGTRRMAKKNAIVRSLPSVETLGCTSVICSDKTGTLTTNQMSVCRM
                                     2

III.  sheep alpha1 (500-513)    MKGAPERILDRCSS
      SR-Ca-ATPase (513-526)    VKGAPEGVIDRCTH

IV.   sheep alpha1 (575-626)    NLCFVGLISMIDPPRAAVPDAVGKCRSAGIKVIMVTGDHPITAKAIAKGVGI
      SR-Ca-ATPase (589-640)    NLTFVGCVGMLDPPRIEVASSVKLCRQAGIRVIMITGDNKGTAVAICRRIGI
                                                    3

V.    sheep alpha1 (683-723)    FARTSPQQKLIIVEGCQRQGAIVAVTGDGVNDSPALKKADI
      SR-Ca-ATPase (675-715)    FARVEPSHKSKIVEFLQSFDEITAMTGDGVNDAPALKKAEI

VI.   sheep alpha1 (737-779)    QAADMILLDDNFASIVTGVEEGRLIFDNLKKSIAYTLTSNIPE
      SR-Ca-ATPase (728-770)    TASEMVLADDNFSTIVAAVEEGRAIYNNMKQFIRYLISSNVGE
```

FIG. 5. Homologous amino-acid sequences between various P-type ATPases. The sequence in the indicated regions from Fig. 4 is shown. Identical amino acids are marked with a dot. Highlighted residues are Asp-369 (1), Lys-501 (2), Asp-710 (3), and Lys-719 (4).

51

2. THE β SUBUNIT

a. Transmembrane Domains. Photochemical labeling (80, 81), proteolytic digestion (82, 83), and immunochemical (84, 85) procedures have led to the suggestion that the β subunit has one to four transmembrane domains. Hydropathy analysis of the deduced amino-acid sequence indicates that the protein has only one transmembrane domain located near the amino terminus (residues 34–60) (20, 21, 31, 39, 42, 43). Also, comparison of sequences of the β subunit from numerous species reveals a high degree of homology in this region (Fig. 2). Evidence to support the importance of this amino-terminal hydrophobic region in membrane insertion was provided by Kawakami and Nagano (86), who constructed various deletion mutations of the human β subunit cDNA clone. Transcription of the mutated cDNA clones, followed by incubation of the synthetic mRNAs in a reticulocyte-lysate translation system, generated β subunits containing various deletions. Analysis of the insertion of these structurally altered proteins into membranes revealed that a sequence of 16 amino acids within the proposed amino-terminal transmembrane domain is sufficient and essential for incorporation of the nascent β subunit, irrespective of the possible presence of other transmembrane segments that have been proposed for the carboxyl-terminal region (85).

b. Extracellular Domains. Electron microscopic studies (87) suggest that a large proportion of the β subunit is located on the extracellular side of the membrane. Hydropathy analysis indicates that sheep β subunit residues 60–302 probably lie on the extracellular side (21). In other studies, β subunit amino-acid sequences of papain-hydrolyzed peptide fragments generated from the extracellular side of dog-kidney membranes (82) exhibited partial homology to the sheep sequence beginning at residue 87, thereby also assigning this segment to the extracellular side.

The presence of three N-linked oligosaccharide chains has been indicated by studies on the biosynthesis of chicken skeletal muscle Na,K-ATPase (88) and by endoglycosidase F treatment of rat kidney and axolemma Na,K-ATPase (89). The deduced primary structure of the sheep β subunit contains three potential N-linked glycosylation sites (Asn-X-Ser/Thr) (21, 90), all located in the predicted extracellular regions of the protein (Asn-157, -192, and -264).

Because of the extensive glycosylation of this subunit, it has been of interest to examine the possible roles of these oligosaccharide chains in Na,K-ATPase biosynthesis and cation transport function. Inhibition of N-linked protein glycosylation of the β subunit with tunicamycin has no influence on subunit assembly, intracellular transport, or degradation rate in cultured chick sensory neurons (91). Furthermore, *Xenopus* oocytes injected with Na,K-ATPase α and β subunit mRNAs and incubated with tunicamycin expressed an oligosaccharide-deficient Na,K-ATPase, with catalytic activity, ouabain binding-site concentration, and Rb^+ transport activity virtually the same as the fully glycosylated enzyme (92). Thus, glycosylation of the β subunit does not appear to have any apparent function with regard to the integrity of Na,K-ATPase activity.

c. Cytoplasmic Domains. Based on hydropathy analysis, the β subunit is proposed to contain a short hydrophilic N-terminal domain (residues 1–33) that appears to be located on the cytoplasmic side of the membrane. Supportive evidence for this proposal is provided by the demonstration (93) that only a small cytoplasmic fragment of 2 kDa is removed by trypsin treatment.

II. Structure-Function Relationships of the Cardiac Glycoside Binding Site

Na,K-ATPase is the pharmacological target for cardiac glycosides. These drugs, such as digoxin and ouabain, bind to and subsequently inhibit the enzyme, causing an increase in intracellular Na^+ concentration (94). This, in turn, leads to an increase in intracellular Ca^{2+} levels by Na^+/Ca^{2+} exchange. The elevated intracellular Ca^{2+} subsequently causes an increase in the force of contraction of the heart.

Although most animal species possess Na,K-ATPases sensitive to the inhibitory effect of cardiac glycosides, there is one notable exception. The α1 isozyme of Na,K-ATPase isolated from rodents is relatively resistant to the inhibitory effect of cardiac glycosides. There is approximately a 1000-fold difference in ouabain sensitivity between rat Na,K-ATPase containing the α1 subunit and the enzyme from human, sheep, monkey, dog, and other sources (95–99). It has been determined that although the association rate for the ouabain/Na,K-ATPase interaction is important, the dissociation rate of the inhibitor from the binding site on the enzyme is a major determinant of ouabain affinity and, therefore, sensitivity (100). Data from immunological (101), biochemical (97), and structure–activity relationship (98, 102) studies indicate that cardiac glycosides dissociate rapidly from the insensitive enzyme because of a structural difference in the actual binding site on the enzyme compared to the corresponding region on sensitive enzymes. Binding of the drug to the sensitive enzymes is apparently followed by a conformational change that results in a stable, enzymatically inactive complex.

The chemical structures of these types of drugs can be divided into three domains: a steroid-like nucleus; an unsaturated lactone ring at the C17 position of the steroid; and one to three sugar residues at the C3 positions (94). Each of these domains may possibly interact with a unique region in the binding site of Na,K-ATPase. Numerous studies using various derivatives of cardiac glycosides have yielded additional insight pertaining to the location and nature of the binding site on the sensitive enzyme. Anthroylouabain, a fluorescent probe for the binding site, binds specifically to human, eel, rabbit, and canine Na,K-ATPase in a hydrophobic pocket that probably contains at least one tryptophan residue (103). A separate report describing the labeling of eel and canine Na,K-ATPase with a photoaffinity derivative of ouabain, p-aminobenzenediazonium (ABD)-ouabain, corroborated the implication that a tryptophan residue is located at or near the binding site (104). The presence of a conserved tryptophan (Trp-310, Figs. 1 and 3) in the second extracellular domain of the α subunit therefore makes this region a possible candidate for part of the ouabain binding site (18). Analysis of a mild tryptic digest of the enzyme labeled with ABD-ouabain indicated that the probe had been incorporated into the amino-terminal half of the α subunit.

Like ABD-ouabain, other affinity derivatives whose reactive group is located on the first or second sugar residue of the glycoside molecule also label the α but not the β subunit (105–108). However, unlike ABD-ouabain, one of these derivatives, N-(4-azido-2-nitrophenyl)ethylenediamine-ouabain, appears to label both the amino and carboxyl halves of the α subunit (109). Cardiac glycoside derivatives with a photoactive group on either the steroid nucleus or the C17 side chain also label the α subunit exclusively (105, 110). Evidence that the β subunit contains part of, or is at least spatially close to, the cardiac glycoside binding site stems from the observation that a photoaffinity derivative whose photolabile group is on the third sugar of the glycoside labels both subunits of Na,K-ATPase (111). Even though identification of the amino acids comprising the cardiac glycoside binding site remains undetermined, it is evident that it is extracellular and may consist of regions from either half of the α subunit as well as portions of the β subunit.

The basis for the differential cardiac glycoside sensitivity of the rodent Na,K-ATPase α1 isozyme compared to other species poses an interesting question. Recent studies using chromosome-mediated gene transfer of murine DNA into monkey CV-1 cells indicate that the chromosome encoding the mouse α1 subunit is sufficient to confer ouabain resistance (112). These findings were confirmed by the observation that expression of the cDNA encoding either the mouse or the rat α1 subunit in CV-1 cells confers ouabain resistance upon those cells (113, 114). When the α subunit from sheep, a species sensitive to ouabain, is transferred to ouabain-sensitive human HeLa cells, resistant cells are not obtained (72). These data show that the determinants involved in resistance are located on the rodent α1 subunit.

The determinants have been localized further by constructing cDNA chimeras containing distinct regions from the ouabain-resistant rat and the ouabain-sensitive sheep α subunit cDNAs (72). Two different chimeras were generated. One encoded an α subunit composed of an amino-terminal half from the rat and a carboxyl-terminal half from the sheep. Conversely, the other chimera contained the amino-terminal half from the sheep and the carboxyl-terminal half from the rat. These gene constructs were used to transfect ouabain-sensitive HeLa cells. As shown in Fig. 6, only the construct containing the amino-terminal half of the rat α1 subunit and the carboxyl-terminal half of the sheep α1 subunit conferred ouabain resistance upon the cells. These cells were biochemically identical to HeLa cells transfected with the intact rat α1 cDNA alone with respect to ouabain-insensitive cell growth, Rb^+ influx, and Na,K-ATPase activity (72). This places the determinants of ouabain resistance somewhere in the amino-terminal half of the rat α1 subunit. A previous comparison of the primary structure of the rat α1 sequence with that of the sheep identified four significant amino-acid differences between these sequences in the first extracellular domain (35). The residues present in this region were postulated to be involved in ouabain resistance. The rat/sheep chimera that conferred resistance to HeLa cells also contains this region of the rat sequence.

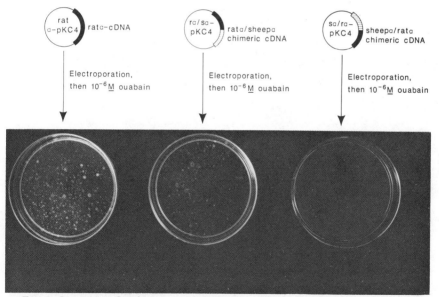

FIG. 6. Generation of ouabain-resistant cells. HeLa cells were transfected with the indicated construct. The parent vector, pKC4, contains SV40-derived promoter and RNA-processing sequences. Ouabain-resistant cells were selected in 1 μM ouabain and the number of resistant colonies was determined after 14 days in culture. Shown are the culture dishes of cells transfected with rat α1 cDNA, the rat/sheep chimeric cDNA, and the sheep/rat chimeric cDNA.

Site-directed mutagenesis has been used to determine the biological effect of the four amino-acid differences found in the first extracellular domain of the rat α1 subunit (72). Five different mutations of the sheep α1 subunit cDNA were generated, inserted into an expression vector, and screened for the capability of a particular mutation to confer ouabain resistance following transfection into HeLa cells (Table II). Stable incorporation of two of these mutated cDNAs into HeLa cells generated transfectants capable of proliferating in 1.0 μM ouabain, indicating that the transfected HeLa cells exhibited a ouabain-resistant phenotype. Mutant A (Table II) encodes amino-acid substitutions in the H1–H2 extracellular region in the sheep α1 polypeptide, converting it to the sequence present in the rat α1 (*Arg-Ser*-Ala-Thr-Glu-Glu-Glu-Pro-*Pro*-Asn-Asp-*Asp*; italicized residues are those that were substituted). Mutant B, on the other hand, alters sheep α1 amino acids present at the borders of the H1–H2 extracellular region, changing them to charged residues (*Arg*-Ala-Ala-Thr-Glu-Glu-Glu-Pro-Gln-Asn-Asp-*Asp*). These transfectants were selected in 1.0 μM ouabain and, similar to the previously described rat/sheep chimera transfectants, were

TABLE II

TRANSFECTION OF HeLa CELLS WITH MUTANT α1 cDNAs OF SHEEP: NUMBER OF OUABAIN-RESISTANT COLONIES[a]

Construct	Ouabain (1 μM)		Ouabain (0.1 μM)
	Trial 1	Trial 2	
Mutant A	240	140	—
Mutant B	170	150	—
Mutant C	0	0	70
Mutant D	0	0	200
Mutant E	0	0	0
sα1-pKC4	0	0	0

Sequences of the H1–H2 Extracellular Domain from Mutant Sheep α1 cDNAs[b]

Mutant A	*Arg-Ser*-Ala-Thr-Glu-Glu-Glu-Pro-*Pro*-Asn-Asp-*Asp*
Mutant B	*Arg*-Ala-Ala-Thr-Glu-Glu-Glu-Pro-Gln-Asn-Asp-*Asp*
Mutant C	*Arg-Ser*-Ala-Thr-Glu-Glu-Glu-Pro-Gln-Asn-Asp-Asn
Mutant D	Gln-Ala-Ala-Thr-Glu-Glu-Glu-Pro-*Pro*-Asn-Asp-*Asp*
Mutant E	Gln-Ala-Ala-Thr-Glu-Glu-Glu-Pro-*Pro*-Asn-Asp-Asn
Wild-type sheep α	Gln-Ala-Ala-Thr-Glu-Glu-Glu-Pro-Gln-Asn-Asp-Asn
	111 112 119 122

[a]HeLa cells were transfected with the indicated sheep α1 mutant. The number of ouabain-resistant colonies that proliferated in either 1.0 μM or 0.1 μM ouabain were quantitated after 14–28 days in culture.

[b]Italicized residue(s) indicates location of mutation(s).

identical to rat α1 transfected cells in terms of ouabain-insensitive cell growth, Rb$^+$ influx, and Na,K-ATPase activity.

Two additional mutations in the sheep α1 cDNA conferred ouabain resistance upon HeLa cells but to a lesser extent than that observed with mutations A and B. These mutations, C and D (Table II), generated cells that proliferated in 0.1 μ*M* ouabain, whereas no colonies were observed in 1.0 μ*M* ouabain. The amino-acid sequence of the H1–H2 extracellular domain encoded by mutation C is *Arg-Ser*-Ala-Thr-Glu-Glu-Glu-Pro-Gln-Asn-Asp-Asn, and that of mutation D is Gln-Ala-Ala-Thr-Glu-Glu-Glu-Pro-*Pro*-Asn-Asp-*Asp*. Note that in these constructs, only one or the other border residue is changed to a charged residue. When mutation C or D transfected HeLa cells were characterized in terms of ouabain-inhibitable cell growth, an increased sensitivity to the drug relative to the previously described transfectants was observed (Fig. 7). Thus, these transfectants exhibit an intermediate sensitivity to ouabain.

At this point, a model depicting the residues involved in cardiac glycoside binding to sensitive forms of Na,K-ATPase would be speculative at best. However, two amino acids that appear to be responsible for the rapid dissociation of ouabain from the binding site on rat kidney Na,K-ATPase seem to be identified, based on results obtained with mutations A and B. These residues are charged amino acids that appear to reside on both borders of the first extracellular domain of the α subunit, as estimated by hydropathy plot analysis. It is of interest to note that all ouabain-sensitive enzymes with

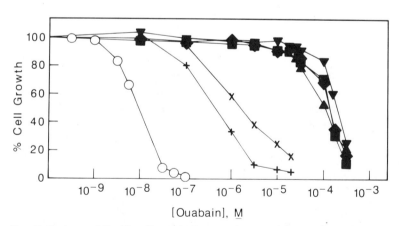

FIG. 7. Ouabain-inhibitable cell growth of mutant sheep α1 transfectants. Cells transfected with various mutated sheep α1 cDNAs were cloned and ascertained for their capability to proliferate in increasing concentrations of ouabain. ▲ and ▼, Mutant A transfectants; ■ and ◆, mutant B transfectants; X, mutant C transfectants; +, mutant D transfectants; ○ wild-type HeLa cells.

known primary sequences possess uncharged residues at this position (cf. Fig. 1). It is reasonable to speculate that the H1–H2 extracellular loop may be involved in conformational changes during ouabain binding, which prevents easy dissociation of ouabain from the enzyme. Such a change may involve an interaction between the uncharged border residues of the H1–H2 extracellular domain and the plasma membrane. When charged amino acids are present at these positions, which is the case in the rat $\alpha 1$ sequence and the aforementioned sheep $\alpha 1$ mutations, such an interaction may be hindered, perhaps due to energy requirements for moving a charged group into the hydrophobic membrane.

The specific regions of the Na,K-ATPase that interact with discrete domains of the cardiac glycoside molecule have yet to be determined. It has been observed that some sequence similarity exists between the H3–H4 extracellular domain of numerous α subunits (Glu-Tyr-Thr-Trp-Leu-Glu) and a region of the putative steroid binding region of either the human estrogen or glucocorticoid receptor (Glu-Cys-Ala-Trp-Leu-Glu or Gln-Tyr-Ser-Trp-Met-Phe) (115). Therefore, the residues of the H3–H4 extracellular region may interact specifically with the steroid-like nucleus of the cardiac glycoside. Interestingly, the H3–H4 extracellular sequence is identical between the rat $\alpha 1$ and other ouabain-sensitive enzymes, such as sheep or human. This may explain why the rodent enzyme is inhibited eventually by high concentrations of ouabain. It is possible that once the cardiac glycoside interacts with the binding pocket via its steroid-like nucleus and the H3–H4 extracellular peptide, a conformation change occurs in sensitive enzymes that requires uncharged residues on the borders of the H1–H2 extracellular region. The amino acids in the H1–H2 region may also interact specifically with additional structures such as the lactone ring on the cardiac glycoside. Of course, this does not exclude other extracellular regions of the α or the β subunit participating in the total binding process.

These observations illustrate the vast potential of recombinant DNA technologies to address structure–function relationships of Na,K-ATPase. In addition. to identifying the amino acids involved in cardiac glycoside resistance and binding, such methods as site-directed mutagenesis and cDNA expression should yield insightful information about other aspects of enzyme function. Future work will hopefully result in the elucidation of the amino acids or structural domains involved in cation transport.

III. Regulation of Na,K-ATPase Expression

The existence of multiple α-isoform genes for Na,K-ATPase has been correlated with the diverse biochemical properties of Na,K-ATPase activity. The different forms of Na,K-ATPase exhibit a tissue-specific and developmental pattern of expression. Furthermore, distinct molecular forms of Na,K-ATPase appear to be modulated by numerous hormones, including peptide, thyroid, and steroid hormones, as well as by monovalent cations. Such observations suggest that the Na,K-ATPase gene family is influenced by a complex series of regulatory pathways that affect a multitude of cellular processes. Characterizing these pathways at the molecular level and understanding their mechanisms of regulation are a major focus of current research, both because of their potential as model systems for differential control of gene family expression, and because of their physiological and therapeutic significance. With regard to the latter, Na,K-ATPase is the only known receptor for cardiac glycosides such as digoxin and ouabain. Cardiac glycosides are known to bind to the biochemically distinct isoforms of the α subunit with different affinities. Hence, differential expression of the α isoforms in heart under various physiological or pathological conditions will influence the therapeutic effectiveness of cardiac glycoside drugs to mediate positive myocardial inotropy.

The following sections review in some detail the more recent studies aimed at examining Na,K-ATPase regulation at distinct levels: (A) tissue- and cell-specific; (B) developmental; and (C) modulators of enzyme activity; such as hormones and cations.

A. Tissue- and Cell-Specific Regulation

Early studies of tissue distribution of the α-isoform proteins of Na,K-ATPase demonstrated that rat kidney contains predominantly the α1 isozyme (116), while both α1 and α2 can be detected in brain (58, 59), adipose (60), skeletal and cardiac muscle (60, 117, 118), and retina (119). However, discovery of the α3 isoform by cDNA cloning complicated interpretation of the protein results (35). While the protein encoded by the α3 gene transcript has yet to be identified in vivo, there is circumstantial evidence that this gene product is present and may exhibit biochemical and biophysical characteristics similar to those of α2 (120, 121). Additional supporting evidence comes from the observation (122) that in rabbit reticulocyte lysates supplemented with rough microsomes, all three rat α-isoform polypeptides can be generated by translation of their respective synthetic mRNAs and analyzed by polyacrylamide gel electrophoresis. The α3 protein possesses an electrophoretic mobility similar to that of α2. Also, the α3 protein can be immunoprecipitated by a presumed α2-specific antiserum, indicating similar antigenic determinants. Hence, this observation suggests that some of the observed properties of Na,K-ATPase in various tissues, attributed previously to the α2 subunit, may, in reality, belong to α3 or a combination of α2 and α3.

Since definitive identification and quantitation of the α isoform proteins are unavailable at present, more sensitive detection of the α isoforms and β subunit in various adult rat tissues has been performed by RNA blot analyses (38, 120, 122, 123). The results reveal that α1 mRNA (3.7 kb in length) is expressed ubiquitously in various tissues, albeit at different levels. The α2 mRNAs (5.3 and 3.4 kb) are expressed primarily in neural and muscle tissues, and to much lesser extents in adipose, kidney, lung, and stomach. The α3 mRNA (3.7 kb) is detected predominantly in neural tissue, and to lesser extents in lung, skeletal muscle, and stomach. The β-subunit mRNAs (primarily 2.7 and 2.35 kb), like α1 mRNA, are present at varying levels in all tissues examined. The relative levels of the α-isoform and β-subunit mRNAs in the various rat adult tissues were quantitated by RNA "slot-blot" analysis (123) and the results are summarized in Table III.

Whole-tissue RNA analyses are valuable for correlating the tissue-specific expression of individual catalytic isoform subunits with known physiological functions of Na,K-ATPase. However, precise delineation of the specific cellular role(s) for each of the Na,K-ATPase isozymes is not possible using this technique because of the multicellular composition of most tissues. Moreover, many tissues express more than one isozyme. In an effort to overcome this limitation, in situ hybridization histochemistry has recently been used to characterize the anatomic distribution of the Na,K-ATPase α3 mRNA in rat brain (122). The α3 RNA probes hybridize intensely to several major neuronal formations, including the hippocampus, dentate gyrus, neocortex, and subiculum. In addition, strong hybridization signals were observed in the thalamus and the habenula. In contrast, white matter was not

TABLE III

RELATIVE ABUNDANCE OF α-ISOFORM AND β-SUBUNIT mRNAs OF Na,K-ATPase IN ADULT RAT TISSUES[a]

Tissue	α1	α2	α3	β	Σα/β
Brain	1.0	1.2	0.8	5.2	0.58
Heart	0.7	0.1	ND	1.0	0.80
Kidney	7.0	<0.06	ND	10.4	0.68
Liver	<0.05	ND	ND	<0.05	1.00
Lung	0.3	<0.06	<0.04	0.3	1.33
Muscle	0.1	1.8	ND	0.5	3.80
Stomach	0.3	<0.06	<0.04	2.6	0.15

[a]Results were derived from RNA "slot-blot" analyses of mRNAs encoding the α isoforms and β subunits of rat Na,K-ATPase (123). The RNAs were hybridized with subunit-specific cDNA probes of similar size and specific activity. The hybridization intensities were measured by densitometry. A value of 1 was assigned to the level of brain α1 mRNA and the level of each mRNA (α1, α2, α3, and β) in the various tissues was normalized with respect to the brain α1 mRNA value. The values presented are only approximate due to experimental variation with this technique. ND, Not detected.

labeled appreciably. In the hippocampus and the neocortex, $\alpha 3$ mRNA was localized to the pyramidal cells. Lastly, in cerebellum, expression of $\alpha 3$ mRNA was restricted primarily to the Purkinje cell layer. Further use of this technique should provide relevant information on cell-specific expression and possible physiological roles for the isozymes of Na,K-ATPase, particularly where tissue architecture is important for gene expression or where cell culture is not available.

To date, most studies examining the regulation of Na,K-ATPase expression have involved analysis of whole tissues or tissue sections of various organs removed from treated animals. As stated above, while these analyses have provided valuable information, their interpretation in some situations is complicated by the presence of multiple Na,K-ATPase isozymes that have not been clearly distinguished. Furthermore, secondary effects of exogenously administered hormones or other modulators to whole animals make direct effects on Na,K-ATPase difficult to establish.

An alternative approach to studying Na,K-ATPase gene expression is through the use of cultured cells. While the availability of certain cell types limits the general applicability of this approach, the capability to distinguish individual isozymes of Na,K-ATPase in various cell lines now allows for detailed analyses of their distinct biochemical, biophysical, and regulatory characteristics in a more controlled manner.

With this objective, the expression of Na,K-ATPase α-isoform and β-subunit mRNAs has been characterized in various rodent cell lines (for a summary, see Table IV). The analyses reveal that multiple α-subunit genes can be expressed in distinct populations of cells. The $\alpha 1$ and β mRNAs are present in all cell lines examined, while $\alpha 2$ and $\alpha 3$ mRNAs exhibit a more restricted pattern of cell-specific expression. In particular, $\alpha 2$ gene expression appears to be restricted to neural- and muscle-derived cell lines, which correlates with its expression in whole tissues. Although this is a limited survey, it is possible to suggest that the $\alpha 1$ gene functions primarily in a housekeeping capacity to maintain osmotic balance and cell-volume regulation, while the other α subunit genes fulfill more specialized requirements for cation transport necessary for differentiated cell-specific function.

In addition, other cell lines have been used successfully to examine various regulatory aspects of Na,K-ATPase α and β-subunit gene expression. These include the amphibian A6 cells (derived from *Xenopus laevis* kidney) (125) and canine MDCK (Madin–Darby canine kidney) cells and the various subclones (D1, L, N, and T) derived from the parental MDCK line (126). However, it is not clear whether the α-subunit mRNAs identified in these kidney cell lines are the homologs of the $\alpha 1$ mRNA found in rodent tissue or cells. Kidney tissue is known to express predominantly $\alpha 1$ mRNA and minor amounts of $\alpha 2$ mRNA, although the cellular origins of these isoforms have

TABLE IV

EXPRESSION OF THE α-ISOFORM AND β-SUBUNIT GENES OF Na,K-ATPase IN CULTURED RODENT CELLS[a]

Cell type	Species	Line	α1	α2	α3	β	References
Adipocyte–embryonal	Mouse	3T3-L1	+	–	–	+	†
Embryonal carcinoma	Mouse	F9	+	+	+	+	†
Kidney–epithelial	Mouse	TCMK-1	+	–	–	+	†
Kidney–epithelial	Rat	NRK-52E	+	–	–	+	†
Liver	Rat	APL-15	+	–	–	+	221–223
Liver	Rat	FAZA	+	–	–	+	†
Liver	Mouse	NMuli	+	–	–	+	†
Liver–normal embryonic	Mouse	BNL-CL2	+	–	–	+	†
Mammary	Mouse	S115	+	–	–	+	†
Neuroblastoma	Mouse	NB41A3	+	+	–	+	†
Prostate adenocarcinoma	Rat	R3327H-G8-A1	+	–	–	+	†
Skeletal muscle	Mouse	C2C12	+	+	–	+	†
Skeletal muscle	Mouse	G8	+	+	–	–	†
Skeletal muscle	Rat	L6E9	+	–	–	+	†
Smooth muscle–thoracic aorta	Rat	A10	+	–	–	+	†

[a] Total cellular RNA was extracted from cultured cells and subjected to RNA blot analyses. The blots were hybridized with restriction endonuclease fragments of rat Na,K-ATPase α-isoform and β-subunit-specific cDNA and the absence (–) or presence (+) of the respective subunit mRNAs was identified. The rat subunit-specific cDNA fragments were shown previously to exhibit similar specificity for the homologous mRNAs in murine tissues (161). († indicates J. Orlowski and J. B Lingrel, unpublished.)

not been established. Variant HeLa cell lines stably resistant to ouabain also have been used to study the mechanisms involved in drug resistance (127, 128). The results suggest that gene amplification and overexpression of the Na,K-ATPase α1 subunit is the primary mechanism responsible for acquisition of the ouabain-resistant phenotype in these cells. Circumstantial evidence indicates that the β subunit also may be amplified severalfold. Lastly, primary rat adipocyte (60, 129), hepatocyte (130, 131), cardiocyte (132, 133), and chick skeletal myocyte (134, 135) cultures have been used to examine Na,K-ATPase expression at the protein level. While this list of useful cell cultures is by no means complete, further characterization of these and other systems should add to the rapidly expanding information on cell-specific expression of the Na,K-ATPase gene family.

B. Developmental Regulation

In addition to tissue- and cell-specific expression, the Na,K-ATPase gene family also exhibits distinctive developmental patterns of expression in various rat tissues and cells. In the following section, we describe changes in Na,K-ATPase gene expression in selected tissues (brain, heart, lung, kidney, and skeletal muscle) and cells (myocytes) that appear to correlate with various physiological processes necessary for maintaining cellular and organismic homeostasis during ontogenesis.

1. TISSUES

a. Brain. From RNA analyses, brain α3 mRNA is the most abundant α-isoform transcript expressed during the fetal stage, reaching maximum levels (10-fold induction) at 7 days of age (120). In contrast, the α1 and α2 mRNA abundances increase more gradually during development, reaching α3 mRNA levels at 25 days of age. Overall, the total α-isoform mRNA in brain increases 10-fold from the fetal to adult stage. The β-subunit mRNA abundance also increases approximately 25-fold during this time period. There are also developmental changes in the relative abundance of distinctive α-isoform proteins of rat brain Na,K-ATPase (136–138). The increase in the total α-isoform mRNA correlates well with rat brain Na,K-ATPase activity, which also increases 10-fold from pre- to postnatal life, reaching adult levels 20–30 days after birth (137, 139), a pattern synchronous with the onset of brain electrical activity (140). The physiological roles of the three distinct catalytic isoforms in brain function remain to be elucidated.

b. Heart. In cardiac muscle, α1 mRNA is the major α-isoform transcript expressed throughout development (120). Both α2 and α3 mRNAs also are present, but in lesser amounts relative to α1 mRNA. Interestingly, a developmental switch in α2 and α3 mRNA abundances occurs between the first and second week of birth. The α3 mRNA appears predominantly in fetal and neonatal myocardium, and then decreases to negligible levels in adult tissue. Conversely, α2 mRNA abundance is low in fetal and neonatal myocardium and gradually increases in juvenile and adult tissue. The transition in α3 and α2 mRNAs between days 7 and 15 after birth is synchronous with the shortening of rat heart action potential duration (*141*). While this does not imply a cause-and-effect relationship, the results suggest that these two α isoforms of Na, K-ATPase may function differently in modulating cardiac physiology. There are also postnatal developmental changes in immunologically different Na, K-ATPase catalytic subunits in rat cardiac ventricles (*142*).

Differential expression of the various α-isoform proteins and their sensitivity to cardiac glycosides should have important consequences for modulating myocardial inotropy during distinct developmental stages and pathological conditions. In regard to the latter, the kinetic properties of ouabain binding to newborn rat heart Na, K-ATPase differs from that of the normal adult heart enzyme, but is similar to that for the hypertrophied adult heart (*143*); the latter condition is induced by chronic pressure overload (i.e., abdominal aortic coarctation). These observations suggest that the α3 gene may be reinduced in hypertrophied adult heart, but this hypothesis has yet to be explored experimentally. However, in a related study examining the effects of hormone-induced hypertension on Na, K-ATPase gene expression, uni-nephrectomized rats treated with deoxycorticosterone-salt or angiotensin II showed a decrease to one-third to one-fifteenth in α2 mRNA abundance in left ventricular myocardium and aorta (*144*). This response was specific for these tissues, as α2 mRNA abundance in skeletal muscle tissue was unaffected. Reexpression or accumulation of α3 mRNA was not observed. However, this effect occurred in hypertensive rats regardless of whether the myocardial tissue was hypertrophied or nonhypertrophied as a consequence of the hormonal treatment. The authors concluded that downregulation of α2 mRNA in the left ventricular myocardium and aorta is elicited by increased intravascular pressure and is not a consequence of hypertrophy. It remains to be established whether similar alterations in α2 mRNA abundance occur in hypertrophied hearts induced by chronic pressure overload. It is known that different models of hypertrophy are associated with distinct physiological responses, including normal, depressed, or increased contractility (*145*). Thus, it is possible that each model of cardiac hypertrophy may be associated with distinct changes in expression of the Na, K-ATPase genes. Interestingly, transitions in isoform abundance of other cardiac muscle-specific genes also occur during ontogenesis (*146*) and hypertrophy (*147–149*). Thus, during these two processes, there occur major gene regulatory events that are poorly understood, but may profoundly influence cardiac function.

c. *Lung.* Lung tissue expresses predominantly the α1 mRNA throughout development (120). Both α1 and β mRNAs are regulated coordinately, with a major increase in abundance of approximately 4- and 10-fold, respectively, around the time of birth. These changes are synchronous with the increased liquid clearance of fetal lungs shortly before and after birth (150, 151). The observation that the α1 and β mRNAs increase temporally at birth supports the hypothesis that active ion transport across the pulmonary epithelium facilitates liquid absorption at birth, as suggested in previous studies using fetal sheep (152). Moreover, cation transport in rabbit lung epithelial cells, as measured by ouabain-sensitive Rb^+ uptake, was increased 4-fold in cells obtained from pups that experienced labor compared to pups that experienced no labor (14). The precise mechanism by which this occurs is not understood. Nevertheless, these results have been interpreted (14) as a possible explanation for the increased lung fluid content that is associated with premature birth and delivery by cesarean section before the onset of labor (150, 151). In addition, the α1 isoform may also play an important role in maintaining the adult alveoli relatively free of fluid (153, 154).

d. *Kidney.* Kidney tissue, like lung, expresses predominantly the α1-isoform mRNA in a coordinate pattern of expression with β mRNA (120). RNA blot analysis reveals that kidney α1 and β mRNAs are the highest in abundance at all stages of development relative to the other tissues examined. Both mRNAs approximately double by 25 days of age and then decrease by approximately 70% by 55 days of age. Similar small increases in Na, K-ATPase activity are observed also in the developing 10- to 40-day-old rat proximal tubule cells (155); these increases parallel those in the renal fluid reabsorptive capacity (156).

e. *Skeletal Muscle.* In fetal skeletal muscle, α1 mRNA is the predominant catalytic isoform transcript; it remains constant at that level throughout development (120). Following birth, however, α2 mRNA abundance increases 89-fold by 15 days of age to become the major α-isoform transcript in skeletal muscle. The α3 mRNA levels also increase but to a much lesser extent. Similarly, the muscle β-subunit mRNA abundance also increases (9-fold) coordinately with α2 mRNA following birth. These changes parallel large increases in ouabain-sensitive binding sites measured in isolated rat soleus muscle during the first 35 days of life (157). Increases in the level of Na, K-ATPase α2 gene expression during myogenesis appear to be coregulated with other muscle-specific proteins involved in electrical excitability, such as acetylcholine receptors (158) and voltage-sensitive Na^+ channels (159).

The possible physiological relevance of α2 protein expression in muscle function can be inferred from the fact that the α2 isozyme exhibits a lower affinity for Na^+ than does $\alpha 1$ in rat adipocytes (*129*). Based on kinetic considerations, the $\alpha 2$ isozyme would be relatively inactive in the presence of normal intracellular Na^+ levels. However, insulin increases the affinity of the $\alpha 2$ subunit for Na^+ sufficiently to activate the enzyme (*129*). Assuming that a similar mechanism occurs in muscle, significant stimulation of the $\alpha 2$ isozyme would occur under conditions stimulating insulin release. Indeed, insulin increases the resting membrane potential of skeletal muscle (*160*). Thus, under such circumstances, muscle would have a large reserve capacity to pump Na^+ and K^+ that would be required for maintenance of the membrane electrical potential, and hence muscle excitability.

2. CELLS

Developmental studies examining the expression of the Na, K-ATPase gene family in predetermined or determined stem cells, or in cell lines capable of undergoing differentiation and activation of cell-specific genes, have been limited. Primary cultures of chick embryo skeletal myoblasts exhibit a severalfold increase in the concentration of Na, K-ATPase molecules in the plasma membrane during formation of multinucleate myotubes, as measured by immunodetection and ouabain-binding techniques (*134, 135*). At present, little is known about the Na, K-ATPase isozyme composition of these cells. A particular cell line that also has the potential to provide useful insight into the developmental aspects of muscle Na, K-ATPase gene regulation is the murine C2C12 myogenic cell line, in which undifferentiated myoblasts express primarily the $\alpha 1$ mRNA (*161*). Fusion of the proliferating myoblasts to form differentiated myotubes in nutrient-reduced culture medium was accompanied by an approximate 12-fold induction of $\alpha 2$ mRNA, while $\alpha 1$ mRNA remained constant throughout myogenesis. The β-subunit mRNA was also induced coordinately with the increase in $\alpha 2$ mRNA, albeit to a lesser extent (2- to 3-fold increase). Quantitatively, the relative abundance of the combined α-subunit mRNAs was severalfold that of the β-subunit mRNAs, similar to what is observed in skeletal muscle tissue. Expression of the rodent $\alpha 2$ gene product, which has a greater affinity for cardiac glycosides such as ouabain, correlates with the appearance of high-affinity, ouabain binding sites and ouabain-sensitive Na, K-ATPase activity in C2C12 myotubes. Thus, this cell line appears to mimic to a reasonable extent the changes in Na, K-ATPase gene expression observed in developing rodent skeletal muscle tissue.

3. REGULATORY CONSIDERATIONS

In most tissues and cells examined, the amount of mRNA transcripts encoding the α isoform and β subunit appears to be regulated coordinately throughout development, possibly mediated by transcriptional and/or posttranscriptional processes that have not been defined precisely. Nevertheless, the coordinate regulation of the α- and β-subunit mRNAs supports the generally accepted view that the β subunit, while its function is unknown, is an integral component of Na, K-ATPase. Analysis of the subunit composition of the enzyme has shown that the α and β subunits are present in equimolar amounts (24). Furthermore, pulse-chase experiments have demonstrated that α- and β-subunit syntheses are concurrent and equal in magnitude (91). However, the same stoichiometric relationship of α-isoform to β-subunit mRNAs was not observed even though they generally exhibit coordinate up- or down-regulation. The combined α- to β-subunit mRNA ratios varied greatly in the different tissues (see Table III) and cells examined (161; J. Orlowski and J. B Lingrel, unpublished). This suggests the possibility that translational or posttranslational regulation of the α isoform and β proteins also may occur to maintain equimolar amounts of both Na, K-ATPase subunits. Alternatively, due to the isolation of human Na, K-ATPase α-like genomic sequences in addition to α1, α2, and α3 (discussed in Section IV), it is not possible to exclude the presence of additional rat α (and possibly β) isoforms which may or may not cross-hybridize with the isoform-specific cDNA probes used in previous studies. This could result in the apparent differences in the ratios of α-isoform to β-subunit mRNA.

Understanding the complex regulatory processes involved in the ontogeny of Na, K-ATPase gene expression in various tissues and cells is a challenging problem. Future advances in defining the role of transcriptional mechanisms in Na, K-ATPase regulation may involve the development of transgenic mice or transiently transfected cells containing chimeric genes constructed with regions of the individual genes linked to a reporter gene, such as bacterial chloramphenicol acetyltransferase. These types of experiments should provide significant information on *cis*-acting DNA regulatory elements involved in tissue-/cell-specific, developmental, or hormonal regulation of the multiple genes. Delineation of these *cis*-acting DNA regulatory elements will aid in the identification of potential *trans*-acting factors involved in regulation of Na, K-ATPase genes.

C. Modulators of Activity

1. HORMONAL REGULATION

Na, K-ATPase activity is modulated by numerous hormones, including vasopressin (162, 163), epidermal growth factor (164), nerve growth factor (165), insulin (60, 63, 129, 130, 166, 167), glucagon (130, 131), catecholamines (168–170), glucocorticoids (174, 175), mineralocorticoids (125, 187, 188, 191–200), and triiodothyronine (T3) (202–211). These modulators provide important potential mechanisms for regulating a multitude of cellular processes. Hormones regulating Na, K-ATPase activity can be divided into two general categories. First, there are hormones (steroid and thyroid hormones) that alter the level of expression of Na, K-ATPase genes, as measured by changes in mRNA and protein abundance. A considerable latent period (hours to days) is required before the effects of these hormones are manifested. Second, there are hormones (peptide hormones and catecholamines) that modulate the activity of existing Na, K-ATPase pumps. Possibly this can occur by effecting changes in membrane ion-channel permeabilities, resulting in rapid changes in the cation substrate concentration. As well, these hormones may modulate activity indirectly through interaction with specific membrane receptors that influence Na, K-ATPase by an undetermined pathway, possibly involving posttranslational modification of the enzyme. Na, K-ATPase responds very rapidly to these hormones, typically on the order of seconds or minutes. Thus, the complexity of Na, K-ATPase regulation by a variety of hormones allows the organism to respond either acutely or chronically to many changes in the internal or external environment.

The precise molecular mechanisms whereby these distinct classes of hormones influence Na, K-ATPase are not well understood. The steroid and thyroid hormones are thought to mediate their effects through a high-affinity hormone–receptor/DNA-binding complex that, directly or indirectly, modulates primarily the rate of Na, K-ATPase gene transcription. Secondarily, this hormone–receptor complex also may influence nuclear processing of the primary transcripts, nuclear to cytoplasmic transport, and mRNA stability by, as yet, undefined mechanisms. While speculative, there is evidence to suggest the existence of additional mechanisms influenced by the hormone–receptor complex that could regulate the rate of Na, K-ATPase mRNA translation as well as the formation of functional α,β dimers necessary for functional activity. The cumulative result would be to regulate the number of Na, K-ATPase molecules synthesized *de novo* and inserted into the plasma membrane.

In general, peptide hormones and catecholamines appear to mediate their effects on Na, K-ATPase by interacting with plasma membrane receptors and stimulating second messengers (cyclic nucleotides and diacylglycerol) and their subsequent activation of protein kinases (169–173). However, the mode of transmission of this signal to activate Na, K-ATPase is unknown. In addition, phosphorylation of the catalytic α subunit by a cAMP-independent protein kinase has been implicated in the regulation of Na, K-ATPase activity (176), although further studies will be required to clearly demonstrate this effect. It remains to be established whether hormones directly influence covalent modification of the enzyme.

In this section, we summarize some of the more recent studies designed to characterize the actions of mineralocorticoids and thyroid hormone on Na,K-ATPase gene expression. We focus on these hormones because they illustrate the regulatory complexity involved in modulating the activity and amount of Na,K-ATPase molecules. Additional information on these and other hormones is in other extensive reviews on hormonal regulation of Na,K-ATPase (*22a, 177–181*).

    a. Mineralocorticoids. Mineralocorticoids, such as aldosterone, are potent stimulators of transepithelial Na^+ transport in a variety of target tissues, including amphibian urinary bladder (*182*), mammalian colon (*183–185*), and kidney cortical collecting tubules (*186–188*). These tissues perform an essential role in regulating Na^+ concentrations, and hence the osmolarity, of extracellular fluids. The mineralocorticoid-mediated changes in electrolyte transport are associated with early increases in the Na^+ channel permeability of apical plasma membrane (*184, 185, 189, 190*) and/or alterations in Na,K-ATPase activity of basolateral membrane (*187, 188, 191–200*). These studies support two models for the mechanism of mineralocorticoid regulation of Na,K-ATPase activity. The first model hypothesizes direct action of mineralocorticoids on Na,K-ATPase gene expression, while the other is based on results indicating that elevated cellular Na^+ influx is a necessary intermediate step for hormone action.

    Initial support for direct mineralocorticoid action came from studies demonstrating increased synthesis of the rat kidney Na,K-ATPase α subunit shortly (3 hours) following aldosterone treatment in adrenalectomized animals (*193*). In more controlled studies using toad-bladder tissue cultures, aldosterone stimulated the rate of α- and β-subunit biosynthesis by 2- to 3-fold following a 3- to 6-hour latent period (*195*). This induction was antagonized by the anti-mineralocorticoid spironolactone, but was not influenced by amiloride, a specific inhibitor of apical Na^+ channel conductance. These results suggest that aldosterone induction of Na,K-ATPase is directed by a hormone–receptor-mediated process that is independent of increased intracellular Na^+ concentration. In addition, actinomycin D inhibits this induction, implying that gene transcription, either of Na,K-ATPase or other intermediate genes, is required (*200*).

    Further supporting evidence for this model was obtained using the *X. laevis* kidney A6 cell line. Aldosterone treatment (6-hour period) resulted in a 2- to 4-fold increase in the abundance of α- and β-subunit mRNAs concomitant with a quantitatively similar increase in biosynthesis of α- and β-subunit polypeptides (*125*). Na^+ transport, as measured electrophysiologically, also was augmented to a similar extent. Spironolactone inhibited the aldosterone response, again implying that induction is mediated by the mineralocorticoid receptor. Cycloheximide, a protein synthesis inhibitor, did not prevent the aldosterone-mediated increase in α and β mRNA abundance, but virtually arrested Na$^+$ transport. Thus, proteins induced secondarily do not appear to be required for mRNA induction. In a separate study, amiloride also had no effect on aldosterone-induced Na,K-ATPase activity in A6 cells, thereby eliminating increased Na$^+$ influx as a primary mediator (199). These results support the concept that the aldosterone–receptor-mediated augmentation of Na,K-ATPase gene expression is a direct effect and not a consequence of intracellular Na$^+$ levels or other intermediate mineralocorticoid-responsive regulatory proteins. Furthermore, both the α- and β-subunit mRNAs and corresponding translation products are regulated coordinately, implying similar control mechanisms for both genes. Alternatively, different mechanisms may independently regulate each gene so that the levels are similarly induced.

While the evidence provided is suggestive of a primary effect of aldosterone on Na,K-ATPase gene transcriptional activity, it cannot be regarded as conclusive. More direct evidence obtained by using nuclear transcription rate assays is required to establish this mechanism. In addition, secondary effects operating at the posttranscriptional, translational, or posttranslation levels have yet to be investigated adequately. Measurements of the rates of the synthesis and degradation of α and β cytoplasmic mRNA and protein are required.

The second model postulates that elevated intracellular Na$^+$ functions as the mediator of aldosterone-induced Na,K-ATPase activity. This is based on time-course studies showing variability in the time of aldosterone-mediated induction of Na$^+$ transport, Na,K-ATPase activity, and inhibition of this response by amiloride. The observation that aldosterone treatment of adrenalecomized rats increased kidney Na$^+$ reabsorption prior to increases in Na,K-ATPase activity showed a correlation between intracellular Na$^+$ levels and Na,K-ATPase activity (186). That aldosterone activation of Na,K-ATPase in cortical collecting tubules of adrenalectomized rabbits is blocked by amiloride (194) supports this correlation. These results suggest that the enhancement of Na,K-ATPase activity is mediated primarily by increased Na$^+$ permeability through the apical membrane Na$^+$ channel.

Nevertheless, it is not clear whether the aldosterone response, possibly elicited via Na$^+$ ions, involves stimulation of existing Na,K-ATPase enzymes or de novo synthesis of active molecules. Similar results also were observed using in vitro suspensions of rat medullary kidney tubules (201). Amiloride inhibits the mineralocorticoid activation of Na,K-ATPase activity. However, when intracellular Na$^+$ levels are elevated by short-term incubation of the tubules in the presence of ouabain, no change in Na,K-ATPase activity is detected within the 2 hours normally required to elicit a maximal steroid response (201). The results suggest that elevated intracellular Na$^+$ is not the primary mediator of mineralocorticoid action, but perhaps may play a permissive role in increasing Na, K-ATPase activity (201).

Thus, while a comprehensive mechanism describing mineralocorticoid action(s) remains elusive, it appears that two steps of hormone action that occur separately or together in a tissue-specific manner may be involved: first, an early response that increases apical Na^+ permeability and, hence, intracellular Na^+ that, in turn, could stimulate the activity of existing basolateral Na, K-ATPase; second, a slower phase mediated by the mineralocorticoid receptor increasing the amount of Na, K-ATPase.

b. *Thyroid Hormones.* It is well established that thyroid hormone T3 stimulates Na, K-ATPase activity and enzyme abundance in a wide variety of tissues, including liver, kidney, intestine, skeletal, and cardiac muscle (202–205). T3 also augments both the activity and the relative abundance of distinctive α isoforms of rat brain Na, K-ATPase during development (137). Interestingly, rat brain Na, K-ATPase becomes unresponsive to T3 stimulation in the adult, although the mechanism is unknown (204). In rat kidney cortex, the T3-induced increase in Na, K-ATPase activity correlates with proportionate increases in the synthesis of both the α and β subunits (206, 207). The initial evidence suggesting that the increased kidney α-subunit synthesis occurs at a pretranslational level came from the fact that kidney poly(A)$^+$-RNA isolated from T3-treated animals exhibits increased α-subunit mRNA translational activity in a rabbit reticulocyte lysate system (208, 209). Subsequent studies using RNA blot analysis corroborated these results by showing increased levels of α1 mRNA (210). Also adult rat brain Na, K-ATPase activity and α1 mRNA abundance are invariant following T3 treatment (210). At present, it is not known if T3 modulates the relative abundance of the other brain α isoforms (α2 and α3) without affecting total brain Na, K-ATPase activity. This does not exclude the possibility of changes in regional brain Na, K-ATPase activity compared to total activity.

Studies using rat kidney cortex were extended further to show that both the Na, K-ATPase α1- and β-subunit mRNAs were induced coordinately to similar quantitative extents (approximately 2-fold) by T3 (177, 211). These changes correlated in a parallel time course with similar increases in Na, K-ATPase activity (211). These results imply that changes in rat renal cortex α1- and β-gene transcription and/or transcript processing and stability must be regulated coordinately by T3. To ascertain the possible mode of T3 regulation, α1- and β-gene transcription rates were measured (212), revealing that both the α1 and β genes were stimulated 2-fold, similar to increases in mRNA abundance and enzyme activity. Thus, in rat kidney cortex, T3 coordinately regulates α1- and β-gene expression primarily by stimulating the rates of gene transcription. This implies that both genes may contain similar

T3-responsive DNA regulatory elements. However, it has not been established whether the primary effect of T3 induction involves direct interaction of a nuclear T3–receptor complex with *cis*-regulatory elements of the α1 and β genes, or whether the induction is secondary to T3 induction of other regulatory proteins that mediate enhanced gene transcription. Another possibility is that increased gene expression may be secondary to T3-induced alterations in ion fluxes that mediate gene expression by unknown mechanisms (*213, 214*). This question remains to be addressed.

Interestingly, while T3 mediates coordinate and quantitatively similar up-regulation of rat kidney cortex α1- and β-gene transcription, mRNA abundance, and enzyme activity, this does not extend to all tissues. In rat cardiac muscle, T3 augmented α1 and β mRNA 9-fold and 22-fold, respectively, with only a doubling of Na,K-ATPase activity (*177*). Conversely, rat liver α1 mRNA was increased approximately 7-fold, with no increase in β mRNA (*212*). These changes were accompanied by only a 1.3-fold stimulation of both α1- and β-gene transcription, implying a predominantly posttranscriptional effect on mRNA levels. Moreover, liver Na,K-ATPase activity was increased only 1.3-fold in response to T3 treatment.

In conclusion, these studies suggest that T3 regulation of Na,K-ATPase gene expression involves a complex interaction of transcription, posttranscriptional, translational, and posttranslational mechanisms. Moreover, a combination of these processes appears to be utilized in a tissue-specific manner.

2. Cations

Intracellular Na^+ has long been purported to stimulate Na,K-ATPase activity. It is proposed that Na,K-ATPase has two distinct stimulatory responses to Na^+ ions, short-term (acute) and long-term (chronic). The short-term (acute) response to increased intracellular Na^+, effected by such mediators as serum (*215–217*), vasopressin (*163*), insulin (*131, 167*), glucagon (*130*), and monensin (*215, 216*), or by brief exposure to low extracellular K^+ (*218*), is a consequence of elevated catalytic turnover rate of existing Na,K-ATPase molecules due to increased Na^+ substrate availability, with no change in the number of active enzyme units. Kinetics measurements show that Na,K-ATPase operates at half-maximal velocity or lower in the presence of normal intracellular Na^+ levels (*22a, 218*).

Conversely, the long-term (chronic) stimulatory response to elevated intracellular Na^+, achieved by prolonged exposure to ouabain (*201, 218*), veratridine (*135, 219*), or low extracellular K^+ (*218–221*), increases the concentration of functionally active enzymes in the plasma membrane, as measured by ouabain binding sites or phosphorylation of the catalytic subunit. This response appears to be related to the increase in intracellular Na^+

rather than a decrease in K^+ (220). The elevated enzyme activity restores the original transmembrane ionic gradient, thereby maintaining cellular homeostasis (218, 221). Protein synthesis is also required, suggesting that the induced amount of Na,K-ATPase is a consequence of increased enzyme biosynthesis (220). However, this does not exclude the possibility that protein synthesis also may be necessary for transport of latent Na,K-ATPase units to the plasma membrane. In cultured avian neurons, a large pool of Na,K-ATPase appears to be stored intracellularly, presumably serving as a reserve capacity of potential pumps (91). This latter alternative remains to be elucidated.

In view of the existence of multiple Na,K-ATPase genes, the rat liver ARL-15 cell line was used (222) to ascertain whether alternate isoforms of Na,K-ATPase are induced in response to long-term low extracellular K^+. Biochemical analysis revealed that basal and induced enzymatic activities in control and low K^+-treated cells, respectively, were kinetically and functionally indistinguishable. Furthermore, RNA blot analysis revealed the presence of only the α1 mRNA in ARL-15 cells under both conditions. The 70% increase in activity and abundance of Na,K-ATPase molecules in response to low K^+-treatment (24 hours) was correlated with an increase in α1- and β-subunit mRNAs (223). This clearly indicates that elevated Na^+ concentrations can elicit increases in Na,K-ATPase gene expression by altering transcriptional and/or posttranscriptional processes. Rate measurements of α1- and β-gene transcription rates and mRNA half-lives are required to determine the respective contributions of these mechanisms.

Both the α1- and β-subunit mRNAs also exhibited coordinate induction, although not to similar quantitative extents (α1, 290%; β, 70%). Moreover, the cellular concentration of α1 mRNA exceeded that for β mRNA more than 30-fold. Based on the observed similarity between the increases in β mRNA and Na,K-ATPase activity, and assuming that both α and β mRNAs are translated with equal efficiency, it was suggested that the regulation of β-subunit abundance may determine the increases in functionally active enzyme (223). This implies that excess α subunit is synthesized but not incorporated into active enzyme units. Alternatively, the translation rates of α1 and β mRNA may differ significantly to produce equimolar amounts of both subunit proteins. Discerning which of these alternative hypotheses is correct will require direct measurements of subunit biosynthesis rates. Alterations in Na,K-ATPase subunit synthesis and degradation have been implicated in regulating enzyme activity in veratridine-treated chick skeletal muscle cells (135). In contrast to ARL-15 cells, Na,K-ATPase in Madin–Darby kidney cells exhibits coordinate and similar quantitative increases ($\sim$2-fold) in α- and β-mRNA abundance, rates of synthesis and abundance of subunits (126). Interestingly, no change in Na,K-ATPase activity was observed and the explanation for this remains to be clarified. In MDCK cells, neither the α- or β-subunit mRNA appears to be rate-limiting, as has been suggested to occur in ARL-15 cells (223).

The molecular pathway for the increase in α- and β-subunit mRNA abundance in response to elevated intracellular Na^+ remains to be established. Nevertheless, it appears to involve increases in nuclear transcription rates and/or posttranscriptional alterations in mRNA steady-state levels. Furthermore, translational and/or posttranslational mechanisms also may play a role in regulating the concentration of active Na,K-ATPase inserted in the plasma membrane. Thus, similar to steroid and thyroid hormones, regulation of Na,K-ATPase gene expression in response to elevated intracellular Na^+ may involve a combination of these mechanisms, which operate in a tissue- or cell-specific manner.

IV. Na,K-ATPase Genes

It is clear from the studies discussed in the previous section that the catalytic subunit isoforms of Na,K-ATPase are expressed in a tissue-specific and developmental-stage-specific manner. In addition, there is considerable evidence demonstrating that Na,K-ATPase levels are regulated by various hormones and in response to certain physiological conditions. An understanding of the genetic mechanisms of regulation of Na,K-ATPase expression requires the characterization of genomic sequences encoding these isoforms, and detailed analyses of *cis*-acting regulatory elements and *trans*-acting factors controlling their expression. In this section, recent studies concerning the identification and characterization of the genes and the mapping of their chromosomal locations are described.

A. The Na,K-ATPase Multigene Family

Although cDNAs encoding the catalytic (α) subunit of Na,K-ATPase have been isolated from many species, including rats (35, 37, 38, 225), sheep (18), humans (44, 45), pigs (40), chickens (41), frogs (226), and *T. californica* (19), the genes for this subunit have been isolated only for humans (227–229). Sverdlov *et al.* identified five classes of human genomic clones, using a pig α-subunit cDNA as a hybridization probe (227). Limited DNA sequence analysis demonstrated that some of these clones represent the α1, α2, and α3 genes. The fourth class, represented by clone λNKαR15-1, appears to encode an H,K-ATPase gene. A fifth class, represented by clone λNKαSW3.2, encodes an amino-acid sequence that is similar to the α-subunit sequences; however, the predicted amino-acid sequence of the phosphorylation domain exhibits only 89% identity to the phosphorylation domain of the three known α-subunit isoforms. In contrast, the three α isoforms are identical to each other around the phosphorylation site. Clone λNKαSW3.2 exhibits 86%,

52%, and 48% amino-acid identity, respectively, to the rat H,K-ATPase (76), rabbit slow-twitch skeletal muscle sarcoplasmic reticulum Ca-ATPase (34), and rat plasma membrane Ca-ATPase (78). Thus, it may represent a gene encoding a related transport ATPase rather than Na,K-ATPase catalytic subunit, although it does not appear to encode the H,K-ATPase, a muscle sarcoplasmic reticulum Ca-ATPase, or a plasma membrane Ca-ATPase. On the other hand, it may represent a pseudogene.

Shull and Lingrel (228) isolated four genes, each spanning approximately 20–35 kilobases, using sheep α1 and rat α2 cDNA probes. Limited sequence analysis demonstrated that two of these genes encode known functional isoforms. The αA (ATP1A1) gene encodes the α1 isoform, while the αB (ATP1A2) gene encodes the α2 isoform. Two genes did not correspond to any known isoform, but did exhibit nucleotide similarity to α-subunit sequences. One of these α-like genes, ATP1AL2 (αC), is located approximately 13 kilobasepairs downstream from the 3' end of the α2 gene and appears to represent a catalytic subunit gene or pseudogene. Based on limited sequence analysis, this gene exhibits high nucleotide (76–80%) and deduced amino-acid sequence (80–89%) identities to the human α1 and to the three rat α-isoform cDNA sequences. Nucleotide and amino-acid similarity comparisons of the other α-like gene, ATP1AL1 (αD), to published Na,K-ATPase sequences suggest that this gene could encode either an additional α isoform or a related cation-transport ATPase. When limited regions of this gene were compared to the corresponding regions of the three rat α-subunit cDNAs, the nucleotide (68–76%) and amino-acid (66–75%) sequence identities observed were less than those seen in pairwise comparisons of the rat α-isoform sequences to each other. For the rat isoforms, nucleotide identities in this region range from 76% to 80%, while amino-acid identities are 87–91%. ATP1AL1 does not appear to represent either an H,K-ATPase or a Ca-ATPase gene, since it exhibits only 72%, 33%, and 34% amino-acid identity, respectively, to the corresponding regions of the H,K-ATPase (76), the slow-twitch sarcoplasmic reticulum Ca-ATPase (34), and the plasma membrane Ca-ATPase isoform 1 (78).

Thus, the Na,K-ATPase catalytic subunit is encoded by a family of genes that is diagrammed in Fig. 8. Three of these genes encode the known α-subunit isoforms: α1, α2, and α3. Genomic cloning studies also reveal the presence of additional genes that may encode novel α-subunit isoforms, related cation transport ATPases, or pseudogenes.

B. Genomic Organization

The sequence of the exons and some of the introns has been determined for the human α3 gene (229). This gene spans more than 25 kilobasepairs (kbp) and consists of 23 exons and 22 introns. Intron–exon boundary sequences in the α3 gene of Na,K-ATPase are shown in Table V. These se-

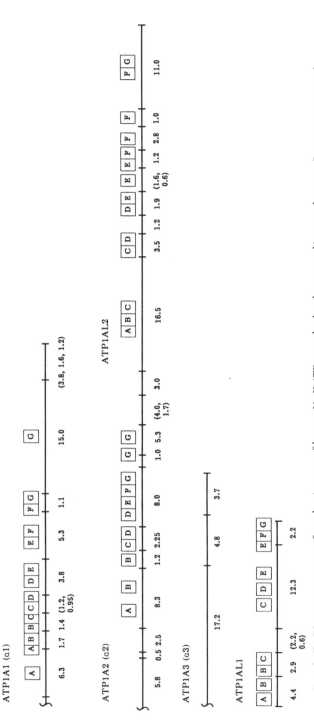

FIG. 8. EcoRI restriction maps of α-subunit genes of human Na,K-ATPase and related genes and/or pseudogenes. Genes representing known α-subunit isoforms (ATP1A1, ATP1A2, and ATP1A3) and related sequences (ATP1AL1 and ATP1AL2) which may represent genes for novel α-subunit isoforms, pseudogenes, or related α-like transport ATPase genes are shown. Location of EcoRI sites are indicated by vertical bars; sizes of resulting fragments are given in kbp. Numbers in parentheses indicate that the order of the fragments has not been determined. Boxed letters above the maps indicate hybridization to sheep kidney α1-subunit cDNA fragments: A, AvaI–AvaI, nucleotides 106–454; B, AvaI–XbaI, nucleotides 455–965; C, XbaI–BamHI, nucleotides 965–1359; D, BamHI–BamHI, nucleotides 1360–1795; E, NcoI–NcoI, nucleotides 1827–2456; NcoI–BglII, nucleotides 2457–3112; G, BglII–AvaI, nucleotides 3113–3523. ATP1A1, ATP1A2, ATP1AL1, and ATP1AL2 are from 228; ATP1A3 is from 229.

TABLE V

EXON/INTRON BOUNDARIES IN THE Na,K-ATPase α3 SUBUNIT GENE[a]

Exon		Intron	Exon
1 ATG GGG		--- 1 ---cacctcgcag/	GAC AAG
Met Gly	(2)		Asp Lys
		2	
2 GCT ATG		/gtaagc--- (99 bp) ---tgttcctcag/	ACA GAG
Ala Met	(31)		Thr Glu
3 GTG CAG		/gtgtgg--- 3 ---ctgtccctag/	GGT TTG
Val Gln	(51)		Gly Leu
4 GAC AAC		/gtgagt--- 4 ---ctccccacag/	CTG TAC
Asp Asn	(119)		Leu Tyr
		5	
5 CCC CAG		/gtgaag--- (113 bp) ---cccacctcag/	CAA GCC
Pro Gln	(157)		Gln Ala
		6	
6 TGC AAG		/gtgggc--- (433 bp) ---ctacccccag/	GTG GAC
Cys Lys	(202)		Val Asp
		7	
7 GAA G		/gtgagg--- (115 bp) ---tggcctgcag/	GC ACG
Gly G(ly)	(241)		(G)ly Thr
8 GTC ACT		/gtaagg--- 8 ---cgtcctccag/	GTG TGT
Val Thr	(331)		Val Cys
		9	
9 TCA G		/gtgagc--- (74 bp) ---cctcccccag/	GG ACC
Ser G(ly)	(397)		(G)ly Thr
		10	
10 AAG AG		/gtgggt--- (84 bp) ---ctccttgcag/	G GAT
Lys Ar(g)	(435)		(Ar)g Asp
11 TAC CAG		/gtactc--- 11 ---cggtccccag/	CTC TCC
Tyr Gln	(479)		Leu Ser
12 CTT G		/gtgcga--- 12 ---ctgccactag/	GT TTC
Leu G(ly)	(542)		(G)ly Phe
		13	
13 ATC AAG		/gtgtgg--- (70 bp) ---atgcctgcag/	GTC ATC
Ile Lys	(602)		Val Ile
14 CCC CG		/gtgagc--- 14 ---ctcttccag/	G GAT
Pro Ar(g)	(648)		(Ar)g Asp
15 AGA CAG		/gtgggc--- 15 ---ctctccccag/	GGT GCA
Arg Gln	(698)		Gly Ala
16 GAG G		/gtgagt--- 16 ---tgtgccacag/	GC CGC
Glu G(ly)	(754)		(G)ly Arg
		17	
17 GAC ATG		/gtgagc--- (77 bp) ---ctccgcctag/	GTC CCT
Asp Met	(806)		Val Pro
18 ATT G		/gtgagg--- 18 ---ctccttccag/	GA ATG
Ile G(ly)	(847)		(G)ly Met

(*continued*)

TABLE V
(*Continued*)

Exon			Intron			Exon
19 CAG TGG		/gtgagt---	19	---gctcctgcag/		ACA TAC
Gln Trp	(896)					Thr Tyr
20 ATG AA		/gtgagg---	20	---gtgcctccag/		G AAC
Met Ly(s)	(940)					(Ly)s Asn
21 CTC AA		/gtgagt---	21	---ctcccctctgcag/		G CCC
Leu Ly(s)	(974)					(Ly)s Pro
22 GGG G		/gtgagg---	22	---gtctctccag/		GT TGG
Gly G(ly)	(1004)					G(ly) Trp

*a*Sequences of the exon–intron boundaries are taken from Ref. 229. Exon sequences are in upper case letters and intron sequences in lower case. Amino-acids encoded by codons bordering the splice junctions are shown and the number of the amino-acid is given in parentheses. When the size of the intron is known, it is shown in parentheses below the intron number (bp, base pairs).

quences are in agreement with splice-junction consensus sequences compiled from other eukaryotic genes (230, 231). Each intron begins with G-T and ends with A-G. This A-G dinucleotide is preceded by a polypyrimidine tract containing no other A-G dinucleotide (232). The locations and sizes of the exons are depicted in Fig. 9. The coding exons vary in size from 60 to 269 basepairs (bp), with the average exon size, 143 bp, falling within the size range suggested to represent the most abundant exon size class for higher eukaryotic protein-coding genes (233). The sizes of all of the α3 gene introns have not been determined; however, for those that have been, the sizes range from 70 bp to over 5 kbp. Three introns (introns 9, 13, and 17) are only 70–77 bp in length. This is slightly less than the approximate minimal intron length, 80 nucleotides, required for efficient splicing of the rabbit β-globin gene (234), but larger than the 31- and 49-bp introns observed in the SV40 (235) and polyoma viruses (236). This size is also above the minimum intron length of 40–50 basepairs observed in surveys of intron lengths in higher eukaryotes (233, 234).

Genomic clones representing the 5′ end of the α3 gene have not been isolated, nor have 5′-end sequences of the other α-isoform genes and the β gene been published. Therefore, information about the promoter regions of these genes is lacking. Comparative studies of the 5′ flanking regions of the various α isoform and β genes should provide useful information concerning potential regulatory sequences such as hormone–receptor and transcription–factor binding sites.

A number of investigators have proposed that exons may encode polypeptide segments representing functional domains (237–239), structural

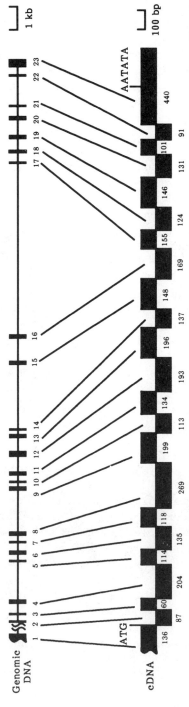

Fig. 9. Intron–exon structure of the α3-subunit gene of human Na,K-ATPase. The locations of the α3-subunit gene exons (from 229) are indicated by solid boxes on line 1. Sizes of the exons in basepairs are shown on line 2. The translation initiation codon (ATG) and the proposed polyadenylation signal (AATATA) are marked.

units (240), or domains of sequential supersecondary structure (241–243), and that intron–exon boundaries are frequently mapped to regions located on the surface of the protein (244–246). The determination of the genomic organization of the Na, K-ATPase α3 gene (229) and also the fast-twitch muscle sarcoplasmic reticulum Ca-ATPase gene (247) has allowed a discussion of the relationship between position of splice sites and proposed protein structural and functional domains of these ATPases (229, 247). However, since many of the functional and structural domains of these proteins have not been clearly delineated (for example, there is even uncertainty about the number of transmembrane domains), it is difficult to make any definite correlations.

When the amino-acid sequences of several P-type ATPases are aligned, regions of high sequence similarity that may correspond to conserved functional domains can be identified (see Fig. 4; 229, 247). The sequences encoding most of these conserved regions are interrupted by introns in either the Na, K-ATPase or sarcoplasmic reticulum Ca-ATPase genes except for the region surrounding the phosphorylation site, which is encoded within a single exon. A comparison of the positions of intron–extron boundaries in the α3 gene with those of the sarcoplasmic reticulum Ca-ATPase gene reveals that the boundary positions in the two ATPase genes are not correlated well with each other. However, exceptions are exon 8, encoding the third and fourth transmembrane domains in both Na, K-ATPase and Ca-ATPase, and exons 19–22, which encode hydrophobic domains in the carboxyl-terminal regions (247).

C. Chromosomal Location

The chromosomal locations of the human α-isoform and β-subunit genes have been determined by somatic cell hybrid mapping studies (248), and for α1, by in situ hybridization to lymphocyte chromosome spreads (45). As shown in Fig. 10, the α1 gene (ATP1A1) has been located on the short arm of human chromosome 1, band p11→p13. The α2 gene (ATP1A2) is located on the long arm of chromosome 1, region cen→q32. The α-related sequence, ATP1AL2 (αC), which is physically linked to the α2 gene, must therefore also be in this region. Another α-related sequence, ATP1AL1 (αD), has been assigned to chromosome 13, tentatively to region q21→q31. The α3 gene, ATP1A3, maps on chromosome 19. Sequences related to the β subunit have been located on chromosomes 1 and 4. The gene corresponding to clone λNKαSW3.2 (227) has not yet been located.

The chromosomal locations of several α- and β-subunit genes in the mouse have been determined (249). The murine homolog of the human ATP1A1 (α1) gene is on *Mus musculus* chromosome 3 (MMU3), homologs of

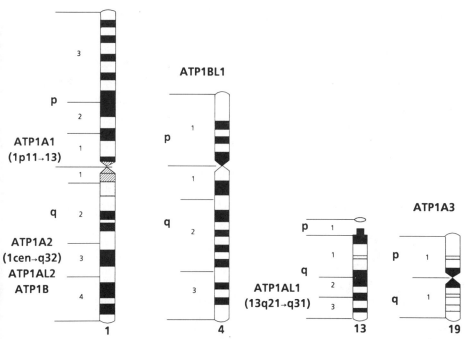

FIG. 10. Chromosomal location of the α- and β-subunit genes of human Na,K-ATPase. Chromosomes are depicted schematically. The regional chromosome location, if known, is indicated in parentheses. Locations are from 45 and 248.

ATP1A2 and ATP1B are on MMU1, and the homolog of ATP1A3 is on MMU7. As pointed out (248), ATP1A1 is a member of a group of syntenic loci on the short arm of human chromosome 1 (HSA1) that have homologs on MMU3. Likewise, ATP1A2 and possibly ATP1B, belong to a group of loci on the long arm of chromosome 1 that are conserved on MMU1. Since only a single site (MMU1) for the β-subunit gene has been identified in the mouse, and since MMU1 contains genes having homologs on human chromosome 1, it seems likely that the human β gene on chromosome 1 is the expressed β gene; the β-like sequence on human chromosome 4 may represent a pseudogene.

D. Future Directions

Characterization of the Na,K-ATPase genes provides the basis for molecular–genetic studies of the determinants that regulate the expression of this enzyme. Both *cis*-acting sequence elements involved in regulation of transcription and *trans*-acting factors interacting with these sequences can be identified. Molecular mechanisms involved in tissue- and cell-specific, developmental, and hormonal regulation of the α and β subunits can be addressed using both *in vitro* and *in vivo* techniques. As mentioned in Section III, DNA sequences influencing expression can be identified using transient expression systems in which putative regulatory regions of the Na,K-ATPase genes are linked to a reporter gene and introduced into cell lines that can be experimentally manipulated. *trans*-Acting factors involved in gene expression can be identified and purified using either these cell culture systems or tissues. Transgenic mice provide an *in vivo* method for studying gene expression. Such studies should greatly enhance our understanding of the regulatory factors crucial to the physiological functioning of this important enzyme.

The isolation of human genomic sequences encoding the Na,K-ATPase isoforms and the mapping of their chromosomal locations will allow a genetic approach to the analysis of inherited disease states that may involve this enzyme. When the chromosomal location of a disease locus is known, the candidacy of a Na,K-ATPase gene as the disease locus can be eliminated if the chromosomal locations do not coincide. Cases in which the locations appear to coincide or in which the location of the disease gene is unknown can be investigated by detailed genetic linkage analysis. In such cases, DNA probes that identify restriction fragment length polymorphisms (RFLPs) within each of the Na,K-ATPase genes can be used to establish the presence or absence of linkage between an Na,K-ATPase gene and the disease locus. This type of genetic analysis provides a powerful tool for investigating the role of Na,K-ATPase in such diseases as familial hypertension, familial obesity, and various kidney transport defects.

V. Summary

Researchers in the past few years have successfully used molecular–genetic approaches to determine the primary structures of several P-type ATPases. The amino-acid sequences of distinct members of this class of ion-transport ATPases (Na,K-, H,K-, and Ca-ATPases) have been deduced by cDNA cloning and sequencing. The Na,K-ATPase belongs to a multiple gene family, the principal diversity apparently resulting from distinct catalytic α isoforms. Computer analyses of the hydrophobicity and potential secondary structure of the α subunits and primary sequence comparisons with homologs from various species as well as other P-type ATPases have identified common structural features. This has provided the molecular foundation for the design of models and hypotheses aimed at understanding the relationship between structure and function. Development of a hypothetical transmembrane organization for the α subunit and application of site-specific mutagenesis techniques have allowed significant progress to be made toward identifying amino acids involved in cardiac glycoside resistance and possibly binding. However, the complex structural and functional features of this protein indicate that extensive research is necessary before a clear understanding of the molecular basis of active cation transport is achieved. This is complicated further by the paucity of information regarding the structural and functional contributions of the β subunit. Until such information is obtained, the proposed model and functional hypotheses should be considered judiciously.

Considerable progress also has been made in characterizing the regulatory complexity involved in expression of multiple α-isoform and β-subunit genes in various tissues and cells during development and in response to hormones and cations. The regulatory mechanisms appear to function at several molecular levels, involving transcriptional, posttranscriptional, translational, and posttranslational processes in a tissue- or cell-specific manner. However, much research is needed to precisely define the contributions of each of these mechanisms. Recent isolation of the genes for these subunits provides the framework for future advances in this area. Continued application of biochemical, biophysical, and molecular genetic techniques is required to provide a detailed understanding of the mechanisms involved in cation transport of this biologically and pharmacologically important enzyme.

REFERENCES

1. K. J. A. Ullrich, *Annu. Rev. Physiol.* **41**, 181 (1979).
2. G. A. Langer, *Annu. Rev. Physiol.* **44**, 435 (1982).
3. K. D. Philipson, *Annu. Rev. Physiol.* **47**, 561 (1985).
4. P. S. Aronson, *Annu. Rev. Physiol.* **47**, 545 (1985).
5. A. D. C. MacKnight and A. Leaf, *Physiol. Rev.* **57**, 510 (1977).
6. M. L. S. Ledbetter and M. Lubin, *Exp. Cell Res.* **105**, 223 (1977).
7. J. M. Larkin, M. S. Brown, J. L. Goldstein and R. G. W. Anderson, *Cell* **33**, 273 (1983).
8. R. C. Thomas, *Physiol. Rev.* **52**, 563 (1972).
9. B. Katz, "Nerve, Muscle and Synapse." McGraw-Hill, New York, 1966.
10. E. M. Wright, *J. Physiol. (London)* **226**, 545 (1972).
11. T. S. Vates, S. L. Bonting and W. W. Oppelt, *AJP* **206**, 1165 (1964).
12. D. F. Cole, *Br. J. Ophthalmol.* **45**, 202 (1961).
13. K. A. Simon, S. L. Bonting and N. M. Hawkins, *Exp. Eye Res.* **1**, 253 (1962).
14. R. D. Bland and C. A. R. Boyd, *J. Appl. Physiol.* **61**, 507 (1986).
15. P. DeWeer, "The Kidney: Physiology and Pathophysiology" (D. W. Seldin and G. Giebisch, eds.), p. 31. Raven, New York, 1985.
16. P. L. Pedersen and E. Carafoli, *Trends Biochem. Sci. (Pers. Ed.)* **12**, 186 (1987).

17. W. S. Craig and J. Kyte, *JBC* **255**, 6262 (1980).
18. G. E. Shull, A. Schwartz and J. B Lingrel, *Nature* **316**, 691 (1985).
19. K. Kawakami, S. Noguchi, M. Noda, H. Takahashi, T. Ohta, M. Kawamura, H. Nojima, K. Nagano, T. Hirose, S. Inayama, H. Hayashida, T. Miyata and S. Numa, *Nature* **316**, 733 (1985).
20. S. Noguchi, M. Noda, H. Takahashi, K. Kawakami, T. Ohta, K. Nagano, T. Hirose, S. Inayama, M. Kawamura and S. Numa, *FEBS Lett.* **196**, 315 (1986).
21. G. E. Shull, L. K. Lane and J. B Lingrel, *Nature* **321**, 429 (1986).
22. A. Askari, *J. Bioenerg. Biomembr.* **19**, 359 (1987).
22a. T. Clausen, *Physiol. Rev.* **66**, 542 (1986).
23. A. Schwartz, G. E. Lindenmayer and J. C. Allen, *Pharmacol. Rev.* **27**, 3 (1975).
24. P. L. Jørgensen, *BBA* **694**, 27 (1982).
25. A. Schwartz and J. H. Collins, in "Membranes and Transport" (A. Martonosi, ed.), Vol. 1, 521 pp. Plenum, New York, 1982.
26. J. Kyte, *Nature* **292**, 201 (1981).
27. W. L. Stahl, *Neurochem. Int.* **8**, 449 (1986).
28. W. L. Stahl and W. E. Harris, *Adv. Neurol.* **44**, 681 (1986).
29. J. G. Nørby, *Chem. Scr.* **27B**, 119 (1987).
31. T. A. Brown, B. Horowitz, R. P. Miller, A. A. McDonough and R. A. Farley, *BBA* **912**, 244 (1987).
32. J. H. Collins, A. S. Zot, W. J. Ball, Jr., L. K. Lane and A. Schwartz, *BBA*, **742**, 358 (1983).
33. J. H. Collins and A. S. Zot, *IRCS Med. Sci.* **11**, 799 (1983).
34. D. H. MacLennan, C. J. Brandl, B. Korczak and N. M. Green, *Nature* **316**, 696 (1985).
35. G. E. Shull, J. Greeb and J. B Lingrel, *Bchem* **25**, 8125 (1986).
36. R. W. Mercer, J. W. Schneider, A. Savitz, J. Emmanuel, E. J. Benz and R. Levenson, *MCBiol* **6**, 3884 (1986).
37. Y. Hara, O. Urayama, K. Kawakami, H. Nojima, H. Nagamune, T. Kojima, T. Ohta, K. Nagano and M. Nakao, *J. Biochem. (Tokyo)* **102**, 43 (1987).
38. V. L. M. Herrera, J. R. Emanuel, N. Ruiz-Opazo, R. Levenson and B. Nadal-Ginard, *J. Cell Biol.* **105**, 1855 (1987).
39. R. M. Young, G. E. Shull and J. B Lingrel, *JBC* **262**, 4905 (1987).
40. Y. A. Ovchinnikov, N. N. Modyanov, N. E. Broude, K. E. Petrukhin, A. V. Grishin, N. M. Arzamazova, N. A. Aldanova, G. S. Monastyrskaya and E. D. Sverdlov, *FEBS Lett.* **201**, 237 (1986).
41. K. Takeyasu, M. M. Tamkun, K. J. Renaud and D. M. Fambrough, *JBC* **263**, 4347 (1988).
42. K. Takeyasu, M. M. Tamkun, N. R. Siegel and D. M. Fambrough, *JBC* **262**, 10733 (1987).
43. K. Kawakami, H. Nojima, T. Ohta and K. Nagano, *NARes* **14**, 2833 (1986).
44. K. Kawakami, T. Ohta, H. Nojima and K. Nagano, *J. Biochem. (Tokyo)* **100**, 389 (1986).
45. F. F. Chehab, Y. W. Kan, M. L. Law, J. Hartz, F.-T. Kao and R. Blostein, *PNAS* **84**, 7901 (1987).
46. K. Taniguchi and S. Iida, *BBA* **288**, 98 (1972).
47. E. Erdmann and W. Schoner, *BBA* **330**, 302 (1973).
48. O. Hansen, *BBA* **433**, 383 (1976).
49. J. S. Charnock, L. P. Simonson and A. F. Almeida, *BBA* **465**, 77 (1977).
50. M. J. Marks and N. M. Seeds, *Life Sci.* **23**, 2735 (1978).
51. F. Medzihradsky, P. S. Nandhasri, V. Idoyaga-Vargas and O. Z. Sellihnger, *J. Neurochem.* **18**, 1599 (1971).
52. F. A. Henn, H. Halijamäe and A. Hamberger, *Brain Res.* **43**, 437 (1972).
53. H. K. Kimelberg, *J. Neurochem.* **22**, 971 (1974).
54. G. Moonen and G. Franck, *Neurosci. Lett.* **4**, 263 (1971).

55. H. K. Kimelberg, S. Biddlecome, S. Narumi and R. S. Bourke, *Brain Res.* **141**, 305 (1978).
56. T. Grisar, J. M. Frère and G. Franck, *Brain Res.* **165**, 87 (1979).
57. T. Grisar, G. Franck and E. Schoffeniels, *Neurochem. Int.* **2**, 311 (1980).
58. K. J. Sweadner, *JBC* **254**, 6060 (1979).
59. T. Matsuda, H. Iwata and J. R. Cooper, *JBC* **259**, 3858 (1984).
60. J. Lytton, J. C. Lin and G. Guidotti, *JBC* **260**, 1177 (1985).
61. J. Lytton, *BBRC* **132**, 764 (1985).
62. P. Mansier and L. G. Lelievre, *Nature* **300**, 535 (1982).
63. R. J. Adams, A. Schwartz, G. Grupp, I. Grupp, S.-W. Lee, E. T. Wallick, T. Powell, V. W. Twist and P. Gathiram, *Nature* **296**, 167 (1982).
64. C. Forest, G. Ponzio, B. Rossi, M. Lazdunski and G. Ailhaud, *BBRC* **107**, 422 1982).
65. M. D. Resh, R. A. Nemenoff and G. Guidotti, *JBC* **255**, 10938 (1980).
66. M. Tamura, T.-T. Lam and T. Inagami, *Bchem* **27**, 4244 (1988).
67. P. L. Jørgensen, E. Skriver, H. Herbert and A. B. Maunsbach, *Ann. N.Y. Acad. Sci.* **402**, 207 (1982).
68. R. A. Farley, C. M. Tran, C. T. Carilli, D. Hawke and J. E. Shively, *JBC* **259**, 9532 (1984).
69. Y. A. Ovchinnikov, K. N. Dzhandzugazyan, S. V. Lutsenko, A. A. Mustayev and N. N. Modyanov, *FEBS Lett.* **217**, 111 (1987).
70. T. Ohta, K. Nagano and M. Yoshida, *PNAS* **83**, 2071 (1986).
71. P. A. Tyson, M. Steinberg, E. Wallick and T. Kirley, *JBC* **264**, 726 (1989).
72. E. M. Price and J. B Lingrel, *Bchem* **27**, 8400 (1988).
73. P. A. G. Fortes and R. Aquilar, *Prog. Clin. Biol. Res.* **268A**, 197 (1988).
74. M. Nagai, K. Taniguchi, K. Kangawa, H. Matsuo, S. Nakamura and S. Iida, *JBC* **261**, 13197 (1986).
75. P. L. Jørgensen and J. H. Collins, *BBA* **860**, 570 (1986).
76. G. E. Shull and J. B Lingrel, *JBC* **261**, 16788 (1986).
78. G. E. Shull and J. Greeb, *JBC* **263**, 8646 (1988).
79. K. Maruyama and D. H. MacLennan, *PNAS* **85**, 3314 (1988).
80. M. Girardet, K. Geering, B. C. Rossier, J. P. Kraehenbuhl and C. Bron, *Bchem* **22**, 2296 (1983).
81. P. L. Jørgensen and J. Brunner, *BBA* **735**, 291 (1983).
82. G. J. Chin, *Bchem* **24**, 5943 (1985).
83. T. Ohta, M. Yoshida, K. Nagano, H. Hirano and M. Kawamura, *FEBS Lett.* **204**, 297 (1986).
84. M. Girardet, K. Geering, J. M. Frantes, D. Geser, B. C. Rossier, J. P. Kraehenbuhl and C. Bron, *Bchem* **20**, 6684 (1981).
85. R. Zibirre, G. Hippler-Feldtmann, J. Kühne, P. Poronnik, G. Warnecke and G. Koch, *JBC* **262**, 4349 (1987).
86. K. Kawakami and K. Nagano, *J. Biochem. (Tokyo)* **103**, 54 (1988).
87. F. Vogel, H. W. Meyer, R. Grosse and K. R. H. Repke, *BBA* **470**, 497 (1977).
88. D. M. Fambrough, *CSHSQB* **48**, 297 (1983).
89. K. Sweadner and R. C. Gilkeson, *JBC* **260**, 9016 (1985).
90. S. C. Hubbard and R. J. Ivatt, *ARB* **50**, 555 (1981).
91. M. M. Tamkun and D. M. Fambrough, *JBC* **261**, 1009 (1986).
92. K. Takeda, S. Noguchi, A. Sugino and M. Kawamura, *FEBS Lett.* **238**, 201 (1988).
93. K. Geering, D. I. Meyer, M. P. Paccolat, J. P. Kraehenbuhl and B. C. Rossier, *JBC* **260**, 5154 (1985).
94. R. E. Thomas, in "Burger's Medicinal Chemistry" (M. E. Wolff, ed.), Part III, p. 47. Wiley, New York, 1981.

86   JERRY B LINGREL ET AL.

95. R. S. Gupta, A. Chopra and D. K. Stetsko, *J. Cell. Physiol.* **127**, 197 (1986).
96. E. T. Wallick, B. J. R. Pitts, L. K. Lane and A. Schwartz, *ABB* **202**, 442 (1980).
97. S. M. Periyasamy, W.-H. Huang and A. Askari, *Comp. Biochem. Physiol.* **76B**, 449 (1983).
98. W. Schonfeld, R. Schonfeld, K.-H. Menke, J. Weiland and K. R. H. Repke, *Biochem. Pharmacol.* **35**, 3221 (1986).
99. K. Repke, M. Est and H. J. Portius, *Biochem. Pharmacol.* **14**, 1785 (1965).
100. T. Tobin and T. M. Brody, *Biochem. Pharmacol.* **21**, 1553 (1972).
101. W. J. Ball and L. K. Lane, *BBA* **873**, 79 (1986).
102. T. Akera, S. Yamamoto, J. Chubb, R. McNish and T. M. Brody, *Naunyn-Schmeideberg's Arch. Pharmacol.* **308**, 81 (1979).
103. P. A. G. Fortes, *Bchem* **16**, 531 (1977).
104. M. P. Goeldner, C. G. Hirth, B. Rossi, G. Ponzio and M. Lazdunski, *Bchem* **22**, 4685 (1983).
105. T. B. Roger and M. Lazdunski, *Bchem* **18**, 135 (1979).
106. A. Ruoho and J. Kyte, *PNAS* **71**, 2352 (1974).
107. B. Forbush, J. H. Kaplan and J. F. Hoffman, *Bchem* **17**, 3667 (1978).
108. B. Rossi, P. Vuilleumier, C. Gache, M. Balerna and M. Lazdunski, *JBC* **255**, 9936 (1980).
109. P. L. Jørgensen, S. J. D. Karlish and C. Gitler, *JBC* **257**, 7435 (1982).
110. T. Deffo, D. S. Fullerton, M. Kihara, R. H. McParland, R. R. Becker, B. M. Simat, A. H. From, K. Ahmed and M. I. Schimerlik, *Bchem* **22**, 6303 (1983).
111. C. C. Hall and A. E. Ruoho, *PNAS* **77**, 4529 (1980).
112. D. Fallows, R. B. Kent, D. L. Nelson, J. R. Emanuel, R. Levenson and D. E. Housman, *MCBiol* **7**, 2985 (1987).
113. R. B. Kent, J. R. Emanuel, Y. B. Neriah, R. Levenson and D. E. Housman, *Science* **237**, 901 (1987).
114. J. R. Emanuel, J. Schulz, X.-M. Zhou, R. B. Kent, D. Housman, L. Cantley and R. Levenson, *JBC* **263**, 7726 (1988).
115. M. E. Baker, *BBRC* **139**, 281 (1986).
116. S. M. Periyasamy, L. K. Lane and A. Askari, *BBRC* **86**, 742 (1979).
117. D. Charlemagne, E. Mayoux, M. Poyard, P. Oliviero and K. Geering, *JBC* **262**, 8941 (1987).
118. T. Akera, Y.-C. Ng, R. Hadley, Y. Katano and T. M. Brody, *Eur. J. Pharmacol.* **132**, 137 (1986).
119. S. C. Specht and K. J. Sweadner, *PNAS* **81**, 1234 (1984).
120. J. Orlowski and J. B Lingrel, *JBC* **263**, 10436 (1988).
121. J. M. Lowndes, A. E. Ruoho and M. Hokin-Neaverson, *Prog. Clin. Biol. Res.* **268B**, 113 (1988).
122. J. W. Schneider, R. W. Mercer, M. Gilmore-Herbert, M. F. Utset, C. Lai, A. Greene and E. J. Benz, Jr., *PNAS* **85**, 284 (1988).
123. R. M. Young and J. B Lingrel, *BBRC* **145**, 52 (1987).
125. F. Verrey, E. Schaerer, P. Zoerkler, M. P. Paccolat, K. Geering, J. P. Kraehenbuhl and B. C. Rossier, *J. Cell Biol.* **104**, 1231 (1987).
126. J. W. Bowen and A. McDonough, *AJP* **252**, C179 (1987).
127. P. G. Pauw, M. D. Johnson, P. Moore, M. Morgan, R. M. Fineman, T. Kalka and J. F. Ash, *MCBiol* **6**, 1164 (1986).
128. J. R. Emanuel, S. Garetz, J. Schneider, J. F. Ash, E. J. Benz, Jr., and R. Levenson, *MCBiol* **6**, 2476 (1986).
129. J. Lytton, *JBC* **260**, 10075 (1985).
130. M. J. A. Ihlenfeldt, *JBC* **256**, 2213 (1981).

131. M. Fehlmann and P. Freychet, *JBC* **256**, 7449 (1981).
132. H. Schwalb, Y. Dickstein and M. Heller, *BBA* **689**, 241 (1982).
133. K. Werdan, B. Wagenknecht, B. Zwissler, L. Brown, W. Krawietz and E. Erdmann, *Biochem. Pharmacol.* **33**, 1873 (1984).
134. P. Vigne, C. Frelin and M. Lazdunski, *JBC* **257**, 5380 (1982).
135. B. A. Wolitzky and D. M. Fambrough, *JBC* **261**, 9990 (1986).
136. S. C. Specht, *BBRC* **121**, 208 (1984).
137. C. A. Schmitt and A. A. McDonough, *JBC* **261**, 10439 (1986).
138. C. K. Atterwill and P. Collins, *Biochem. Pharmacol.* **36**, 2679 (1987).
139. J. M. Bertoni and G. J. Seigel, *J. Neurochem.* **31**, 1501 (1978).
140. A. A. Abdel-Latif, J. Brody and H. Ramahi, *J. Neurochem.* **14**, 1133 (1967).
141. G. A. Langer, A. J. Brady, S. T. Tan and S. D. Serena, *Circ. Res.* **36**, 744 (1975).
142. K. J. Sweadner and S. K. Farshi, *PNAS* **84**, 8404 (1987).
143. D. Charlemagne, J.-M. Maixent, M. Preteseille and L. G. Lelievre, *JBC* **261**, 185 (1986).
144. V. L. M. Herrera, A. V. Chobanian and N. Ruiz-Opazo, *Science* **241**, 221 (1988).
145. W. Grossman, B. A. Carabella, S. Gunther and M. A. Fifer, in "Myocardial Hypertropy and Failure" (N. R. Alpert, ed.), p. 1. Raven, New York, 1983.
146. A.-M. Lompre, B. Nadal-Ginard and V. Mahdavi, *JBC* **259**, 6437 (1984).
147. K. Schwartz, D. dela Bastie, P. Bouveret, P. Oliviero, S. Alonso and M. Buckingham, *Circ. Res.* **59**, 551 (1986).
148. S. Izumo, A.-M. Lompre, R. Matsuoka, G. Koren, K. Schwartz, B. Nadal-Ginard and V. Mahdavi, *J. Clin. Invest.* **79**, 970 (1987).
149. S. Izumo, B. Nadal-Ginard and V. Mahdavi, *PNAS* **85**, 339 (1988).
150. R. D. Bland, T. N. Hansen, C. N. Haberskern, M. A. Bressack, T. A. Hazinski, J. U. Raj and R. B. Goldberg, *J. Appl. Physiol.* **53**, 992 (1982).
151. R. D. Bland, *Acta Paediatr. Scand. Suppl.* **305**, 12 (1983).
152. R. E. Olver, C. A. Ramsden and L. B. Strang, *J. Physiol. (London)* **219**, 55 (1981).
153. M. A. Matthay, C. C. Landolt and N. C. Staub, *J. Appl. Physiol.* **53**, 96 (1982).
154. R. J. Mason, M. C. Williams, J. H. Widdicombe, M. J. Sanders, D. S. Misfeldt and L. C. Berry, *PNAS* **79**, 6033 (1982).
155. A. Aperia, L. Larsson and R. Zetterstrom, *AJP* **241**, F356 (1981).
156. A. Aperia and L. Larsson, *Acta Physiol. Scand.* **105**, 11 (1979).
157. K. Kjeldsen, A. Norgaard and T. Clausen, *BBA* **686**, 253 (1982).
158. D. Fambrough and J. E. Rash, *Dev. Biol.* **26**, 55 (1971).
159. J. Baumgold, J. B. Parent and I. Spector, *J. Neurosci.* **3**, 1004 (1983).
160. K. L. Zierler and E. M. Rogus, *BBA* **640**, 687 (1981).
161. J. Orlowski and J. B Lingrel, *JBC* **263**, 17817 (1988).
162. S. A. Mendoza, N. M. Wigglesworth and E. Rozengurt, *J. Cell. Physiol.* **105**, 153 (1980).
163. V. M. Reznik, R. J. Shapiro and S. A. Mendoza, *AJP* **249**, C267 (1985).
164. Y. Yarden, A. B. Schreiber and J. Schlessinger, *J. Cell. Physiol.* **92**, 687 (1982).
165. N. Inoue, H. Matsui and H. Hatanaka, *J. Neurochem.* **50**, 230 (1988).
166. Y. Marunaka, *Comp. Biochem. Physiol.* **89A**, 103 (1988).
167. N. K. Rosic, M. L. Sandaert and R. J. Pollet, *JBC* **260**, 6206 (1985).
168. T. Clausen and J. A. Flatman, *J. Physiol. (London)* **270**, 383 (1977).
169. C. J. Lynch, P. B. Wilson, P. F. Blackmore and J. H. Exton, *JBC* **261**, 14551 (1986).
170. P. H. Wu and J. W. Phillis, *Int. J. Biochem.* **12**, 353 (1980).
171. W. P. Weismann, S. Sinha and S. Klahr, *AJP* **232**, F307 (1977).
172. D. J. Stewart and A. K. Sen, *AJP* **240**, 207 (1981).
173. B. G. Kennedy and J. E. Lever, *J. Cell. Physiol.* **121**, 51 (1984).
174. B. M. Rayson and I. S. Edelman, *AJP* **243**, F463 (1982).

175. L. C. Garg, W. Narang and C. S. Wingo, *AJP* **248**, F487 (1985).

176. L. Ling and L. Cantley, *JBC* **259**, 4089 (1984).

177. G. G. Gick, F. Ismail-Beigi and I. S. Edelman, *Prog. Clin. Biol. Res.* **268B**, 277 (1988).

179. F. Morel and A. Doucet, *Physiol Rev.* **66**, 377 (1986).

180. N. J. Karin and J. S. Cook, *Curr. Top. Membr. Transp.* **19** (1983).

181. R. D. Moore, *BBA* **737**, 1 (1983).

182. M. Girardet, K. Geering, H. P. Gaeggeler and B. C. Rossier, *AJP* **251**, F662 (1986).

183. C. P. Bastl, H. J. Binder and J. P. Hayslett, *AJP* **238**, F181 (1980).

184. W. Clauss, J. E. Durr, D. Guth and E. Skadhauge, *J. Membr. Biol.* **96**, 141 (1987).

185. S. G. Schultz, *Annu. Rev. Physiol.* **46**, 435 (1984).

186. P. L. Jørgensen, *J. Steroid Biochem.* **3**, 181 (1972).

187. L. C. Garg, M. A. Knepper and M. B. Burg, *AJP* **240**, F536 (1981).

188. G. El Mernissi and A. Doucet, *Pfluegers Arch.* **399**, 139 (1983).

189. G. J. Schwartz and M. B. Burg, *AJP* **235**, F576 (1978).

190. J. Crabbe, *Nature* **200**, 787 (1963).

191. S. K. Mujais, M. A. Chekal, W. J. Jones, J. P. Hayslett and A. I. Katz, *J. Clin. Invest.* **76**, 170 (1985).

192. C. F. Chignell and E. Titus, *JBC* **241**, 5083 (1966).

193. W. H. Knox and A. K. Sen, *Ann. N.Y. Acad. Sci.* **242**, 471 (1974).

194. K. J. Petty, J. P. Kokko and D. Marver, *J. Clin. Invest.* **68**, 1514 (1981).

195. K. Geering, M. Girardet, C. Bron, J.-P. Kraehenbühl and B. C. Rossier, *JBC* **257**, 10338 (1982).

196. C. S. Park and I. S. Edelman, *AJP* **246**, F509 (1984).

197. C. S. Park and I. S. Edelman, *AJP* **246**, F519 (1984).

198. C. Barlet-Bas, C. Khadouri, S. Marsy and A. Doucet, *PNAS* **85**, 1707 (1988).

199. J. P. Johnson, D. Jones and W. P. Wiesmann, *AJP* **251**, C186 (1986).

200. B. C. Rossier, *Curr. Top. Membr. Transp.* **20**, 125 (1984).

201. B. M. Rayson and R. K. Gupta, *JBC* **260**, 12740 (1985).

202. C. S. Lo, T. R. August, U. A. Liberman and I. S. Edelman, *JBC* **251**, 7826 (1976).

203. G. D. Curfman, T. J. Crowley and T. W. Smith, *J. Clin. Invest.* **59**, 586 (1977).

204. M. H. Lin and T. Akera, *JBC* **253**, 723 (1978).

205. U. A. Liberman, Y. Asano and I. S. Edelman, *Biophys. J.* **27**, 127 (1979).

206. C. S. Lo and I. S. Edelman, *JBC* **251**, 7834 (1976).

207. C. S. Lo and T. N. Lo, *JBC* **255**, 2131 (1980).

208. I. S. Edelman, T. A. Pressley and A. Hiatt, *in* "The Sodium Pump" (I. Glynn and C. Ellory, eds.), p. 153. Co. Biol. Cambridge, England, 1985.

209. A. McDonough, *in* "The Sodium Pump" (I. Glynn and C. Ellory, eds.), p. 161. Co. Biol., Cambridge, England, 1985.

210. S. Chaudhury, F. Ismail-Beigi, G. G. Gick, R. Levenson and I. S. Edelman, *Mol. Endocrinol.* **1**, 83 (1987).

211. A. A. McDonough, T. A. Brown, B. Horowitz, R. Chiu, J. Schlotterbeck, J. Bowen and C. A. Schmitt, *AJP* **254**, C323 (1988).

212. G. G. Gick, F. Ismail-Beigi and I. S. Edelman, in press.

213. R. S. Haber and J. N. Loeb, *Endocrinology (Baltimore)* **115**, 291 (1984).

214. G. Capasso, J.-T. Lin, N. G. DeSanto and R. Kinne, *Pfluegers Arch.* **403**, 90 (1985).

215. S. A. Mendoza, N. M. Wigglesworth, P. Pohjanpelto and E. Rozengurt, *J. Cell. Physiol.* **103**, 17 (1980).

216. J. B. Smith and E. Rozengurt, *PNAS* **75**, 5560 (1978).

217. V. M. Reznik, J. Villela and S. A. Mendoza, *J. Cell. Physiol.* **117**, 211 (1983).

218. L. R. Pollack, E. H. Tate and J. S. Cook, *J. Cell. Physiol.* **106**, 85 (1981).

219. D. Kim, J. D. Marsh, W. H. Barry and T. W. Smith, *Circ. Res.* **55**, 39 (1984).
220. L. Boardman, M. Huett, J. F. Lamb, J. P. Newton and J. M. Polson, *J. Physiol. (London)* **241**, 771 (1974).
221. T. A. Pressley, R. S. Haber, J. N. Loeb, I. S. Edelman and F. Ismail-Beigi, *J. Gen. Physiol.* **87**, 591 (1986).
222. F. Ismail-Beigi, T. A. Pressley, R. S. Haber, G. G. Gick, J. N. Loeb and I. S. Edelman, *JBC* **263**, 8162 (1988).
223. T. A. Pressley, F. Ismail-Beigi, G. G. Gick and I. S. Edelman, *AJP* **255**, C252 (1988).
225. J. W. Schneider, R. W. Mercer, M. Caplan, J. R. Emanuel, K. J. Sweadner, E. J. Benz, Jr., and R. Levenson, *PNAS* **82**, 6357 (1985).
226. F. Verrey, P. Kairouz, E. Schaerer, P. Fuentes, T. R. Kleyman, K. Geering, B. C. Rossier and J. P. Kraehenbuhl *AJP* **256**, F1034 (1989).
227. E. D. Sverdlov, G. S. Monastyrskaya, N. E. Broude, Y. A. Ushkaryov, R. L. Allikmets, A. M. Melkov, Y. V. Smirnov, I. V. Malyshev, I. E. Dulobova, K. E. Petrukhin, A. V. Grishin, N. I. Kijatkin, M. B. Kostina, V. E. Sverdlov, N. N. Modyanov and Y. A. Ovchinnikov, *FEBS Lett.* **217**, 275 (1987).
228. M. M. Shull and J. B Lingrel, *PNAS* **84**, 4039 (1987).
229. Y. A. Ovchinnikov, G. S. Monastyrskaya, N. E. Broude, Y. A. Ushkaryov, A. M. Melkov, Y. V. Smirnov, I. V. Malyshev, R. L. Allikmets, M. B. Kostina, I. E. Dulubova, N. I. Kiyatkin, A. V. Grishin, N. N. Modyanov and E. D. Sverdlov, *FEBS Lett.* **233**, 87 (1988).
230. R. Breathnach and P. Chambon, *ARB* **50**, 349 (1981).
231. S. M. Mount, *NARes* **10**, 459 (1982).
232. I. Seif, G. Khoury and R. Dhar, *NARes* **6**, 3387 (1979).
233. H. Naora and N. J. Deacon, *PNAS* **79**, 6196 (1982).
234. B. Wieringa, E. Hofer and C. Weissman, *Cell* **37**, 915 (1984).
235. P. K. Ghosh, V. B. Reddy, J. Swinscoe, P. Lebowitz and S. M. Weissman, *JMB* **126**, 813 (1978).
236. R. Treisman, U. Novak, J. Favaloro and R. Kamen, *Nature* **292**, 595 (1981).
237. W. Gilbert, *Nature* **271**, 501 (1978).
238. H. Sakano, J. H. Rogers, K. Hüppi, C. Brack, A. Traunecker, R. Maki, R. Wall and S. Tonegawa, *Nature* **277**, 627 (1979).
239. W. Gilbert, *Science* **228**, 823 (1985).
240. M. Go, *Nature* **291**, 90 (1981).
241. C. C. F. Blake, *Nature* **273**, 267 (1978).
242. N. Lonberg and W. Gilbert, *Cell* **40**, 81 (1985).
243. C. C. F. Blake, *Int. Rev. Cytol.* **93**, 149 (1985).
244. C. S. Craik, S. Sprang, R. Fletterick and W. J. Rutter, *Nature* **299**, 180 (1982).
245. C. S. Craik, W. J. Rutter and R. Fletterick, *Science* **220**, 1125 (1983).
246. P. Argos and J. K. M. Rao, *BBA* **827**, 283 (1985).
247. B. Korczak, A. Zarain-Herzberg, C. J. Brandl, C. J. Ingles, N. M. Green and D. H. MacLennan, *JBC* **263**, 4813 (1988).
248. T. L. Yang-Feng, J. W. Schneider, V. Lindgren, M. M. Shull, E. J. Benz, Jr., J. B. Lingrel and U. Francke, *Genomics* **2**, 128 (1988).
249. R. B. Kent, D. A. Fallows, E. Geissler, T. Glaser, J. R. Emanuel, P. A. Lalley, R. Levenson and D. E. Housman, *PNAS* **84**, 5369 (1987).

Retroviral-Mediated Gene Transfer

JEANNE R. MCLACHLIN,*
KENNETH CORNETTA,*
MARTIN A. EGLITIS† AND
W. FRENCH ANDERSON*

*National Heart, Lung and Blood
   Institute
National Institutes of Health
Bethesda, Maryland 20892
†Genetic Therapy, Inc.
Gaithersburg, Maryland 20878

Abbreviations

ADA, adenosine deaminase (EC 3.5.4.4)

AKR, strain of inbred mouse

β-vector, retroviral vector containing the β-globin gene

BAG, retroviral vector containing β-galactosidase and neo^r genes

$βpV_4Δneo$, retroviral vector containing β-globin and neo^r genes

BPV, bovine papilloma virus

CFU-B, -GM, -S, colony-forming unit—B lymphocyte; —granulocyte, monocyte; —spleen

CFU-GEMM, colony-forming unit—granulocyte, erythrocyte, monocyte, megakaryocyte

CM, conditioned medium

DE, double expression vector containing two genes

DHFR, dihydrofolate reductase (EC 1.5.1.3)

F-MuLV, Friend murine leukemia virus

91

Progress in Nucleic Acid Research
and Molecular Biology, Vol. 38

G418 (G418 sulfate, Geneticin), antibiotic related to gentamicin and used to
   select for expression of the bacterial neomycin-resistance gene; a glycoside
   of streptamine
GC, glucocerebrosidase
GH, growth hormone
gpt, guanine phosphoribosyltransferase (similar to HPRT, below)
HaMuSV, Harvey murine sarcoma virus
HBGF-1, class-I heparin-binding growth-factor (endothelial cell growth-
   factor)
hCMV, human cytomegalovirus
HERV, human endogenous retroviral sequences
Hmdr, retroviral vector containing a multidrug-resistance gene and H4 his-
   tone promoter
HPRT, hypoxanthine phosphoribosyltransferase (EC 2.4.2.8)
IL-3, interleukin-3
LDL, retroviral vector containing a DHFR gene (Table I)
LDLR, low-density-lipoprotein receptor
LHM$_s$AL, retroviral vector containing an HPRT gene and a ADA gene with
   a short metallothionein promoter (Fig. 6)
LMTPL, retroviral vector containing an HPRT gene and metallothionein
   promoter
LNB*SA, retroviral vector containing the neo^r and β-globin genes (Table II)
LNSAL, retroviral vector containing the neo^r and ADA genes with the SV40
   promoter (Table II)
LNSV, HPRT$^-$ Lesch–Nyhan fibroblasts transformed with the SV40 virus
LPGHL, retroviral vector containing an HPRT gene and a growth hormone
   gene in the same orientation (Table II)
LPHGL, retroviral vector containing a growth hormone gene in the reverse
   orientation to the HPRT gene (Table II)
LPL, retroviral vector containing an HPRT gene (Table I)
LSDL, retroviral vector containing the DHFR gene and SV40 promoter
   (Table I)
LSΔPΔM, retroviral vector containing an HPRT gene (Table I)
LSTRA, murine T-cell lymphoma cell line
LTR, retroviral long-terminal-repeat sequence
MCF, mink-cell focus-forming virus
MEL, murine erythroleukemia cells
MLV-NeoI, retroviral vector containing a neo^r gene (Fig. 5)
MT, metallothionein
Mtx, methotrexate
MoMSV, Moloney murine sarcoma virus
MoMuLV, Moloney murine leukemia virus

MoTN, retroviral vector containing the neo^r gene and the thymidine kinase
   promoter (Fig. 5)
MuMPSV, murine myeloproliferative sarcoma virus
MuMTV, murine mammary tumor virus
N2, retroviral vector containing the neo^r gene (Fig. 5)
Neoμ, retroviral vector containing ned^r gene
neo^r bacterial gene coding for NPT
NG, retroviral vector containing a β-globin gene (Table II)
NHP, retroviral vector containing an HPRT gene and the hCMV promoter
NPT, neomycin phosphotransferase (kanamycin kinase, EC 2.7.1.95)
PA12, amphotropic packaging-cell line
PA317, amphotropic packaging-cell line
PBMC, peripheral blood mononuclear cells
PGK, phosphoglycerate kinase (EC 2.7.2.3; 2.7.2.10)
PNP, purine-nucleoside phosphorylase (EC 2.4.2.1)
pPAM3, plasmid construct containing structural genes for retroviruses used
   in the amphotropic packaging-cell line PA317
ψ2, ecotropic packaging-cell line
ψAM, amphotropic packaging-cell line
ψCRE, ecotropic packaging-cell line
pSV2neo, plasmid containing the neo^r gene and the SV40 promoter
Rev, reticuloendotheliosis virus
RMH, retroviral vector containing an HPRT gene and a metallothionein
   promoter
RSV, Rous sarcoma virus
SAX, retroviral vector containing a neo^r and an ADA gene (Fig. 6)
SCID, severe combined immunodeficiency
SFFV, spleen focus-forming virus
SNV, spleen necrosis virus
SV40, simian virus 40
SVBADA211, retroviral vector containing the neo^r and ADA genes (Fig. 6)
SVXβ(RO), retroviral vector containing a neo^r gene with a β-globin gene in
   the reverse orientation
SV(X)HPRT, retroviral vector containing an HPRT gene and the neo^r gene
TK, thymidine kinase of herpes simplex virus (EC 2.7.1.21)
Tn5, bacterial transposon from which the gene for neo^r was derived
U3, region in retroviral long-terminal-repeat sequence containing enhancer
   and promoter elements (Fig. 1)
WEHI-3B, myelomonocytic cell line from a BALB/c mouse that con-
   stitutively produces a mouse bone marrow multi-colony-stimulating factor
WHHL, Watanabe-heritable-hyperlipidemic rabbit
ZIP-NeoSV(X), retroviral vector containing a neo^r gene (Fig. 5)

Gene transfer by retroviral vectors has become a widely used approach to study expression of foreign gene sequences in mammalian cells. Although other methods of gene transfer exist, investigators have taken advantage of both the structure and the life cycle of retroviruses to achieve efficient transduction of cells. The field of retroviral-mediated gene transfer has expanded dramatically and the development of retroviral vectors has been discussed in several reviews (1–6). There is an overview of the biology of retroviruses and how they are central in the study of several areas of biology in a recent article by Varmus (7).

The objective of this review is to present a survey of the literature describing the use of retroviral vectors for gene delivery. Specifically, our discussion focuses on vector design, the development of different packaging cell lines, and the employment of single and multiple gene vectors in different model systems. Several retroviruses have been used to generate recombinant gene transfer vectors; these include Rous sarcoma virus (RSV) (8), reticuloendotheliosis virus (Rev) (9), murine mammary tumor virus (Mu-MTV) (10), murine myeloproliferative sarcoma virus (MuMPSV) (11), and Harvey murine sarcoma virus (HaMuSV) (12, 13). To narrow the scope of this review, we restrict the discussion to only those retroviral vectors derived from Moloney murine leukemia virus (MoMuLV).

In the final section, we address some of the issues concerning the use of recombinant retroviruses for human gene therapy. Many questions are still unresolved concerning the efficiency of transduction, attaining appropriate levels of expression, the possibility of specific cell targeting, and long-term safety questions that arise when this form of therapy is considered for use in humans.

I. Methods of Gene Transfer

Many techniques have been developed for gene transfer to vertebrate cells. Direct microinjection of cloned genes is widely used for mammalian cells in culture (14–19), as well as mammalian embryos to achieve germ-line transformation (reviewed in 20). Transgenic animals carry, and in some cases express, foreign DNA sequences; however, the process of integration of the injected DNA is poorly understood. Often, multiple tandem copies of the introduced genes integrate into the host cell chromosome. In addition, at least in preimplantation embryos, de novo methylation of the microinjected sequences appears to be correlated with a lack of gene expression (21–23). Although DNA microinjection is suitable for gene transfer to small numbers of cells or embryos, it is not practical for tissues such as bone marrow, in which a large number of cells must be transduced simultaneously.

Other modes of gene delivery include fusion of mammalian cells with protoplasts (24, 25) or liposomes (26), and electroporation (27, 28). Gene transfer using electroporation is based on the finding that cells can be briefly and reversibly permeabilized by applying high voltage. This method, also called electro-transfection, has been used successfully with a number of mammalian cell types, and appears to be, under optimal conditions, of equal or slightly better efficiency than that of chemical transfection (29, 30).

One of the most widely used biochemical techniques for gene transfer to cultured mammalian cells is calcium-phosphate-mediated transfection (31, 32), in which cells incorporate a DNA-containing precipitate of calcium phosphate. This procedure has been used extensively for transformation of cultured fibroblasts and cells of hematopoietic origin (33–37). However, a disadvantage is that this technique is very inefficient, with a tranduction frequency as low as one cell in 10^5. For this reason, the introduced DNA must either contain or be co-transfected with a selectable marker gene to facilitate isolation of transfected cells. A recent report (38) outlines modifications that can lead to a several-fold improvement in transfection efficiency in certain cell types.

Gene-transfer vectors derived from animal viruses provide an alternative to the methods outlined above. Both RNA and DNA viruses have been utilized as vectors for gene transfer (39, 40). Vectors using DNA virus backbones have been derived from simian virus 40 (SV40) (41, 42), adenovirus (43–45), adeno-associated virus (46–48), and bovine papilloma virus (BPV) (49–51). However, some of these vectors have limited capabilities. For instance, DNA introduced by BPV-based vectors remains episomal and is currently best suited only for examining short-term expression in transduced cells. On the other hand, the structure and life cycle of retroviruses makes them ideally suited to be gene-transfer vehicles. Retroviruses replicate through a DNA intermediate that integrates into the host genome. Although the site of integration is apparently random with respect to the host genome, the provirus integrates with a defined structure in low copy-number. Most of the viral gene sequences can be removed and replaced with foreign DNA with the missing viral functions supplied in *trans*. In addition, the host range for infection can be manipulated by the choice of envelope used for vector packaging. Finally, vectors can accommodate single or multiple gene inserts under the transcriptional control of sequences contained in either the viral long-terminal-repeat (LTR) or linked to an internal, heterologous promoter.

II. Retroviral Vectors

A. Structure of Moloney Murine Leukemia Virus

The genome of retroviruses contains two single-stranded RNAs that replicate through a DNA intermediate in the host cell (52). The ability to infect a variety of cell types is determined by the glycoproteins of the virion envelope, so that murine retroviruses can be classified according to their host-cell range (53). Ecotropic retroviruses are those that infect and replicate only in mouse (and a few rat) cells. Amphotropic retroviruses can infect cells of other species as well as mouse cells. Xenotropic retroviruses can infect many species, but not mice.

Virions contain two copies of genomic RNA, which serve as the template for generating a double-stranded DNA copy using the viral reverse transcriptase. [There is a detailed description of the sequence of events of retroviral DNA synthesis in Varmus (54).] Briefly, infectious viral particles containing an RNA–protein core bind to and enter the host cell in a way thought to resemble receptor-mediated endocytosis (7). The genomic RNA is reverse-transcribed to the linear duplex DNA, which enters the cell nucleus. Integration is poorly understood, but requires a viral integrase and appears to occur at random, accessible sites within the cellular genome. The integrated DNA structure, called a provirus, is depicted in Fig. 1. The structure and nucleotide sequence of Moloney MuLV has been described (55, 56) and in its integrated form is 8.8 kilobases (kb) long. The provirus is bounded on each end by a repetitive sequence designated LTR. The LTRs contain enhancer and promoter elements in addition to signals for the initiation and termination of viral transcripts. Internal sequences contain the necessary information coding for the products of the three retroviral genes: *gag*, *pol*, and *env*. The *gag* (group-specific antigens) gene encodes the structural core

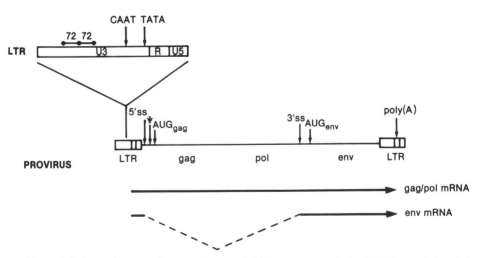

Fig. 1. Schematic diagram of MoMuLV proviral DNA structure and the 5′ LTR containing viral enhancer and promoter sequences in the U3 region. LTR, Long-terminal-repeat; ss, splice site; ψ, viral packaging signal.

proteins. The *pol* gene encodes the viral reverse transcriptase as well as integrase and a protease function. The *env* gene encodes the outer envelope protein of the virion. The proteins from *gag* and *pol* are produced from a full-length mRNA, while the protein from *env* is produced from a spliced transcript utilizing a 5′ splice donor site and a 3′ splice acceptor site. Other sequences internal to the two LTR regions necessary for replication include the packaging signal (ψ), which directs the encapsidation of viral transcripts.

B. Design of Retroviral Vectors

Several generalized designs of retroviral vectors are illustrated in Fig. 2. Some factors to be considered in vector design are: the size capacity of the recombinant retrovirus; the use of single or multiple gene arrangements; the inclusion of a selectable marker gene; the orientation of the inserted DNA; the positioning of genes relative to viral splice sites; the choice of internal promoter sequences; and deletions of the viral enhancer/promoter sequences.

In general terms, the minimum size limit for MuLV vectors is approximately 2 kb based on the insertion of a bacterial guanine phosphoribosyltransferase (EC 2.4.2.8) gene (*gpt*) in a Moloney murine sarcoma virus (MoMSV) backbone and recovery of infectious particles with MoMuLV

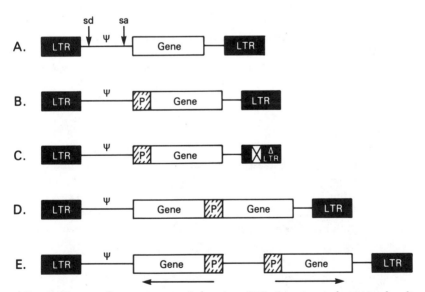

FIG. 2. Diagram of prototype retroviral vectors. LTR, Long-terminal-repeat; sd, splice donor; ψ, viral packaging signal; sa, splice acceptor; P, promoter; ΔLTR, deletion of enhancer/promoter region in 3′ LTR. Arrows indicate possible orientation of inserted genes.

helper (57). The upper size limit that vectors can accommodate without a reduction in titer is around 10 kb for RSV (8, 58, 59) and MuLV based vectors (60); however, it has not been determined that this represents the maximum size.

Although small genomic fragments have been used in retroviral constructs—for example, human β-globin (61–67)—cDNA sequences are more widely used. Many considerations contribute to the general preference for cDNAs. A major advantage is that cDNAs are generally smaller in size than genomic fragments, and their expression can be regulated by either the viral LTR or by an internal heterologous promoter. In addition, cDNAs do not require splicing.

Vectors with a single gene insert (Fig. 2A and B) are the least complex, and transcription of the inserted DNA can be regulated by sequences contained in the viral LTR or from an internal promoter. Single-gene vectors containing an internal promoter can be in either the same or the reverse orientation relative to the viral LTR (60, 68) (Fig. 2B). Expression from an exogenous promoter might be required in cells in which the viral promoter sequences are inactive, as observed in embryonal carcinoma cells (69–71). It is also possible, in this type of internally promoted construct, to choose promoters that are inducible or confer tissue-specific expression. A disadvantage of this type of vector is that if the single gene is not a selectable marker gene, then transduced cells are difficult to isolate from an infected population. Most of the early single-gene retroviral vectors contained a selectable marker gene such as the bacterial gene for neomycin resistance (neo^r) (35, 60) or the human hypoxanthine phosphoribosyltransferase (EC 2.4.2.8) (HPRT) gene (72). One particular neo^r vector, designated N2 (discussed in detail in Section III,A), has an exceptionally good titer and has been used extensively by several investigators. An important element in this vector, described in 73, is the identification of a cryptic 3′ splice site contained within the gag coding region. A shorter version, N4, which does not include as much of the viral gag sequence, has a titer that is a tenth to a fortieth that of N2 (73). The assertion that viral gag sequences play a role in the efficient expression of introduced DNA has become an important factor in vector design (74).

Several vectors containing a deletion in the 3′ LTR (dLTR) that eliminates the viral promoter and enhancer elements have been developed (Fig. 2C). During replication, the U3 region of the 3′ LTR serves as the template for generating the U3 region of both the 5′ and 3′ LTRs in the provirus. Therefore, it is possible to generate a vector where, after reverse transcription, the regulatory sequences in the 5′ LTR are absent while the other regions necessary for LTR function are left intact. These constructs have been referred to as "self-inactivating" (75), "clipped wing" (76), and "handicapped" (77). In deleted LTR vectors, transcription can be regulated entirely from an internal promoter, and the possibility of activating a cellular oncogene by the presence of viral promoter sequences near the site of integration is reduced. Examples of this type of vector have been described (68, 75–79) and their use is discussed in Section III, B. One disadvantage of this type of vector is that a reduced viral titer often results if the 3' deletion interferes with other LTR functions during DNA replication or integration.

Retroviral vectors containing multiple gene inserts (Fig. 2D), also referred to as "double expression" (DE) vectors (5), are widely used. Expression of both genes can be regulated by the viral LTR sequences with separate gene transcripts generated by splicing. Alternatively, an internal promoter can be linked to the second gene. An advantage of DE vectors is that transduced cells expressing a nonselectable gene can easily be isolated if the vector also contains a dominant selectable marker.

One of the first DE parent vectors to be described was the shuttle vector, ZIP-NeoSV(X) (80). It contains intact LTR sequences, a 3' splice acceptor site upstream from neo^r, the SV40 origin of replication for amplification in COS cells, and the pBR322 origin of replication for plasmid rescue. For use as a multigene vector, cDNA fragments can be cloned into ZIP-NeoSV(X) at a location 5' to the splice acceptor site and the neo^r gene. Vectors containing the human HPRT (81, 82) and human adenosine deaminase (ADA) (EC 3.5.4.4) genes (83) employ this strategy. A variant of this construct, designated ZIP-NeoSV(B), has the neo^r insert 5' to the splice acceptor, and cDNA sequences can be placed where neo^r is located in SV(X). This gene arrangement has been used for a neo^r/human ADA gene construct (81, 84).

Another parent vector used to produce DE vectors, discussed above, is N2 (73). The SAX vector (85–87) was produced by inserting a cDNA for the human ADA gene linked to the SV40 early promoter into a unique XhoI site that is 3' to the neo^r gene of N2 (similar to Fig. 2D). Analysis of RNA from SAX-infected NIH-3T3 cells indicates that three sorts of transcripts are generated: a full-length transcript; a spliced transcript using the 3' cryptic splice site of N2; and an SV40-promoted transcript. With this vector, selection for expression of neo^r does not reduce expression of the ADA gene (73). This is in contrast to studies done with spleen necrosis virus (SNV) vectors, in which expression of one gene was suppressed when selection was exerted for the other gene regardless of the relative position of the two genes (88).

Another possible arrangement of genes in a multiple-gene vector is illustrated in Fig. 2E. These two-gene, two-internal promoter constructs can be made in several orientations. For example, both genes and their associated promoter sequences can be inserted in the same orientation as the viral LTR, or one of the promoter/gene sequences can be inserted in the opposite orientation. A vector, named F-TK-N, employing the latter strategy with the addition of a deletion in the 3' LTR, has been constructed (75). It contains the mouse c-*fos* gene that includes a poly(A) signal linked to a human metallothionein (MT) promoter upstream from a *neo*^{r} gene linked to the thymidine kinase (TK; EC 2.7.1.21) promoter. The c-*fos* portion was in the opposite orientation with respect to the *neo*^{r} gene. Analysis of infected NIH-3T3 cells showed the c-*fos* transcript to be of the predicted length, and expression from the MT promoter could be induced with cadmium. No full-length transcripts were observed, confirming that the deletion in the 3' LTR had led to the inactivation of the 5' LTR in the intact provirus.

C. Packaging Systems for Retroviral Vectors

Recombinant retroviruses as genetic vectors are replication-defective because the structural genes have been removed. Consequently, they require "help" to produce infectious vector particles. In naturally occurring defective retroviruses, such as the spleen focus-forming virus (SFFV), this help is provided by a helper virus (F-MuLV) containing intact structural genes. When a cell is infected simultaneously by both SFFV and F-MuLV, infectious virions are produced only because the helper virus provides the structural proteins needed for the SFFV genome to be packaged.

Superinfection with wild-type retroviruses can be used to package recombinant vectors. However, the general purpose in using retroviruses for gene transfer is the unidirectional introduction of an exogenous gene into the target cell. This consideration has led to efforts to develop cell lines that provide packaging "help" without the generation of wild-type retroviruses (Fig. 3). To accomplish this, a plasmid(s) (see Fig. 4), encoding the retroviral structural genes *gag*, *pol*, and *env*, is introduced into a tissue cell line (most often NIH-3T3) by conventional calcium-phosphate-mediated DNA transfection (89). This "packaging cell line" can be maintained as such or a plasmid carrying the cloned proviral form of a retroviral vector can be introduced into it. In the latter case, the genomic RNA generated by the vector construct combines with the constitutively expressed retroviral structural proteins of the packaging line, resulting in the release of retroviral vector into the culture medium. A stable cell line containing both virion and structural gene sequences may be termed a vector "producer cell line."

Within the retroviral genome, as described above, between the LTR and the beginning of *gag*, lies an area that enables the packaging mechanism to recognize an RNA transcript as one to be encapsidated. Early packaging lines were developed based on deletions of this "packaging signal" (Fig. 4). Such cell lines, e.g., the ecotropic ψ2 (90) and the amphotropic PA12 (91), contained plasmids that encoded all of the structural genes of a retrovirus, under the control of the regulatory sequences within the LTR. However, without a packaging signal, the full-length genomic transcript could not be

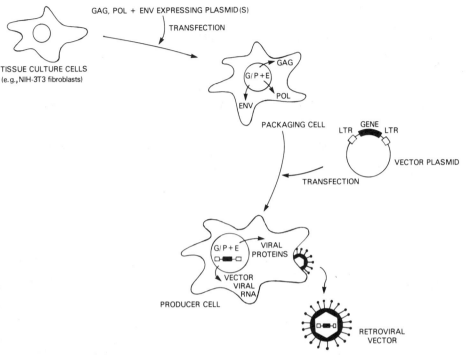

FIG. 3. Sequence of events for the generation of producer-cell lines.

encapsidated. Therefore, the cell line produces "empty" (i.e., genome-defi-cient) virions. When a retroviral vector, in which the structural genes are removed but the packaging signal remains intact, is introduced into such a packaging cell line, transcripts of the vector are recognized by the packaging mechanism, and a vector virion is produced.

Unfortunately, wild-type virus could still be generated from such packag-ing cell lines. A single recombination event between certain vectors and these early packaging proviruses could yield a wild-type retrovirus (92). To increase the number of recombinatorial events required to generate helper virus, Miller and Buttimore (93) developed the PA317 packaging line. In these cells, the structural genes of the retrovirus were introduced with the pPAM3 plasmid (Fig. 4). To provide the structural proteins without generat-ing wild-type retrovirus, two changes were made in the structure of the provirus within pPAM3. In addition to deleting the packaging signal, the LTRs of the helper provirus were altered so that more than one recom-binatorial event was required to regenerate a wild-type virus. Sequences at

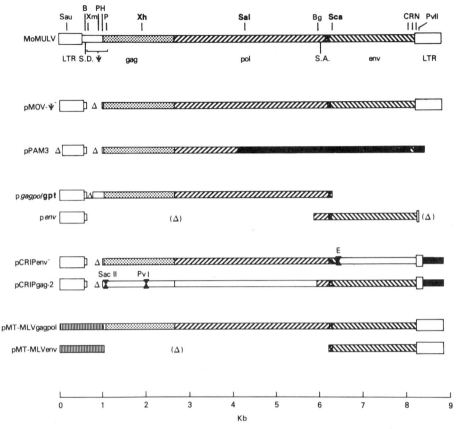

FIG. 4. Comparison of the structure of several helper proviruses used to construct packaging-cell lines. All of these examples are derivatives of Moloney murine leukemia virus, whose structure, including pertinent restriction enzyme sites, is shown at the top. S.D., splice donor; ψ, packaging signal; S.A., splice acceptor. [Refer to the text (Section II,C) for detailed descriptions of the various packaging-cell lines.] pMOV-ψ⁻ was used to generate the ecotropic ψ2 packaging-cell line (90), while pPAM3 was used to generate the PA317 packaging-cell line (93). The shaded region of *pol* and *env* in pPAM3 is derived from the amphotropic 4070A retrovirus. pgagpolgpt and penv were used to generate the GP+E packaging-cell line (95). pCRIPenv⁻ and pCRIPgag-2 were used by Danos and Mulligan (96) for their packaging-cell line. pMT-MLVgagpol and pMT-MLVenv were used by Bosselman et al. (97) to generate their packaging-cell line. Restriction enzyme sites: Sau, *Sau*3A; B, *Bal*I; Xm, *Xma*III; P, *Pst*I; H, *Hae*III; Xh, *Xho*I; Sal, *Sal*I; Bg, *Bgl*II; Xb, *Xba*I; Sca, *Sca*I; C, *Cla*I; R, *Rsa*I; N, *Nhe*I; PvII, *Pvu*II; E, *Eco*RI; PvI, *Pvu*I. Unique sites are indicated in boldface. ‖‖‖, Metallothionein promoter; (in pCRIPenv⁻ and pCRIPgag-2), polyadenylation sites derived from the SV40 virus.

the 5' end of the 5' LTR were deleted and almost the entire 3' LTR was deleted, with polyadenylation signals provided instead by sequences derived from SV40.

With these changes, two recombinations are necessary to regenerate wild-type virus. Nonetheless, after long-term culture, wild-type viruses are still generated at detectable frequencies. Therefore, further efforts have been made to develop packaging lines almost completely refractory to the generation of wild-type retroviruses caused by recombinations between vector and helper. The strategy of such packaging systems was laid out in one of the first packaging systems reported, that of Watanabe and Temin (94) for the avian reticuloendotheliosis virus. This strategy entailed the complete separation of *gag/pol* expression from *env* expression. Rather than relying on the wild-type spliced transcript expression of the viral proteins, each was generated using a separate transcript under individual regulatory control.

Recently, similar MoMuLV-based packaging systems have been described (Fig. 4). Markowitz *et al.* (95) designed a packaging line incorporating two plasmid constructs for the separate expression of *gag/pol* and *env*. In these plasmids, the retroviral structural genes remain under the control of the LTR. For expression of *gag* and *pol* genes, Markowitz *et al.* constructed the pgagpolgpt plasmid, where *gag/pol* is expressed but both *env* and the 3' LTR were deleted. The packaging signal adjacent to the 5' LTR was also deleted. The *env* gene is expressed in the reciprocal construction, p*env*, where the packaging signal and *gag/pol* are deleted, leaving only *env* under the regulation of the retroviral LTR. For a cell containing these constructs to produce a replication-competent virus, three separate recombination events would be required.

Danos and Mulligan used a slightly different strategy in their pCRIPenv⁻ and pCRIPgag-2 constructs (96). Although they still utilized deletions to eliminate packaging, they used point mutations to eliminate expression of the second gene in both the *gag/pol* and *env* constructs. In pCRIPenv⁻, two tandem *Eco*RI linkers were inserted into position 5987 of the MoMuLV genome to disrupt the reading frame of *env*. Likewise, they used the insertion of a *Sac*II linker at position 623 and the conversion of the *Xho*I site at position 1560 to a *Pvu*I site to disrupt the *gag/pol* reading frame of pCRIPgag-2. In the latter construct, the envelope protein is still translated from a spliced transcript. A third strategy was used by Bosselman and colleagues in their pMT-MLVgag/pol and pMT-MLVenv constructs. They exchanged the regulatory sequences provided by the retroviral LTR with the metallothionein promoter (97). This permits specific, inducible regulation of expression of the packaging genes.

In all packaging systems, the targeting of the vector is provided by the choice of envelope expressed by the packaging cells. The MoMuLV ecotropic envelope is used in ψ2 (90), the GP+E cell line of Markowitz *et al.* (95), and ψCRE (96) to create vectors with a mouse-specific tropism. To enable the infection of non-rodent species, the ecotropic envelope was exchanged with the amphotropic envelope derived from the murine 4070A virus. This envelope has been used in the ψAm (98), PA12 (91), PA317 (93), and ψCRIP (96) packaging-cell lines.

III. Gene Transfer and Expression in Mammalian Cells

A. Single-Gene Retroviral Vectors

Recombinant retroviruses have been used extensively to introduce functioning genes into cells in culture as well as into animals. Table I presents a survey of several single gene vectors based on Moloney MuLV. The use of these vectors is discussed here and comparisons are made concerning the extent of gene transfer and expression in different types of target cells using similar vectors. Initially, retroviral-mediated gene transfer was used to transfer selectable marker genes into cultured cell lines or murine bone marrow. New approaches have employed more complex vectors, the development of refined packaging cell lines to eliminate the presence of helper virus, modifications of infection protocols, and the use of varied animal model systems to test expression *in vivo*.

1. NEOMYCIN-RESISTANCE VECTORS

The expression of the gene for neomycin resistance (*neo*[r]), originally derived from the bacterial transposon Tn5 (99, 100), has been studied in a variety of systems using several different vectors. Most vectors contain intact LTR sequences to drive expression of *neo*[r], although some have included a second internal promoter in the vector (Fig. 5). One of the earliest *neo*[r] vectors used was MLV-Neo1, containing *neo*[r] and the SV40 early-promoter in the opposite orientation to the viral LTRs. In a population of bone marrow cells infected with MLV-Neo1, 0.3% of the CFU-GM (colony-forming units, granulocyte/monocyte) were resistant to G418 (a neomycin analogue) at concentrations toxic to uninfected marrow cells. In addition, *neo*[r]-specific RNA was detected by dot-blot (60).

Using several modifications of the infection protocol, much higher efficiencies of gene transfer with the MLV-Neo1 vector have been achieved (101–103). These modifications included: pretreatment of the mice used for donor marrow with 5-fluorouracil to enrich for primitive progenitor cells; cocultivation of the marrow and vector-producing cells; preselection of infected marrow for 48 hours in high levels of G418 to enrich for cells expressing the *neo*[r] gene ("preselection"); and the use of WEHI-3B-conditioned

TABLE I

SINGLE-GENE RETROVIRAL VECTORS[a]

Gene	Vector designation	Promoter	Target cell	References
neo[r]	MLV-Neo1	SV40	Murine BM	60, 101–103
	MLV-Neo1	SV40	1° Murine hepatocytes	116
	Neoμ	Murine Ig heavy-chain enhancer	Murine BM	101
	Neoμ	Murine Ig heavy-chain enhancer	Murine B-lymphocytes	103
	N2	LTR	Murine BM	102, 104, 105
	N2	LTR	Human BM	110–113
	N2	LTR	K562 (human leukemic cell line)	112
	N2	LTR	Human fetal liver cells	112
	N2	LTR	Canine BM	106–108
	N2	LTR	CF2TH (canine fibroblast cell line)	106
	N2	LTR	NIH-3T3 cells	73, 106
	N2	LTR	1° Rat hepatocytes, 208F (rat HPRT⁻ cell line)	28
	N2	LTR	Human myeloid leukemia blast cells	114
	ZIP-NeoSV(X)	LTR	Murine BM	115
	ZIP-NeoSV(X)	LTR	Human BM	112
	ZIP-NeoSV(X)	LTR	K562 cells	112
	ZIP-NeoSV(X)	LTR	Human fetal liver cells	112
	ZIP-NeoSV(X)	LTR	1° Murine hepatocytes	116
	ZIP-NeoSV(X)	LTR	Murine B-lymphocytes	103

(continued)

TABLE I
(Continued)

Gene	Vector designation	Promoter	Target cell	References
	ΔeΔpMoTN	TK	SP1 (mouse mammary adenocarcinoma cell line)	76
	MoTN	TK	Murine BM	102
	MoTN	TK	1° Murine hepatocytes	116
	MT-N	MT	NIH-3T3 cells	75
	SV-N	SV40	NIH-3T3 cells	75
Human HPRT	LPL	LTR	208F (rat HPRT− fibroblasts)	72
	LPL	LTR	LNSV, D98 (human HPRT− fibroblasts)	72
	LPL	LTR	Murine BM	118
	LSΔPΔLM	LTR	1° Rat hepatocytes	28
	LMTPL	MT	HPRT− 208F cells	79
	RMH			
DHFR	LDL	LTR	NIH-3T3 TK− cells	91
	LSDL	SV40	LNSV human HPRT− cells	
hph	LHL	LTR	Murine fibroblasts, human ADA− fibroblasts	110, 119
Murine *mdr*	Hmdr	Human histone H4	NIH-3T3 cells	120
Human ADA	PGK-ADA	Human pgk	Murine BM	68
Human LDLR	LTR-LDLR	LTR	1° Rabbit hepatocytes	123
	BA-LDLR	β-Actin	1° Rabbit hepatocytes	123
	TK-LDLR	TK	1° Rabbit hepatocytes	123
	H4-LDLR	Histone H4	1° Rabbit hepatocytes	123

*a*Abbreviations: neo*r*, neomycin resistance gene; SV40, early gene promoter of simian virus 40; BM, bone marrow; TK, thymidine-kinase gene promoter of herpes simplex type 1; LTR, viral long-terminal-repeat; MT, metallothionein promoter; HPRT, hypoxanthine phosphoribosyltransferase; DHFR, dihydrofolate reductase; *hph*, hygromycin-B phosphotransferase; *mdr*, multiple drug resistance gene; ADA, adenosine deaminase; pgk, phosphoglycerate kinase; LDLR, low-density-lipoprotein receptor.

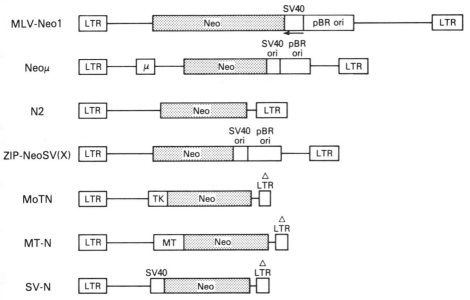

FIG. 5. Schematic diagrams of several retroviral vectors containing the gene for neomycin resistance (*neo^r*). [Refer to Table I for references.] LTR, Long-terminal-repeat; SV40, simian-virus-40 early promoter; pBR ori, pBR322 origin of replication; μ, mouse immunoglobulin heavy-chain enhancer; SV40 ori, SV40 origin of replication; TK, thymidine kinase promoter; MT, metallothionein promoter; ΔLTR, partial deletion of LTR.

medium throughout the infection and preselection steps. Using the MLV-NeoI vector or Neoμ, in which the mouse Ig heavy-chain enhancer has been inserted into pZIP-NeoSV(X) (Fig. 5), *in vitro* assay of infected marrow showed 60–100% of the CFU to be resistant to G418 (*101*). In the same study, infected marrow was used to reconstitute normal, lethally irradiated mice. Examination of spleen colonies 11–13 days after transplant of the preselected MLV-Neo1-infected marrow revealed that 8/8 spleen colonies (CFU-S) contained vector DNA, in contrast to only 1/11 DNA-positive CFU-S from marrow that was not preselected in G418 (*101*).

A similar infection efficiency (10/10 positive CFU-S) was seen with the Neoμ vector after injection of preselected marrow (*101*). In the same study, the Neoμ vector was used to infect marrow for reconstitution of W/W^v mice (a mutant anemic strain) to examine long-term stable transfer and expression in primitive stem cells 11–17 weeks after transplantation. Hematopoietic reconstitution with *neo^r*-containing stem cells was detected in 7 of 15 mice, and examination of several individuals showed the presence of vector DNA in cells of the bone marrow, thymus, and spleen: marrow from one of these mice was used to reconstitute secondary recipients, and neo^r-specific sequences were detected in the spleens of these animals 14 days after transplantation, indicating that gene transfer had occurred in the population of stem cells capable of reconstituting animals. Most important was the demonstration that G418-resistant CFU-GM could be recovered from the long-term reconstituted animals, indicating functioning of the transferred gene *in vivo*.

Additional work with the MLV-Neo1 and Neoµ vectors showed that normal mouse B-lymphocytes can be infected and express the *neo^r* gene (*103*). Greater levels of *neo^r* expression (42% G418^r CFU-B) were observed in infected B-lymphocytes using Neoµ compared to either MLV-Neo1 or the parent vector, ZIP-NeoSV(X) (9–10% G418^r CFU-B) under the same infection conditions, suggesting a direct effect of the Igµ chain enhancer (*103*).

To date, one of the most widely used *neo^r* vectors is N2 (Fig. 5). The design has been discussed in detail above (Section II,B), but unlike MLV-Neo1 and Neoµ, transcription of *neo^r* in N2 is regulated only by the viral LTR rather than a heterologous internal promoter. It has been used in many cell types, such as murine (*102, 104, 105*), canine (*106–108*), primate (*109*), and human (*110–113*) bone marrow, as well as rat fibroblasts and primary rat hepatocytes (*28*), and human leukemic cells (*112, 114*).

Hematopoietic progenitor cells of mice can be readily infected with the N2 vector and express *neo^r*. We (*104*) and Keller *et al.* (*105*) independently showed transfer and expression of the *neo^r* gene in both short-term (10–12 days post-transplant) and long-term reconstituted animals (6 weeks to 4 months). In our study, a high rate of infection was obtained by cocultivation with producer cells, as measured by DNA-positive CFU-S, without 5-fluorouracil treatment of donor marrow or enrichment for *neo^r*-expressing cells in the infected marrow by culturing in high concentrations of G418 for 48 hours prior to transplantation (*104*). We also included the purified growth factor, interleukin-3 (IL-3), in some of the bone marrow infections but found no appreciable difference in the efficiency of infection.

Keller *et al.* (*105*) used an infection protocol similar to that of Dick *et al.* (*101*) with 5-fluorouracil treatment of mice for the donor marrow and preselection of the infected marrow in G418 before transplant. The proportion of G418-resistant (G418^r) CFU *in vitro* was approximately 25% without G418 preselection, and increased 2- to 3-fold with preselection in G418 prior to transplant. Marrow recovered from long-term reconstituted animals (7–11 weeks) that had been transplanted with preselected marrow had 13–37% G418^r CFU (*105*). In addition, neomycin phosphotransferase (NPT) activity was detected in spleen, bone marrow, thymus, and lymph node tissue taken from both primary and secondary reconstituted mice, indicating that *neo^r* was expressed in hematopoietic cells of both the myeloid and lymphoid cell lineages.

The N2 vector has been used by several investigators to study gene transfer in canine hematopoietic cells (106–108). Kwok et al. (106) compared infection rates by cocultivation, using either N2 packaged by PA12 cells containing amphotropic helper virus or N2 packaged by the helper-free amphotropic packaging cell line, PA317. The percentage of G418-resistant CFU-GM was greater with PA12-N2 (16–25%) compared to PA317-N2 (6%). Eglitis et al. (107) found only 3–5% G418-resistant CFU-GM after infection with virus-containing supernatant from PA12-N2 cells, and no evidence of CFU expressing neo if the bone marrow was cocultivated with producer cells. This finding is difficult to explain in light of the fact that cocultivation with producer cells did not affect the viability of the dog bone marrow.

In a third study of gene transfer into canine hematopoietic cells (108), using cocultivation with helper-contaminated PA12-N2 cells, an infection rate of only 2.8% G418^r CFU-GM was found (assayed before transplantation). Unfortunately, this was the result of only one infection. None of the above studies used preselection of marrow in G418; the variability reported may also have stemmed from other factors such as different sources of donor marrow.

The efficiency of infection by cocultivation with producer cells or using a cell-free virus-containing supernatant may vary depending on the viral titer and/or the target cell. These two types of infection methods have been compared in a human leukemic cell line, K562, using either the ZIP-NeoSV(X) vector or N2 (112). In this study, the ZIP-NeoSV(X) vector was packaged by either the helper-free amphotropic ψAM cell line or helper-contaminated PA12 cells, and the N2 vector was packaged by PA12 or the helper-negative PA317 cell line. With titers less than 10^5 cfu/ml, the infection efficiency was 4-fold greater by cocultivation, whereas with viral titers of 5×10^5 or greater there was little difference seen in the level of infection by either cocultivation or supernatant infection. Also, the presence or absence of helper virus did not affect infection efficiency.

Studies using the N2 vector for gene transfer demonstrate an infection efficiency in human bone marrow comparable to that seen in marrow of dogs, although generally somewhat lower than that seen in mice. Similar cocultivation infection protocols were used by three independent groups to examine the marrow infection rate, using either PA12-N2 or PA317-N2 producer cell lines. For marrow infected with PA12-N2, the percentage of G418-resistant CFU-GM ranged from 4 (111) to 7% (112), and for PA317-N2 from 4 (112) to 20% in in vitro colony assay (113). The highest level of infection was achieved using a PA317 producer cell line and conditioned medium from 5637 cells. In the same study, preselection of infected marrow for 48 hours in G418 to enrich for expressing cells increased the proportion of resistant CFU recovered to 60% (113).

Another neo^r vector, ZIP-NeoSV(X) (Fig. 5), in which expression of neo^r is regulated by the viral LTR, has been used in a number of studies to examine the transduction of murine bone marrow (*115*), B-lymphocytes (*103*), and hepatocytes (*116*), as well as human bone marrow (*112*). The ZIP-NeoSV(X) vector was used to infect mouse bone-marrow progenitor and stromal cells maintained in long-term bone-marrow culture (*115*). Cells were infected by exposure to virus-containing supernatants on day 7 in culture. Colonies that were resistant to G418 were isolated at 9 weeks and represented 4–42% of the progenitor cells. These G418-resistant progenitor cells were assayed according to their ability to form colonies in response to WEHI-3B-conditioned medium (CM), L-cell CM, or a combination of spleen cell CM and erythropoietin. The presence of the ZIP-NeoSV(X) virus along with MoMuLV helper in the cultures did not lead to an overall increase in the number of resistant colonies detected. Nonetheless, it is difficult to interpret these results relative to the level of transduction of mouse bone marrow with the N2 vector in short-term culture because of the continuous infection over a period of several weeks in culture, and in some instances, the presence of MoMuLV helper virus.

Several studies have used another *neo*[r] vector, MoTN (Fig. 5), containing an internal herpes-simplex-virus/thymidine-kinase (HSV-TK) promoter upstream from *neo*[r] in the same orientation as the viral LTR. This vector has been used to transduce mouse bone marrow with high efficiency (*117*). The percentage of G418-resistant CFU-GM ranged from 17% without preselection in high concentrations of G418 to 77% with preselection prior to plating. It was also observed that the sizes of G418-resistant colonies from MoTN-, Neoμ-, and N2-infected marrows were larger than the colonies from marrow infected with other *neo*[r] vectors such as MLV-Neo1 or ZIP-Neo(SV)X, suggesting higher levels of *neo*[r] expression. In this case, it is difficult to draw conclusions about the effectiveness of different promoters on gene expression without examination of the nature of the RNA transcripts produced. In both the Neoμ and MoTN vectors, the promoter sequences in the 5' viral LTR are intact, so that *neo*[r] expression could be directed from the LTR, as well as the internal promoter. The MoTN vector was used in the same study to infect rat fibroblast cells (Rat-2 cell line), and *neo*[r] was only weakly expressed compared to the NPT activity detected in Rat-2 cells infected with MLV-Neo1, Neoμ, or N2. In contrast to these results is the finding that the MoTN vector transduces primary rat hepatocytes much more efficiently than either ZIP-NeoSV(X) or the MLV-Neo1 vector with comparable viral titers (*116*). The variability observed with these vectors may be related to the target cells used for infection or the type of infection protocol, or it may be vector-specific rather than simply a function of different promoters.

2. HYPOXANTHINE PHOSPHORIBOSYLTRANSFERASE VECTORS

Lesch–Nyhan syndrome, brought about by a deficiency of hypoxanthine phosphoribosyltransferase (HPRT), is a potential candidate for somatic cell gene therapy. A vector designated LPL, which contains a cDNA for human HPRT under the transcriptional regulation of the viral LTR, has been used (72) for gene transfer. In these experiments, HPRT⁻ 208F rat fibroblast cells, D98 HeLa cells, and SV40-transformed Lesch–Nyhan (LNSV) fibroblasts were infected; these subsequently expressed HPRT, as evidenced by their growth in HAT (hypoxanthine plus aminopterin plus thymidine) medium. Cell extracts from both HATʳ rat and human fibroblasts had detectable HPRT activity with similar electrophoretic mobility to that observed in normal human HPRT⁺ cells. This vector was also used to infect mouse bone marrow (118). Because of the presence of MoMuLV helper virus, spleen and bone marrow recovered from transplanted mice 31–133 days post-transplant continued to produce virions capable of generating HPRT⁺ colonies in HPRT-deficient BALB/3T3 cells. The presence of a putative human/mouse HPRT heterodimer isolated from the spleen of an animal 2 months after transplant indicated long-term expression.

Using a vector derived from LPL, containing a mutant HPRT, Wolff *et al.* (28) transferred a functioning HPRT cDNA to primary rat hepatocytes. Expression of the LSΔPΔM vector was dependent on cell proliferation. Rat liver cell cultures exposed to LSΔPΔM on day 2 or 3 in culture (when the cells are actively dividing) expressed the mutant HPRT, whereas cells exposed after five days in culture did not. Exposing cells to mitogens to stimulate cell division also had no effect. The authors suggest that the restricted period of infectibility of primary rat liver cells may be a reflection of a change in membrane receptors for amphotropic retroviruses rather than simply a lack of active cell division that may be required for integration to occur.

Another vector containing the human HPRT cDNA was produced by inserting the promoter from human metallothionein (MT) into LPL. This MT-promoter vector, LMTPL, was then modified further by deleting the enhancer and promoter sequences in the 3′ LTR to generate the vector designated RMH (79). Analysis of RNA from rat 208F cells infected with either the LMTPL or RMH vector revealed vector-specific transcripts of appropriate length, initiated either in the 5′ LTR for LMTPL-infected cells or from the internal MT promoter for RMH-infected cells, in which the 5′ LTR promoter sequences should not be active. In this study, the MT promoter was also inducible by the heavy metal, cadmium, leading to a threefold increase in human HPRT RNA in transduced cells.

3. DIHYDROFOLATE REDUCTASE VECTORS

Another selectable marker gene, the gene for dihydrofolate reductase (DHFR), which confers resistance to the folate analogue methotrexate (Mtx), has been used in several retroviral constructs (91). The cDNA used is derived from a mutant DHFR that has reduced affinity for Mtx. It is possible to select for resistant cells that have undergone amplification of the DHFR gene by gradually increasing the concentration of Mtx. At the time when the gene for DHFR was introduced as a selectable marker, there was speculation that it would provide a means for *in vivo* Mtx selection. It may also be useful clinically for protecting bone marrow cells from Mtx-induced myelosuppression, thereby allowing the use of higher dosages for human chemotherapy. However, these applications have not yet been successfully developed in animal model systems.

The single-gene vectors containing a cDNA for DHFR (*91*) are LDL, where expression of the DHFR gene is regulated from the 5′ LTR, and LSDL containing an internal SV40 early promoter in addition to DHFR. These investigators were able to increase the viral titer of DHFR producer cells by selection in increasing concentrations of Mtx. The strategy of inducing gene amplification with a corresponding increase in transcripts available for packaging increased the DHFR viral titer from 4×10^6 to 6×10^7 cfu/ml for cells grown at Mtx concentrations from 10^{-7} M to 10^{-5} M. The LDL DHFR virus produced could infect HPRT$^-$ LNSV human fibroblast cells to generate Mtx-resistant cells.

4. Hygromycin-B Phosphotransferase* Vectors

The bacterial gene for hygromycin-B phosphotransferase* (*hph*), which confers resistance to hygromycin B, has been used as a selectable marker for gene transfer to both murine and human fibroblasts (*110, 119*). The LHL vector contains *hph* without an internal promoter, and approximately 400 base-pairs of *gag* coding sequence from MoMuLV similar to the N2 vector (*119*). The LHL vector had a higher titer than LSHL, which was generated using LTR sequences from MoMSV and an internal SV40 early promoter linked to *hph*. Infection of human fibroblasts from four donors with the LHL vector gave rise to hygromycin-resistant colonies with an infection efficiency in the range of 33–55% for fetal fibroblasts, 41–46% for newborn fibroblasts, and 19–52% for adult human diploid fibroblasts.

5. Multidrug-Resistance Vectors

Both a human (*12*) and a murine (*120*) cDNA for the multidrug-resistance (MDR) gene have been isolated and used in retroviral constructs for gene transfer. The MDR gene encodes a plasma membrane glycoprotein that serves as a drug efflux pump, resulting in decreased accumulation of cytotoxic drugs. Although the human MDR cDNA was cloned into a MoMuLV vector, it was used initially only for introduction into cells by transfection

---

* Hygromycin-B kinase (EC 2.7.1.119) is the recommended name (and number) of the Nomenclature Committee of the International Union of Biochemistry (NC-IUB); see *Eur. J. Biochem.* **179**, 509 (1989). [Eds.]

(*12*). Nonetheless, using this technique, resistance was conferred to murine and human fibroblasts for several drugs, including colchicine, vinblastine, and doxorubicin (Adriamycin). In a later study, the human MDR cDNA was shown to express in infected human fibroblasts and a dog kidney cell line, using a retroviral vector based on Harvey murine sarcoma virus (*13*).

The murine MDR cDNA has been cloned into a retroviral vector along with the human H4 histone promoter (*120*). This construct also had a deletion of the viral enhancer sequences in the 3' LTR so that transcription should be regulated from the internal histone promoter (*120*). This vector, Hmdr, was used to infect NIH-3T3 cells, which subsequently became resistant to both colchicine and doxorubicin. Analysis of integrated DNA in resistant clones growing in moderate or high concentrations of drug revealed only one or two copies of the Hmdr vector. For future retroviral constructs, the inclusion of the MDR gene may prove useful for both *in vitro* and *in vivo* selection.

6. ADENOSINE DEAMINASE VECTORS

A series of vectors containing only the gene for human adenosine deaminase (ADA) with a human phosphoglycerate kinase (PGK) promoter have been used by Lim *et al.* (*68*). They were constructed using the ZIP-DHFR backbone by removing the DHFR cDNA and inserting a PGK-promoted ADA cDNA in the sense orientation (PGK-ADA, Fig. 6). A similar vector was produced that contained a deletion in the enhancer region of the 3' LTR with the PGK-promoted ADA in either the sense or anti-sense orientation. Because these vectors do not contain a selectable marker gene such as *neo^r*, producer cell clones were isolated in "ADA selection" medium containing xylofuranosyl arabinoside (Xyl-A) and deoxycoformycin (dCF), which would select for cells expressing levels of ADA higher than the endogenous murine ADA constitutively expressed in the producer cells. Producer cell clones were then screened for ADA virus production by a qualitative measure of human ADA enzyme activity in infected NIH-3T3 cells. We have used a similar strategy for ADA vectors not containing a selectable marker gene (B2A, Fig. 6); however, we could isolate putative high-titer producer-cell clones without the use of Xyl-A/dCF selection medium by initially co-transfecting ADA vector DNA with pSV2neo DNA and selecting in G418 (J. R. McLachlin, unpublished observations).

The PGK-ADA vectors developed by Lim *et al.* (*68*) were used to infect mouse bone marrow progenitor cells followed by preselection in Xyl-A/dCF for 48 hours prior to transplantation into lethally irradiated recipients. *In vitro* assays of infected marrow showed that most of the colonies (CFU-GEMM, i.e., colony-forming units–granulocyte, erythrocyte, monocyte megakaryocyte) selected in Xyl-A and dCF were producing human ADA enzyme, and expression appeared to be at levels comparable to the endogenous mouse ADA. The presence or absence of enhancer sequences in the viral LTR did not affect the ADA expression detected in murine bone-marrow colonies. These investigators also found evidence of vector DNA in 9% of the spleen colonies (CFU-S) isolated from animals reconstituted with unselected bone marrow. Human ADA isozyme activity was observed in every DNA-positive CFU-S. From animals reconstituted with marrow pre-selected in Xyl-A/dCF, a greater proportion (27%) contained intact vector DNA, and all of those expressed human ADA. This study was unique in its demonstration of the effectiveness of a single-gene vector without a selectable marker gene for obtaining expression in primary murine bone marrow *in vitro* and in spleen colonies recovered from short-term reconstituted animals. This is in contrast to the lack of ADA expression *in vivo* in mice reported previously for other ADA vectors (*121, 122*), which is discussed in more detail in a later section (Section III,B,2). At least, comparing the results obtained with this series of vectors, the presence of intact viral LTR sequences did not lead to down-regulation of vector ADA expression in animals.

7. Low-Density Lipoprotein Vectors

A group of retroviral constructs containing a cDNA for the low-density-lipoprotein receptor (LDLR) gene have been used to infect hepatocytes from the Watanabe rabbit (*123*). The Watanabe-heritable-hyperlipidemic (WHHL) rabbit provides a useful model system because of a defect in LDL receptors which leads to hypercholesterolemia. The LTR-LDLR vector does not contain an internal promoter, although it was modified by substituting a portion of the MoMuLV 3' LTR with sequences from the 3' LTR of myeloproliferative sarcoma virus. Three other recombinant vectors used a backbone containing a deletion of the 3' LTR enhancer, inclusion of additional *gag*-coding sequences from MoMuLV, and an internal promoter linked to the LDLR sequences (chicken β-actin, HSV-TK, or human histone H4). Cultured hepatocytes from WHHL rabbits were infected on day 2 of culture for 12 hours and assayed on day 5 for expression of the LDLR gene. Analysis of hepatocytes infected with any of the LDLR vectors showed the presence of intact vector DNA. RNA analysis revealed the presence of LDLR transcripts exceeding the level of detectable endogenous RNA that were initiated either from the LTR or from the internal promoter in the deleted LTR constructs.

In an attempt to quantify the LDLR expression, the degradation of ^{125}I-LDL was measured in infected populations of cells for a 5-hour period. The greatest level of activity was found in the LTR-LDLR-infected hepatocytes, whereas the levels measured for the other internally promoted vectors did not differ from mock-infected WHHL cells. The authors suggest (*123*) that the lower variable expression obtained with the internally promoted recombinant retroviruses may be only partially due to differences in promoter strength; it may also arise from differences in RNA stability.

B. Multiple-Gene Retroviral Vectors

Retroviral vectors containing two exogenous genes have been widely used (Table II). In most of these constructs, transcription of the first gene is regulated from the 5' LTR promoter sequences, while the second gene is linked to an internal heterologous promoter. The inclusion of a selectable marker gene in conjunction with a nonselectable gene in a retroviral construct greatly facilitates the isolation and identification of high-titer producer-cell clones to be used for the production of infectious, but replication-incompetent virus carrying both genes.

1. MULTIPLE-GENE VECTORS WITH HUMAN HPRT

Several retroviral vectors containing HPRT in addition to a nonselectable gene have been designed (*122, 124, 125*), as have vectors containing two selectable genes, i.e., HPRT/neo^r vectors (*79, 81, 82*). Some examples of these types of constructs are discussed briefly.

A cDNA for human HPRT has been included in retroviral constructs that also contain the genes for rat growth hormone (GH) (*124*), HSV-TK (*125*), human adenosine deaminase (ADA) (*122*), or human purine nucleoside phosphorylase (PNP) (*122*). The LPGHL vector contained a rat growth hormone "minigene" with its own promoter and polyadenylation signal inserted in the "sense" orientation or in the reverse orientation (LPHGL) to the HPRT gene, which was expressed from the 5' LTR. Both constructs were used to infect HPRT$^-$ rat 208F cells and BALB/3T3 cells. About half of the infected cells expressing HPRT also expressed GH regardless of the orientation of the growth hormone minigene. Examination of RNA in the infected cells by S_1 nuclease analysis demonstrated the correct initiation and termination of transcripts from the vector GH gene. These results confirmed that retroviruses can be used for the cotransfer and expression of two heterologous genes.

Vectors containing both HPRT and neo^r have been described (*79, 81, 82*). The SV(X)HPRT vector contains the human HPRT cDNA upstream from neo^r in ZIP-NeoSV(X). Infected HPRT$^-$ NIH-3T3 cells simultaneously expressed HPRT and neo^r (*81, 82*). The level of HPRT expression ranged from 4 to 56% of wild-type activity. An interesting finding (*82*) was the unstable nature of some infected cell clones. Cells expressing th SV(X)HPRT vector cultured in the absence of selective pressure lost both the HAT^r and the G418^r phenotypes. In some cases, the lack of expression resulted from the loss or gross rearrangement of the vector DNA. The SV(X)HPRT vector was

TABLE II

MULTIPLE-GENE RETROVIRAL VECTORS[a]

Genes	Vector designation	Promoter	Target cell	References
Human HPRT/rGH	LPHGL	LTR/GH	HPRT⁻ rat 208F cells	124
Human HPRT/TK	HT2	LTR	HPRT⁻ rat 208F cells, rat-2 TK⁻ rat cells	125
Human HPRT/ADA	LHMAL	LTR/mMT	Murine fibroblasts, murine BM	122
Human HPRT/PNP	LHMPL	LTR/mMT	Murine fibroblasts, murine BM	122
Human HPRT/neo^r	SV(X) HPRT	LTR	NIH-3T3 cells, murine BM, human fibroblasts	82, 82
neo^r/human HPRT	LHP	LTR/hCMV	HPRT⁻ rat 208F cells	79
Human GC/neo^r	DOL-MP10	LTR	NIH-3T3 cells, GM1260 (Gaucher fibroblast line)	129
DHFR/ADA	ZIP-DHFR-ADA	LTR	NIH-3T3 cells	121
	ZIP-DHFR-SVADA	LTR/SV40	Murine lymphoid cell line, GM2471 ADA⁻ B cells, murine BM	121
Human ADA/neo^r	ZIP-ADA	LTR	NIH-3T3 cells	126
	SV(X) ADA	LTR	Murine lymphoid cell line	83
	SV(B)ADA211	LTR	Murine BM	81, 84
neo^r/human ADA	LNSAL	LTR/SV40	Human ADA⁻ skin fibroblasts	119
	SAX	LTR/SV40	Human ADA⁻ T cells, human ADA⁻ B cells	85
	SAX	LTR/SV40	NIH-3T3 cells, CV-1 monkey kidney cell line	86
	SAX	LTR/SV40	Monkey BM	87

Human PAH/neor	ZPAH	LTR	hepal-a* cells, NIH-3T3 cells	130
Human α1AT/neor	Zα1AT(+)	LTR	Human hepatoma cell lines, NIH-3T3 cells	131
neor/human αIAT	N2-FAT	LTR/SV40	NIH-3T3 cells	132
neor/human AS	ZNXAS	LTR	NIH-3T3 cells, rat XC cells	117
Human β-globin/neor	SVX	LTR/globin	MEL cells	61
	βpV4Δneo	LTR/globin	NIH-3T3 cells, MEL cells	63
	HX19	LTR/globin	Murine BM	66
neor/human β-globin	NG	LTR/globin	MEL cells	64
	LNB*WT	LTR/globin	MEL cells	65
	LNB*MG		Human BM	65
	LNB*SA	LTR/globin	MEL cells, murine BM	67
c-fos/neor	F-TK-N	mMT/TK	NIH-3T3 cells	75
λ1Ig/neor	SVλ1	LTR	NIH-3T3 cells, 1881Y and 70Z B-cell lines	133
				133
Human GH/neor	DOL-hGH	LTR/SV40	1° Human epidermal cells	134
neor/IL-3	N2-IL3	LTR	FDC-P1 cells,b fetal liver cells	135
Factor IX/neor	AFFIXSVNeo	LTR/SV40	1° Murine skin fibroblasts	140
β-gal/neor	BAG	LTR/SV40	Rat retina, cerebral cortex, 1° rat hepatocytes	137–139
				136
Human IL-2/neor	ZIPSVIL2	LTR	Murine T-cell line	141

aAbbreviations: rGH, rat growth hormone; ADA, human adenosine deaminase; mMT, mouse metallothionein; PNP, human purine-nucleoside phosphorylase; hCMV, human cytomegalovirus; GC, glucocerebrosidase; PAH, phenylalanine hydroxylase; αIAT, α1-antitrypsin; AS, argininosuccinate synthetase; MEL, murine erythroleukemia cells; λ1IG, murine λ1 immunoglobulin gene; GH, growth hormone; β-gal, β-galactosidase; *, hepal-a cells (murine hepatoma cell line).

bFDC-P1 cell, murine factor-dependent cells (myeloid lineage)

117

also used to infect mouse bone marrow. Only about 0.5% of the cultured CFU were resistant to G418; however, human HPRT activity could be demonstrated in a pooled population of neo^r-expressing CFU.

Yee *et al.* (79) modified the HPRT parent vector, LPL (72), by inserting *neo*^{r} and linking the human cytomegalovirus (hCMV) promoter to HPRT. The resulting NHP-1 vector had intact LTR sequences, while NHP-2 had a deletion of the 3′ LTR enhancer and promoter elements. Rat 208F cells had greater levels of HPRT activity after NHP-2 infection, when transcription should be regulated primarily by the hCMV promoter. On the other hand, expression seen with the NHP-2 vector was much less than the HPRT activity measured using the parent LPL vector, which does not contain either a *neo*^{r} or an internal promoter (i.e., HPRT promoted by the LTR).

2. MULTIPLE-GENE VECTORS WITH HUMAN ADA

Gene therapy using retroviral-mediated gene transfer may some day be a mode of treatment for severe combined immunodeficiency (SCID) resulting from a deficiency of ADA. To investigate the potential for gene therapy, there has been a large effort devoted to the development of ADA gene vectors. Several vectors containing a cDNA for human ADA are illustrated in Fig. 6. Most are multiple-gene vectors containing *neo*^{r}, *DHFR*, or *HPRT* in addition to ADA.

Valerio *et al.* (126) used an ADA construct derived from the ZIP-Neo-SV(X) backbone to infect NIH-3T3 cells. Human ADA activity was demonstrated in infected cell lines with or without selection in G418. The introduced genes were stable in transduced cells; continued passage in the absence of G418 did not lead to loss of either neo^r or human ADA activity. Another ADA vector based on the ZIP-neoSV(X) backbone was used by Friedman (83) to infect BL/VL$_3$ cells, a mouse T-cell lymphoma line, which subsequently expressed the transduced human ADA gene.

The SAX vector (Fig. 6) was generated by inserting an ADA cDNA linked to the SV40 early promoter into the *Xho*I site of *neo*^{r} in the N2 vector. It has been used to transfer a functioning human ADA gene to ADA-deficient human T and B cells (85), as well as NIH-3T3 and CV-1 cells (a monkey kidney cell line) (86). Selection for expression of *neo*^{r} enriched for cells which were concomitantly expressing high levels of human ADA. The NIH-3T3 or CV-1 G418-selected cells expressed levels of human ADA equal to or greater than the endogenous enzyme activity.

We have used the SAX vector to infect hematopoietic cells of monkeys for autologous bone marrow transplantation (87). Cells were infected by either 24-hour cocultivation with producer cells or a 2-hour exposure to viral supernatant. Low levels of human ADA activity (approximately 0.01–0.5% of endogenous monkey ADA) were detected in 4 out of 5 reconstituted animals.

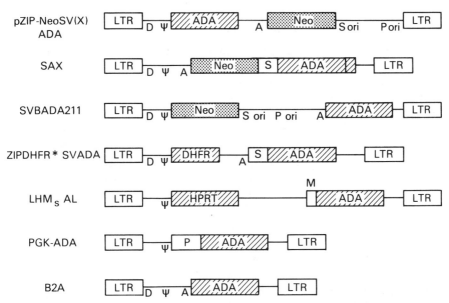

FIG. 6. Schematic diagrams of various retroviral vectors that contain a cDNA for human adenosine deaminase (ADA). Refer to text (Section III,B,1) for references. LTR, Long-terminal-repeat; D, splice donor site; ψ, packaging signal; A, slice acceptor site; Neo, neomycin resistance gene (*neo^r*); S ori, SV40 origin of replication; P ori, pBR322 origin of replication; S, SV40 early gene promoter; DHFR, dihydrofolate reductase; HPRT, hypoxanthine phosphoribosyltransferase; M, metallothionein promoter; P, phosphoglycerate kinase promoter.

Two animals with the highest levels (0.2 and 0.5% of endogenous monkey ADA) had detectable levels only between 60 and 120 days post-transplant, and there was no evidence of human ADA activity in the peripheral blood mononuclear cells (PBMC) of either animal at 6 months post-transplant. Expression of *neo^r* was examined by *in situ* hybridization and 0.8% of the PBMC showed hybridization to a neo-specific probe at 4 months. For two animals, G418^r T cells could be isolated from the peripheral blood at 6–7 months post-transplant. Our inability to detect vector DNA sequences in the PBMC or bone marrow of most transplanted animals led us to conclude that only a small fraction of the cells contained and expressed the introduced genes.

A vector very similar to SAX, containing the *neo^r* gene and an SV40-promoted ADA gene (LNSAL), has been used to infect ADA-deficient human skin fibroblasts (*119*). The LNSAL vector expressed high levels of hADA in G418-resistant cells.

The ADA vector "SVBADA211" (*84*) (Fig. 6) was produced by inserting an ADA cDNA into the ZIP-NeoSV(B) backbone. Expression of both the *neo*[r] and ADA genes were demonstrated in mouse hematopoietic progenitor cells. Approximately 10% of the CFU were resistant to G418, and human ADA activity could be demonstrated in pooled populations of G418-selected cells.

Two other ADA vectors illustrated in Fig. 6 contain either a DHFR cDNA, ZIPDHFR-SVADA (*121*), or a cDNA for HPRT, LHM$_s$AL (*122*). ZIPDHFR-ADA vector was constructed with or without an SV40 promoter linked to ADA; however, NIH-3T3 cells infected with the ZIPDHFR-SVADA vector with the SV40 promoter expressed much higher levels of ADA enzyme. Although this particular vector was capable of infecting murine bone marrow, as indicated by the presence of intact vector sequences in the spleens or CFU-S of reconstituted animals, there was no measurable human ADA activity (*121*). We have not been able to detect any human ADA expression in individual CFU-S or pooled spleen foci from mice reconstituted with marrow infected with the SAX vector (*127*).

Inactivity of the SV40 promoter in mouse hematopoietic progenitor cells has been encountered by other investigators. ZIPDHFR-SVADA vector (Fig. 6) has been used (*121*) to introduce a functioning human ADA gene into an ADA-deficient B-cell line (GM2471) that subsequently expressed high levels of ADA activity even without enrichment for expressing cells, using Mtx selection. However, when the same vector was used to infect mouse bone marrow, there was no detectable ADA activity in the spleens of reconstituted mice at 1–2 weeks, even though intact vector sequences were present.

The HPRT/ADA vector (Fig. 6), LHM$_s$AL, has a short mouse metallothionein promoter linked to the ADA gene. Both LHM$_s$AL and a similar vector with a longer metallothionein promoter were used (*122*) to infect cultured mouse cells and all the clones analyzed produced human ADA at levels similar to endogenous mouse ADA activity. Use of these vectors to infect mouse bone marrow led to results similar to those of Williams *et al.* (*121*). Analysis of spleen colonies from mice reconstituted with infected marrow showed evidence of integrated LHM$_s$AL proviral DNA but not of human ADA activity.

There may be some mechanism of suppression of the SV40-promoted ADA gene in murine hematopoietic cells *in vivo* that is not present in transformed murine fibroblasts. In experiments using the SAX vector to infect preimplantation mouse embryos, several substrains of mice carrying intact vector sequences were analyzed for expression of ADA (*128*). No transcripts were detected from either the 5' LTR or the internal SV40 promoter; further analysis showed the SAX vector sequences to be hypermethylated. A high degree of methylation may only be coincident to the lack of human ADA expression in these transgenic mice. *De novo* methylation and restricted gene expression are associated with genes introduced into pre-implantation mouse embryos rather than into embryos in postimplantation stages (21). In some cases, expression in later-stage embryos is affected not only by demethylation but also by the site of integration (22). The presence of inhibitors in cells of the early embryo may only influence the expression of certain introduced sequences (e.g., the SV40-promoted neo^r gene). In one study (128), other transgenic mice generated in the same manner by retroviral infection of early embryos all expressed neo^r linked to an internal TK promoter. This observation suggests that inactivation may be gene- and/or promoter-specific.

3. MULTIPLE-GENE VECTORS WITH HUMAN β-GLOBIN

Transfer of genomic sequences of the human β-globin gene using retroviral vectors has been investigated in many laboratories (61–67). All of the vectors used contain neo^r but differing lengths of the human β-globin gene. Cone et al. (61) introduced a 3.0-kb fragment of β-globin in both orientations into the ZIP-NeoSV(X) backbone containing either an intact 3' LTR or one with the 3' enhancer elements deleted [ZIP-NeoSV(X)en⁻]. The vectors were used to infect NIH-3T3 cells and murine erythroleukemia (MEL) cells. The only construct that gave measurable viral titers (by $G418^r$) was the reverse orientation β-globin with intact LTR sequences, designated SVXβ(RO). In these experiments, infected MEL cell clones were analyzed; 11 out of 15 contained a single vector insert. Human β-globin transcripts could be detected in the $G418^r$ MEL cell clones, and levels increased in induced MEL cells following exposure to Me_2SO. It is interesting that there were little or no human globin transcripts detected in infected NIH-3T3 cells that were G418-resistant, suggesting erythroid-specific expression of the introduced globin gene in MEL cells.

Karlsson et al. (64) constructed β-globin vectors containing either a 2.5-kb β-γ globin gene hybrid inserted in reverse orientation in the N2 parent vector (NG vector), or a 3.4-kb genomic fragment of human β-globin (β vector). With the NG virus, transcription of the human β–γ globin hybrid increased significantly (5- to 10-fold) in induced populations of infected MEL cells. However, much higher levels of human β-globin synthesis were detected in MEL cells infected with the β vector; these levels approached 10% of endogenous mouse globin.

The $βpV_4Δneo$ vector used by Lerner et al. (63) contained a longer (4.4-kb) fragment of the human β-globin gene in either the reverse or the forward orientation. In contrast to Cone et al. (61), positioning the β-globin gene in the forward orientation did not interfere with the production of infectious virus; however, portions of the vector were deleted in several clones of infected NIH-3T3 cells. Consequently, the vector with β-globin sequences in the reverse orientation to the viral LTR was used primarily in this study. Compared to similar β-globin constructs used in other studies, the level of human β-globin RNA in induced MEL cells was much higher (25–50% of endogenous). The authors suggest that the higher levels of human β-globin expression may result from the presence of SV40 enhancer sequences in this vector as well as the additional 5′ flanking sequence included in the human β-globin fragment.

More recently, studies have been undertaken to examine β-globin expression in hematopoietic cells. Bender *et al.* (65), using a vector containing a 3.0-kb fragment of human β-globin, observed gene transfer and expression in MEL cells and human bone marrow-derived erythroid colonies (BFU-E). In the latter, levels of human β-globin produced approached 5% of endogenous β-globin. It was possible to identify vector-specific transcripts because of additional sequences inserted in the 5′ noncoding region of the β-globin fragment. This was the first demonstration of expression in normal (non-transformed) human cells of erythroid lineage. However, because of a low rate of infection, only five G418[r] colonies were analyzed for the presence of vector-specific transcripts. Also, the bone marrow colony assay conditions only favored growth of erythroid hematopoietic progenitors, so expression of either the β-globin or *neo*[r] was not assessed in other hematopoietic cell lineages. In the same study, a second construct containing human β-globin genomic sequences with the introns removed was not expressed at detectable levels in either the producer cells or infected MEL cells, regardless of orientation.

Another group of investigators examined the expression of human β-globin *in vivo* in mice transplanted with infected marrow. Dzierzak *et al.* (66) used either a 3.0-kb or 4.1-kb human β-globin genomic fragment inserted in the reverse orientation in the ZIP-NeoSV(X) vector. Vector sequences were detected at 1–2 months post-transplant in only 18 of 104 animals reconstituted with infected marrow. A detailed analysis of eight animals was presented. All of these received marrow from donor mice pretreated with 5-fluorouracil, and two had been reconstituted with marrow preselected in G418 for 48 hours prior to transplant. Variable levels of human β-globin expression were demonstrated in peripheral blood, where 10–50% of the erythrocytes stained positively with human β-globin-specific antibodies. Reconstituted mice were also analyzed for the presence of vector transcripts in tissues of various hematopoietic origin; in most cases expression was erythroid-specific. Expression in peripheral blood varied in individual animals from 0.4 to 4.0% of endogenous β-globin when copy-number was accounted for. Although there was a low rate of infection, it now appears possible to infect murine bone-marrow stem-cells and achieve tissue-specific expression of human β-globin *in vivo* in long-term reconstituted animals.

More recently, Miller *et al.* (67) investigated several factors contributing to low titers of virus and low levels of globin expression, using a series of modified β-globin vectors. One important finding was that there are sequences within the 5' flanking region and in intron 2 of the reverse orientation β-globin gene that interfere with the generation of full-length transcripts, thus decreasing titer. Although portions of the 5' flanking region could be removed, the presence of intron 2 was necessary for expression. The LNB*SA vector, containing the SphI–AvrII genomic fragment of β-globin in reverse orientation downstream from neo^r, was used to infect mouse bone marrow. The infected marrow was preselected in G418 before transplanting to enrich for cells expressing neo^r. At 12 days post-transplant, CFU-S were analyzed; intact vector sequences were present in a high proportion of CFU-S (6/9 and 10/10 for separate experiments). All CFU-S that contained vector expressed variable levels of human β-globin.

This work underlined some of the problems encountered with the use of genomic fragments in retroviral vectors. In the case of β-globin, there are sequences within the flanking regions or introns that are important for expression, but that in the reverse orientation may contain consensus poly(A) addition signals that result in early termination of transcripts. A low level of full-length transcripts appears to correlate with a low virus titer.

4. OTHER MULTIPLE-GENE VECTORS

Retroviral vectors have been used to transfer a variety of other genes. These include genes for human glucocerebrosidase (129), human phenylalanine hydroxylase (130), human α_1-antitrypsin (131, 132), human argininosuccinate synthetase (117), mouse λ1 immunoglobulin (133), human growth hormone (134), interleukin-3 (135), β-galactosidase (136–139), human factor IX (140), human interleukin-2 (141), and rat growth hormone (142).

Transfer of a cDNA for human glucocerebrosidase has been demonstrated in both murine fibroblasts (NIH-3T3 cells) and a human Gaucher fibroblast cell line (GM1260) deficient in this enzyme (129). Somatic cell gene therapy may also be useful for the treatment of other enzyme deficiency diseases. Gene transfer and expression of human Phe hydroxylase have been demonstrated in a mouse liver cell line and mouse fibroblasts by retroviral infection (130). Two groups have shown expression of a human α_1-antitrypsin cDNA in mouse fibroblasts using either an N2 (132) or ZIP-NeoSV(X) backbone (131), and a functioning human argininosuccinate synthetase has been introduced into rat cells (117).

Retroviral-mediated gene transfer has also been used to transfer a marker gene so that histochemical staining can be used to identify expressing cells. The BAG vector contains both the β-galactosidase gene from *Escherichia coli* and *neo*[r]. It has been developed and used in a number of studies for the purpose of cell tagging in developing rat retina and cerebral cortex (*137–139*). In addition, the BAG vector has been used to infect adult rat liver cells in culture; it shows expression of β-galactosidase by histochemical staining (*136*).

IV. Use of Retroviral Vectors for Human Gene Therapy

Advances in recombinant DNA technology and the development of vectors for the efficient delivery of genes have generated a great deal of interest in the potential for human gene therapy. Several reviews have addressed this subject and how it may apply to various genetic disorders (*1, 143–145*), as well as some of the ethical issues (*146–148*).

A. Model Systems

Although the concept of gene therapy is straightforward, the practical implementation of it is not. For a disease to be corrected by introducing a functioning therapeutic gene, several criteria must be met. The gene must be isolated, the delivery system should provide a means of efficient, stable transfer, and there should be adequate, long-term expression in the target cells. Because existing technology for gene transfer is relatively unsophisticated, only those diseases resulting from a single-gene defect that does not require complex regulation of expression are usually considered possible candidates for this form of therapy. Some examples of genes with potential for gene therapy are ADA, β-globin, HPRT, PNP, α_1-antitrypsin, glucocerebrosidase, argininosuccinate synthetase, Factor VIII, Factor IX, phenylalanine hydroxylase, and the gene for LDLR.

The most direct approach to gene therapy using retroviral vectors has focused on the treatment of bone-marrow cells because they can easily be removed, infected with a vector carrying the normal gene, and returned to the donor to form a renewable population of cells. A notable advance toward human gene therapy was the demonstration that human bone marrow can efficiently be transduced by a retroviral vector without the presence of contaminating helper virus (*111*). Unfortunately, showing that genes can be expressed *in vitro* in hematopoietic progenitor cells may not be truly representative of the level of expression that might be attainable in more primitive stem-cells *in vivo*. In the case of some retroviral vectors carrying the human ADA gene, although the introduced gene was expressed at high levels in cultured cell lines (*86, 121, 122, 126*) or ADA-deficient human cells (*85, 119*), there was no detectable expression *in vivo* in transplanted mice (*121, 122*), and only low levels of activity in transplanted monkeys (*87*). Gene expression under regulation of the viral LTR may be suppressed in pluripotent stem-cells of bone marrow in a manner similar to the restriction of expression in early preimplantation embryos (21–23). For long-term gene therapy, there is little value in inserting genes into bone-marrow cells that are approaching terminal differentiation.

Recently, Spangrude et al. (149) developed a technique to isolate a relatively pure population of murine bone-marrow stem-cells by the selective removal of more differentiated bone-marrow cells, using antibodies specific for various stem-cell lineages. Once purified stem-cells are isolated, there is the possibility of generating antibodies specific for stem-cells and directly infecting this subpopulation with retroviral vectors. A similar approach may be applicable to the isolation of human bone-marrow stem-cells in the future.

Diseases affecting target cells other than cells of the bone marrow will require different approaches to gene delivery by means of retroviruses. St. Louis and Verma (140) have described a system in which transduced mouse skin fibroblasts expressing the human Factor-IX protein can be transplanted into mice in a collagen implant. The Factor-IX protein was detectable in the serum of mice for several days. Another potential method, reported recently by Thompson et al. (150), utilizes a gelatin sponge treated with class-I heparin-binding growth factor (HBGF-1). The sponges, surgically implanted in both the neck and the peritoneal cavity of rats, supported vascularization of the matrix as well as the growth of N2-infected hepatocytes expressing neo^r.

B. Gene Transfer Safety Issues

A number of theoretical risks must be considered when applying retroviral-mediated gene transfer in humans for the purpose of somatic cell gene therapy. At present, potential risk factors can be studied only in animal models; at best, they provide only an approximation of what might apply in humans. Two areas of concern—the implications of accidental exposure to replication-competent murine amphotropic virus, and the risk of malignancy secondary to retroviral insertion—are addressed here.

1. EXPOSURE TO REPLICATION-COMPETENT MURINE AMPHOTROPIC VIRUS

Amphotropic packaging cell lines are used to obtain amphotropic retroviral vector preparations capable of infecting primate cells, but free of replication-competent (helper) virus (92, 93, 96, 151, 152). These cell lines contain a mutated helper-virus genome with the necessary trans factors required for virion formation, but lack the cis sequences needed for packaging of the helper virus genome into virions (see Section II,C). When a retroviral vector containing the cis packaging sequence is introduced into a packaging cell line, selective encapsidation of vector RNA occurs, so that viral particles contain only the vector genome (i.e., are free of helper virus). Unfortunately, recombination can occur between vector and viral sequences, so that the deleted packaging sequence can be restored, thereby producing replication-competent viral particles (74, 92, 93, 96, 97, 151, 152).

Packaging cell lines that produce retroviral vectors capable of infecting primate cells have utilized the envelope from the murine amphotropic retrovirus 4070A (153). Wild-type 4070A can infect a wide number of primate cell types, and human fibroblasts can produce virus at a titer approximately equivalent to that of murine 3T3 cells (154).

We have studied the fate of amphotropic murine leukemia retrovirus in rhesus monkeys to assess the potential pathogenicity of these viruses in primates (154). Retrovirus was infused intravenously into three normal animals and one immunosuppressed animal (mean dose, 7.2×10^7 focus-forming units). Virus was cleared rapidly (less than 15 minutes) from the circulation and subsequent viremia has not been detected (mean follow-up, 15.7 months). The only acute event, occurring in two of the four animals, was the development of transient asymptomatic lymphadenopathy approximately 1 week after virus infusion. Surgical resection of some enlarged lymph nodes was performed and tissue was evaluated for evidence of virus integration and production. Viral sequences could not be detected by Southern blot analysis, and lymph node lymphocytes grown in culture did not produce detectable virus [using the $S+/L-$ assay (155)]. Lymph nodes returned to normal size within 7 days. Since virus was not recovered from the animal, it is possible that the lymphadenopathy represented an immune response to injected antigens, not a response to viral replication (the viral preparations used in this study contained 10% fetal calf serum in addition to viral antigens). Clinically, the animals have remained afebrile and have exhibited no adverse change in behavior, appetite, weight, complete blood counts, or blood chemistries throughout their course (154).

The rapid disappearance of injected virus may, in part, be related to the ability of primate serum to inactivate murine retroviruses (154, 156). This serum component, a heat-labile factor (presumably complement) may have protected the animals receiving intravenous virus. To maximize virus exposure, another immunosuppressed monkey was transplanted with infected autologous skin fibroblasts shown to be producing amphotropic virus, in addition to an intraperitoneal injection of virus. Clinically, this animal developed transient asymptomatic lymphadenopathy without other clinical symptoms. Unlike the animals injected intravenously with virus, this animal was viremic for two days post-inoculation. Isolated lymphocytes, from lymph nodes and from peripheral blood, were producing virus 8, 16, and 22 days after exposure. When the animal was again studied on days 84 and 125, virus could not be recovered from lymphocytes or serum, suggesting successful viral clearance. While this study demonstrates that the murine amphotropic virus can lead to viral infection and subsequent production *in vivo*, this animal has not shown evidence of pathology with a follow-up of 6.2 months.

In addition, we have collected information on cynomolgus and rhesus monkeys followed for up to 3 years after exposure of their bone-marrow cells to helper-contaminated retroviral vectors as part of a bone-marrow transplantation/gene-therapy protocol (87). These animals have remained free of illness or pathology and replicating virus has not been detected in follow-up studies (K. Cornetta, unpublished).

The evidence indicates that murine amphotropic viruses are not acute pathogens in primates. Continued follow-up of these animals is needed before the true long-term risk of such exposure is known.

2. INSERTIONAL MUTAGENESIS

Retroviruses produce tumors in animals. The biology and *in vivo* interactions of murine leukemia viruses in rodents make it difficult to determine accurately their malignant potential in humans. The following discussion is limited to MoMuLV, a slowly transforming retrovirus that has been used as the backbone for most of the retroviral vectors intended for human use. We address the risk of malignancy when primates are exposed to retroviral vectors based on MoMuLV.

MoMuLV induces T-cell lymphomas when injected into mice. Animals must be infected by the retrovirus as newborns, when persistent retroviremia develops. Viral expression continues in infected tissues, with most thymocytes expressing viral sequences throughout their lifetime. Despite this continued exposure to retrovirus, tumors that develop are clonal and occur only after a relatively long latency (months). While retroviruses integrate throughout the genome, cell transformation is associated with integration in or near certain proto-oncogenes that change gene expression (reviewed in 157). In MoMuLV-induced tumors, abnormal gene regulation is usually mediated by the enhancer region within the viral LTR. Another potential mechanism, promoter insertion, is not commonly associated with MoMuLV-induced lymphomas.

Retroviral insertion has been found near the *pim-1* domain in approximately 50% of MoMuLV-induced T-cell lymphoma studies (158). Usually, enhanced *pim-1* expression is associated with retroviral insertion within its 3'-terminal exon (159). *pim-1* is most homologous to serine protein kinases (EC 2.7.1.37) and is presumably a lymphoid-specific protein kinase involved with lymphocyte proliferation (159). While the majority of lymphomas are associated with insertion near the *pim-1* gene, insertion near other genes has been described, including c-*myc* (158, 160, 161) and Mlvi-2 (162) in the mouse, and c-*myc* (*160*), Mlvi-1 (*163*), Mlvi-2, and Mlvi-3 in the rat (*164*). The murine T-cell lymphoma line LSTRA has arisen by promoter insertion near the lck gene, another T cell-specific protein kinase (*165–168*).

While the interaction of MoMuLV and specific proto-oncogenes appears important in cellular transformation, a direct causal relationship has not been determined. In most studies, the proto-oncogenes of interest are identified and the adjacent genome is probed for the presence of retroviral sequences. Unfortunately, this approach does not identify other factors that may be required for transformation. Rat thymomas usually have ten or more MoMuLV proviral insertions (*160*), and it is possible that abnormal regulation is required in a number of genes before cellular transformation occurs.

Although MoMuLV is associated with T-cell lymphoma, it is likely that a recombinant virus is responsible for cell transformation. In AKR mice (a strain with a high frequency of leukemia occurring after 6 months of age), ecotropic murine leukemia viruses are expressed early in life with the subsequent emergence of mink-cell focus-forming (MCF) viruses. Injection of these viruses into newborn mice accelerates the development of lymphoma, and they are believed to be the most likely cause of leukemia in these mice. MCF viruses arise from recombination among ecotropic, xenotropic, and endogenous MCF *env*-related sequences. Concurrent expression of RNAs from the three murine leukemia virus classes occurs only in the thymic tissues of young mice (*169*). MoMuLV appears to function in a similar way, since viral exposure is required early in life. MoMuLV-MCF are produced and are oncogenic (*170*), and thymic lymphomas develop as a result of retroviral integration. A MoMuLV-MCF virus has recently been shown (*168*) to have integrated near *lck* in the T-cell lymphoma line Thy 19, resulting in abnormal RNA transcripts and an elevated level of its gene product, a tissue-specific protein-tyrosine kinase (EC 2.7.1.112).

If MCF viruses are responsible for the tumorigenicity of MoMuLV, then the chance of a replication-defective MoMuLV-based vector recombining with endogenous sequences in primate cells and producing a replication-competent, tumorigenic virus appears to be very low. Human endogenous retroviral (HERV) sequences share some homology with murine leukemia viruses, but the parts of MoMuLV retained in retroviral vectors (namely, the LTR and a small portion of *gag*) share little homology, if any, with known HERV sequences (K. Cornetta, unpublished; see also letter to *Science* **228**, 653). While HERV sequences can be transcribed (*171, 172*), they contain numerous mutations that make them replication-defective (*171, 173, 174*). The HERV sequences required for restoration of replicative function (i.e., *gag, pol,* and/or *env*) are missing from MoMuLV-based retroviral vectors. Therefore, recombination between retroviral vectors and HERV sequences leading to the production of a replication-competent virus, with or without tumorigenicity, appears to be a very rare event and has so far not been reported.

In assessing the risk of malignancy in humans, another consideration is cell tropism. MoMuLV causes T-cell lymphoma in rodents. The susceptibility of the T cell to transformation involves an interaction with the rodent T cell and a region in the U3 enhancer region of the viral LTR. Removal of this region can prevent malignancy, even though the virus still retains the ability to produce viremia (175). Substitution of the MoMuLV U3 region with that of the erythroleukemia-producing Friend virus leads to the development of erythroleukemia rather than lymphoma (176). The converse experiment, substitution of the Friend U3 regions with the MoMuLV U3, leads to lymphoma production by Friend virus (176–178). Since MoMuLV infects many cell types *in vivo* without subsequent tumor formation, interaction between the MoMuLV and the rodent T cells is important in tumorigenesis. What primate cell, if any, shares this tropism is not known.

Taken together, it appears that the transformation rate of primate cells by replication-defective MoMuLV-based vectors is very low because: (1) the frequency of cell transformation by MoMuLV is low even in a permissive environment (newborn mice); (2) transformation is associated with multiple viral insertions, while cells infected with retroviral vectors usually contain a single copy of the vector genome; (3) persistent viremia, an important factor in tumorigenesis, would not develop when replication-defective vectors are used; (4) replication-defective vectors make the development of a recombinant virus, the probable cause of MoMuLV-induced leukemias, very unlikely, and; (5) no known tropism exists between primate cells and the MoMuLV.

Murine leukemia virus does not appear to cause an acute disease in primates. While exposure to these viruses may have no detrimental effect in humans, follow-up of exposed animals is needed. Nevertheless, every effort should be made to insure that retroviral preparations used for humans are free of contaminating replication-competent retrovirus. Even when vector preparations are free of replication-competent virus, malignant transformation remains a theoretical risk. Thus, patients treated by retroviral-mediated gene transfer need to be carefully studied, both short- and long-term, to assess the true risks of retroviral insertion.

V. Future Prospects

Up to this point, most *in vivo* gene expression with retroviral vectors has been obtained with hematopoietic cells. However, the use of blood cells limits the potential scope of genetic therapy. Although a number of diseases, such as adenosine deaminase deficiency and β-thalassemia, specifically affect the hematopoietic system, there are many more diseases in which gene transfer into bone-marrow cells would be unlikely to provide complete amelioration of the disease.

Techniques for using alternative tissues as targets for retroviral mediated gene transfer are being developed. Recent reports of the successful transduction of liver cells (28, 116, 136), fibroblasts (119, 140), and vascular endothelial cells (142) suggest that a wider array of tissues will one day be targets for gene therapy. Indeed, an aim of retroviral-mediated gene transfer might likely be targeted gene transfer, where *ex vivo* tissue manipulations would no longer be necessary for the introduction of corrective genes into the affected cells. Instead, vectors would have been engineered to combine selective infectivity with selective gene regulation, resulting in vectors capable of targeting specific tissues. Ultimately, techniques might be found that overcome the apparent randomness of retroviral gene integration, permitting the insertion of corrective genes into precise chromosomal locations. Thus, gene therapy would become a sort of genetic surgery, where the defective gene is replaced by its normal homologue.

Besides gene therapy, retroviral-mediated gene transfer may find a number of other clinical applications. Cancer therapy might be accomplished by using targeted vectors to deliver toxic agents to tumor cells, or by activating cells of the immune system to stimulate natural defenses against cancer. Other diseases might also be amenable to prevention or attack by retroviral vector gene transfer. For example, genes to interfere with the life cycle of the human immunodeficiency virus could be introduced into the target cell population in an effort to combat AIDS.

Retroviral-mediated gene transfer holds considerable promise for combating human diseases. However, significant obstacles still exist before this promise becomes a reality. Gene transfer efficiencies still need improvement, particularly if mechanisms for the selection of transduced cells are not available. In addition, the *in vivo* studies of gene expression in hematopoietic cells suggest that accurate regulation of transferred genes continues to be a serious problem. Nonetheless, retroviral-mediated gene transfer remains the best current technology for introduction of clinically relevant genes into diseased cells for the purpose of gene therapy.

Acknowledgments

We are grateful to Elizabeth Russo and Mary Beth Daucher for assistance in preparation of the manuscript.

References

1. W. F. Anderson, *Science* **226**, 401 (1984).
2. H. M. Temin, *in* "Gene Transfer" (R. Kucherlapati, ed.), p. 149. Plenum, New York, 1986.

3. J. E. Dick, M. C. Magli, R. A. Phillips and A. Bernstein, *Trends Genet.* **2**, 165 (1986).
4. E. Gilboa, *Bioessays* **5**, 252 (1986).
5. E. Gilboa, M. A. Eglitis, P. W. Kantoff and W. F. Anderson, *BioTechniques* **4**, 504 (1986).
6. M. A. Eglitis and W. F. Anderson, *BioTechniques* **6**, 608 (1988).
7. H. Varmus, *Science* **240**, 1427 (1988).
8. J. Sorge and S. H. Hughes, *J. Mol. Appl. Genet.* **1**, 547 (1982).
9. P. K. Bandyopadhyay and H. M. Temin, *MCBiol* **4**, 743 (1984).
10. W. H. Gunzburg and B. Salmons, *Virology* **155**, 236 (1986).
11. C. Laker, C. Stocking, U. Bergholz, N. Hess, J. F. DeLamarter and W. Osterberg, *PNAS* **84**, 8458 (1987).
12. K. Ueda, C. Cardarelli, M. Gottesman and I. Pastan, *PNAS* **84**, 3004 (1987).
13. I. Pastan, M. Gottesman, K. Ueda, E. Lovelace, A. V. Rutherford and M. C. Willingham, *PNAS* **85**, 4486 (1988).
14. D. Stacey and V. Allfrey, *Cell* **9**, 725 (1976).
15. C. Liu, D. Slate, R. Gravel and F. Ruddle, *PNAS* **76**, 4503 (1979).
16. A. Graessmann, M. Graessmann, W. Topp and M. Botchan, *J. Virol.* **32**, 989 (1979).
17. W. F. Anderson, L. Killos, L. Sanders-Haigh, P. J. Kretschmer and E. G. Diacumakos, *PNAS* **77**, 5399 (1980).
18. M. Capecchi, *Cell* **22**, 479 (1980).
19. W. F. Anderson and E. G. Diacumakos, *Sci. Am.* **245**, 106 (1981).
20. R. D. Palmiter and R. L. Brinster, *ARGen* **20**, 465 (1986).
21. D. Jahner, H. Stuhlmann, C. L. Stewart, K. Harbers, J. Lohler, I. Simon and R. Jaenisch, *Nature* **298**, 623 (1982).
22. D. Jahner and R. Jaenisch, *MCBiol* **5**, 2212 (1985).
23. R. D. Palmiter, H. Y. Chen and R. L. Brinster, *Cell* **29**, 701 (1982).
24. W. Schaffner, *PNAS* **77**, 2163 (1980).
25. V. Oi, S. Morrison, L. Herzenberg and P. Berg, *PNAS* **80**, 825 (1988).
26. R. J. Mannino and S. Gould-Fogerite, *BioTechniques* **6**, 682 (1988).
27. G. L. Andreason and G. A. Evans, *BioTechniques* **6**, 650 (1988).
28. J. A. Wolff, J.-K. Yee, H. F. Skelly, J. C. Moores, J. G. Respess, T. Friedman and H. Leffert, *PNAS* **84**, 3344 (1987).
29. K. Shigekawa and W. J. Dower, *BioTechniques* **6**, 742 (1988).
30. M. A. McNally, J. S. Lebkowski, T. B. Okarma and L. B. Lerch, *BioTechniques* **6**, 882 (1988).
31. M. Wigler, A. Pellicer, S. Silverstein and R. Axel, *Cell* **14**, 725 (1978).
32. M. Wigler, R. Sweet, G. K. Sim, B. Wold, A. Pellicer, E. Lacy, T. Maniatis, S. Silverstein and R. Axel, *Cell* **16**, 777 (1979).
33. K. E. Mercola, H. D. Stang, J. Browne, W. Salser and M. J. Cline, *Science* **208**, 1033 (1980).
34. M. J. Cline, H. Stang, K. Mercola, L. Morse, R. Ruprecht, J. Browne and W. Salser, *Nature* **284** 422 (1980).
35. L. H. Hwang and E. Gilboa, *J. Virol.* **50**, 417 (1984).
36. C. Young, M. Donovan-Peluso, K. Bloom, M. Allan, J. Paul and A. Bank, *PNAS* **81**, 5315 (1984).
37. R. F. Selden, M. J. Skoskiewicz, K. Burke Howie, P. S. Russell and H. M. Goodman, *Science* **236**, 714 (1987).
38. C. A. Chen and H. Okayama, *BioTechniques* **6**, 632 (1988).
39. B. H. Howard, *Trends Biochem. Sci. (Pers. Ed.)* **8**, 209 (1983).
40. V. R. Baichwal and B. Sugden, in "Gene Transfer" (R. Kucherlapati, ed.), p. 117. Plenum, New York, 1986.

41. R. Mulligan, B. Howard and P. Berg, *Nature* **277**, 108 (1979).

42. D. Hamer, K. D. Smith, S. Boyer and P. Leder, *Cell* **17**, 725 (1979).

43. K. Van Doren, D. Hanahan and Y. Gluzman, *J. Virol.* **50**, 606 (1984).

44. K. Van Doren and Y. Gluzman, *MCBiol* **4**, 1653 (1984).

45. K. L. Berkner, *BioTechniques* **6**, 616 (1988).

46. J. D. Tratschin, I. L. Miller, M. G. Smith and B. J. Carter, *MCBiol* **5**, 3251 (1985).

47. J. S. Lebkowski, M. M. McNally, T. B. Okarma and L. B. Lerch, *MCBiol* **8**, 3988 (1988).

48. S. K. McLaughlin, P. Collis, P. L. Hermonat and N. Muzyczka, *J. Virol.* **62**, 1963 (1988).

49. M. Law, D. Lowy, I. Dvoretzky and P. Howley, *PNAS* **78**, 2727 (1981).

50. N. Sarver, P. Gruss, M. Law, G. Khoury and P. Howley, *McBiol* **1**, 486 (1981).

51. K. Zinn, P. Mellon, M. Ptashne and T. Maniatis, *PNAS* **79**, 4897 (1982).

52. J. M. Bishop, *ARB* **47**, 35 (1978).

53. R. Risser, J. M. Horowitz and J. McCubrey, *ARGen* **17**, 85 (1983).

54. H. E. Varmus, *Science* **216**, 812 (1982).

55. C. Shoemaker, S. Goff, E. Gilboa, M. Paskind, S. W. Mitra and D. Baltimore, *PNAS* **77**, 3932 (1980).

56. T. M. Shinnick, R. A. Lerner and J. G. Sutcliffe, *Nature* **293**, 543 (1981).

57. A. S. Perkins, P. T. Kirschmeier, S. Gattoni-Celli and I. B. Weinstein, *MCBiol* **3**, 1123 (1983).

58. D. A. Foster and H. Hanafusa, *J. Virol.* **48**, 744 (1983).

59. P. A. Norton and J. M. Coffin, *MCBiol* **5**, 281 (1985).

60. A. L. Joyner and A. Bernstein, *MCBiol* **3**, 2180 (1983).

61. R. D. Cone, A. Weber-Benavous, D. Baorto and R. C. Mulligan, *MCBiol* **7**, 887 (1987).

62. A. Bank, M. Donovan-Peluso, N. Lerner and D. Rund, *Blood Cells* **13**, 269 (1987).

63. N. Lerner, S. Brigham, S. Goff and A. Bank, *DNA* **6**, 573 (1987).

64. S. Karlsson, T. Papayannopoulou, S. G. Schweiger, G. Stamatoyannopoulos and A. Nienhuis, *PNAS* **84**, 2411 (1987).

65. M. A. Bender, A. D. Miller and R. E. Gelinas, *MCBiol* **8**, 1725 (1988).

66. E. A. Dzierzak, T. Papayannopoulou and R. C. Mulligan, *Nature* **331**, 35 (1988).

67. A. D. Miller, M. A. Bender, E. A. S. Harris, M. Kaleko and R. E. Gelinas, *J. Virol.* **62**, 4337 (1988).

68. B. Lim, D. A. Williams and S. H. Orkin, *MCBiol* **7**, 3459 (1987).

69. J. L. Rubenstein, J. F. Nicolas and F. Jacob, *PNAS* **81**, 7137 (1984).

70. J. Sorge, A. E. Cutting, V. D. Erdman and J. W. Gautsch, *PNAS* **81**, 6627 (1984).

71. M. Taketo, E. Gilboa and M. I. Sherman, *PNAS* **82**, 2422 (1985).

72. A. D. Miller, D. J. Jolly, T. Friedmann and I. M. Verma, *PNAS* **80**, 4709 (1983).

73. D. Armentano, S.-F. Yu, P. W. Kantoff, T. von Ruden, W. F. Anderson and E. Gilboa, *J. Virol.* **61**, 1647 (1987).

74. M. A. Bender, T. D. Palmer, R. E. Gelinas and A. D. Miller, *J. Virol.* **61**, 1639 (1987).

75. S. F. Yu, T. von Ruden, P. W. Kantoff, C. Garber, M. Seilberg, U. Ruther, W. F. Anderson, E. F. Wagner and E. Gilboa, *PNAS* **83**, 3194 (1986).

76. B. Korczak, I. Robson, C. Lamarche, A. Bernstein and R. Kerbel, *MCBiol* **8**, 3143 (1988).

77. R. G. Hawley, L. Covarrubias, T. Hawley and B. Mintz, *PNAS* **84**, 2406 (1987).

78. E. Linney, B. Davis, J. Overhauser, E. Chao and H. Fan, *Nature* **308**, 470 (1984).

79. J.-K. Yee, J. C. Moores, D. J. Jolly, J. A. Wolff, J. G. Respess and T. Friedmann, *PNAS* **84**, 5197 (1987).

80. C. L. Cepko, B. E. Roberts and R. C. Mulligan, *Cell* **37**, 1053 (1984).

81. D. L. Nelson, S. M. W. Chang, J. Henkel-Tiggs, K. Wager-Smith, J. W. Belmont and C. T. Caskey, *CSHSQB* **51**, 1065 (1986).

82. S. M. W. Chang, K. Wager-Smith, T. Y. Tsao, J. Henkel-Tiggs, S. Vaishnav and C. T. Caskey, *MCBiol* **7**, 854 (1987).

83. R. L. Friedman, *PNAS* **82**, 703 (1985).
84. J. W. Belmont, J. Henkel-Tiggs, S. M. W. Chang, K. Wager-Smith, R. E. Kellems, J. E. Dick, M. C. Magli, R. A. Phillips, A. Bernstein and C. T. Caskey, *Nature* **322**, 385 (1986).
85. P. W. Kantoff, D. B. Kohn, H. Mitsuya, D. Armentano, M. Sieberg, J. Zwiebel, M. Eglitis, J. R. McLachlin, D. A. Wiginton, J. J. Hutton, S. D. Horowitz, E. Gilboa, R. M. Blaese and W. F. Anderson, *PNAS* **83**, 6563 (1986).
86. J. R. McLachlin, S. Bernstein and W. F. Anderson, *Anal. Biochem.* **163**, 143 (1987).
87. P. W. Kantoff, A. P. Gillio, J. R. McLachlin, C. Bordignon, M. A. Eglitis, N. A. Kernan, R. C. Moen, D. B. Kohn, S.-F. Yu, E. Karson, S. Karlsson, J. Zwiebel, E. Gilboa, R. M. Blaese, A. Nienhuis, R. J. O'Reilly and W. F. Anderson, *J. Exp. Med.* **166**, 219 (1987).
88. M. Emerman and H. M. Temin, *Cell* **39**, 459 (1984).
89. M. Wigler, S. Silverstein, L. S. Lee, A. Pellicer, Y. C. Cheng and R. Axel, *Cell* **11**, 223 (1977).
90. R. Mann, R. C. Mulligan and D. Baltimore, *Cell* **33**, 153 (1983).
91. A. D. Miller, M. F. Law and I. M. Verma, *MCBiol* **5**, 431 (1985).
92. A. D. Miller, D. R. Trauber and C. Buttimore, *Somatic Cell Mol. Genet.* **12**, 175 (1986).
93. A. D. Miller and C. Buttimore, *MCBiol* **6**, 2895 (1986).
94. S. Watanabe and H. M. Temin, *MCBiol* **3**, 2241 (1983).
95. D. Markowitz, S. Goff and A. Bank, *J. Virol.* **62**, 1120 (1988).
96. O. Danos and R. C. Mulligan, *PNAS* **85**, 6460 (1988).
97. R. A. Bosselman, R.-Y. Hsu, J. Bruszewski, S. Hu, F. Martin and M. Nicolson, *MCBiol* **7**, 1797 (1987).
98. R. D. Cone and R. C. Mulligan, *PNAS* **81**, 6349 (1984).
99. R. A. Jorgenson, S. J. Rothstein and W. S. Reznikoff, *MGG* **177**, 65 (1979).
100. F. Colbere-Garapin, F. Horodniceanu, P. Kourilsky and A. C. Garapin, *JMB* **150**, 1 (1981).
101. J. E. Dick, M. C. Magli, D. Huszar, R. A. Phillips and A. Bernstein, *Cell* **42**, 71 (1985).
102. M. C. Magli, J. E. Dick, D. Huszar, A. Bernstein and R. A. Phillips, *PNAS* **84**, 789 (1987).
103. D.-D. Wu, D. Huszar, J. E. Dick, D. Bernstein and R. A. Phillips, *J. Immunol. Methods* **101**, 279 (1987).
104. M. A. Eglitis, P. Kantoff, E. Gilboa and W. F. Anderson, *Science* **230**, 1395 (1985).
105. G. Keller, C. Paige, E. Gilboa and E. F. Wagner, *Nature* **318**, 149 (1985).
106. W. W. Kwok, F. Schuening, R. B. Stead and A. D. Miller, *PNAS* **83**, 4552 (1986).
107. M. A. Eglitis, P. W. Kantoff, J. D. Jolly, J. B. Jones, W. F. Anderson and C. D. Lothrop, Jr., *Blood* **71**, 717 (1988).
108. R. B. Stead, W. W. Kwok, R. Storb and A. D. Miller, *Blood* **71**, 742 (1988).
109. W. F. Anderson, P. Kantoff, M. Eglitis, J. McLachlin, E. Karson, J. Zwiebel, A. Nienhuis, S. Karlsson, R. M. Blaese, D. Kohn, E. Gilboa, D. Armentano, E. D. Zanjani, A. Flake, M. R. Harrison, A. Gillio, C. Bordignon and R. O'Reilly, *CSHSQB* **51**, 1073 (1986).
110. A. D. Miller, T. D. Palmer and R. A. Hock, *CSHSQB* **51**, 1013 (1986).
111. R. A. Hock and A. D. Miller, *Nature* **320**, 275 (1986).
112. D. E. Hogge and R. K. Humphries, *Blood* **69**, 611 (1987).
113. P. Laneuville, W. Chang, S. Kamel-Reid, A. A. Fauser and J. E. Dick, *Blood* **71**, 811 (1988).
114. L. Smith and S. Benchimol, *MCBiol* **8**, 974 (1988).
115. P. Anklesaria, M. A. Sakakeeny, V. Klassen, L. Rothstein, T. J. FitzGerald, M. Appel, J. S. Greenberger and C. A. Holland, *Exp. Hematol.* **15**, 195 (1987).
116. F. D. Ledley, G. J. Darlington, T. Hahn and S. L. C. Woo, *PNAS* **84**, 5335 (1987).
117. M. C. Magli, J. E. Dick, D. Huszar, A. Bernstein and R. A. Phillips, *PNAS* **84**, 789 (1987).

118. A. D. Miller, R. J. Eckner, D. J. Jolly, T. Friedmann and I. M. Verma, *Science* 225, 630 (1984).

119. T. D. Palmer, R. A. Hock, W. R. A. Osborne and A. D. Miller, *PNAS* 84, 1055 (1987).

120. B. C. Guild, R. C. Mulligan, P. Gros and D. E. Housman, *PNAS* 85, 1595 (1988).

121. D. A. Williams, S. H. Orkin and R. C. Mulligan, *PNAS* 83, 2566 (1986).

122. R. S. McIvor, M. J. Johnson, A. D. Miller, S. Pitts, S. R. Williams, D. Valerio, D. W. Martin and I. M. Verma, *MCBiol* 7, 838 (1987).

123. J. M. Wilson, D. E. Johnston, D. M. Jefferson and R. C. Mulligan, *PNAS* 85, 4421 (1988).

124. A. D. Miller, E. S. Ong, M. G. Rosenfeld, I. M. Verma and R. M. Evans, *Science* 225, 993 (1984).

125. J. C. Stone, N. A. Dower and L. Siminovitch, *Somatic Cell Mol. Genet.* 12, 575 (1986).

126. D. Valerio, M. Duyvesteyn and A. van der Eb, *Gene* 34, 163 (1984).

127. J. A. Zwiebel, P. W. Kantoff, M. A. Eglitis, D. Kohn, D. Muenchau, J. R. McLachlin, E. Karson, R. Wieder, S. F. Yu, R. M. Blaese, E. Gilboa and W. F. Anderson, *Blood* 68, 307a (1986) (abstr.).

128. C. L. Stewart, S. Schuetze, M. Vanek and E. F. Wagner, *EMBO J.* 6, 383 (1987).

129. P. V. Choudary, J. A. Barranger, S. Tsuji, J. Mayor, M. E. LaMarca, C. L. Cepko, R. C. Mulligan and E. I. Ginns, *Mol. Biol. Med.* 3, 293 (1986).

130. F. D. Ledley, H. E. Grenett, M. McGinnis-Shelnutt and S. L. Woo, *PNAS* 83, 409 (1986).

131. F. D. Ledley, H. E. Grenett, D. P. Bartos and S. L. C. Woo, *Gene* 61, 113 (1987).

132. R. I. Garver, A. Chytil, S. Karlsson, G. A. Fells, M. L. Brantly, M. Courtney, P. W. Kantoff, A. W. Nienhuis, W. F. Anderson and R. G. Crystal, *PNAS* 84, 1050 (1987).

133. R. D. Cone, E. B. Reilly, H. N. Eisen and R. C. Mulligan, *Science* 236, 954 (1987).

134. J. R. Morgan, Y. Barrandon, H. Green and R. C. Mulligan, *Science* 237, 1476 (1987).

135. P. M. C. Wong, S.-W. Chung and A. W. Nienhuis, *Genes Dev.* 1, 358 (1987).

136. J. M. Wilson, D. M. Jefferson, J. R. Chowdhury, P. M. Novikoff, D. E. Johnston and R. C. Mulligan, *PNAS* 85, 3014 (1988).

137. J. Price, D. Turner and C. Cepko, *PNAS* 84, 156 (1987).

138. D. L. Turner and C. L. Cepko, *Nature* 328, 131 (1987).

139. C. Walsh and C. L. Cepko, *Science* 241, 1342 (1988).

140. D. St. Louis and I. M. Verma, *PNAS* 85, 3150 (1988).

141. G. Yamada, Y. Kitamura, H. Sonoda, H. Harada, S. Taki, R. C. Mulligan, H. Osawa, R. Diamantstein, S. Yokoyama and T. Taniguchi, *EMBO J.* 6, 2705 (1987).

142. J. A. Zwiebel, S. M. Freeman, P. W. Kantoff, K. Cornetta, U. S. Ryan and W. F. Anderson, *Science* 243, 220 (1989).

143. W. F. Anderson, *Clin. Obstet. Gynecol.* 29, 586 (1986).

144. J. W. Belmont and C. T. Caskey, in "Gene Transfer" (R. Kucherlapati, ed.), p. 411. Plenum, New York, 1986.

145. S. H. Orkin, *Clin. Immunol. Immunopathol.* 40, 151 (1986).

146. W. F. Anderson, *J. Med. Philos.* 10, 275 (1985).

147. J. C. Fletcher, *J. Med. Philos.* 10, 293 (1985).

148. L. Walters, *Nature* 320, 225 (1986).

149. G. J. Spangrude, S. Heimfeld and I. L. Weissman, *Science* 241, 58 (1988).

150. J. A. Thompson, K. D. Anderson, J. M. DiPietro, J. A. Zwiebel, M. Zametta, W. F. Anderson and T. Maciag, *Science* 241, 1349 (1988).

151. J. Sorge, D. Wright, V. D. Erdman and A. E. Cutting, *MCBiol* 4, 1730 (1984).

152. R. D. Cone and R. C. Mulligan, *PNAS* 81, 6349 (1984).

153. S. K. Chattopadhyay, A. I. Oliff, D. L. Linemeyer, M. R. Lander and D. R. Lowy, *J. Virol.* 39, 777 (1981).

154. K. Cornetta, R. C. Moen, K. Culver, R. A. Morgan, J. R. McLachlin, S. Storm, J. E. Selegue, W. London, R. M. Blaese and W. F. Anderson, manuscript submitted.

155. D. K. Haapala, W. G. Robey, S. D. Oroszlan and W. P. Tsai, *J. Virol.* **53**, 827 (1985).
156. B. Banapour, J. Sernatinger and J. A. Levy, *Virology* **152**, 268 (1986).
157. R. Nusse, *Trends Genet.* **2**, 244 (1986).
158. H. T. Cuypers, G. Selten, W. Quint, M. Zijlstra, E. R. Maandag, W. Boelens, P. van Wezenbeek, C. Melief and A. Berns, *Cell* **37**, 141 (1984).
159. G. Selten, H. T. Cuypers, W. Boelens, E. Robanus-Maandag, J. Verbeek, J. Domen, C. van Beveren and A. Berns, *Cell* **46**, 603 (1986).
160. D. Steffen, *PNAS* **81**, 2097 (1984).
161. L. M. Corcoran, J. M. Adams, A. R. Dunn and S. Cory, *Cell* **37**, 113 (1984).
162. P. N. Tsichlis, P. G. Strauss and C. A. Kozak, *MCBiol* **4**, 997 (1984).
163. P. N. Tsichlis, P. G. Strauss and L. F. Hu, *Nature* **302**, 445 (1983).
164. P. N. Tsichlis, M. A. Lohse, C. Szpirer, J. Szpirer and G. Levan, *J. Virol.* **56**, 938 (1985).
165. A. F. Voronova, J. E. Buss, T. Patschinsky, T. Hunter and B. M. Sefton, *MCBiol* **4**, 2705 (1984).
166. J. D. Marth, R. Peet, E. G. Krebs and R. M. Perlmutter, *Cell* **43**, 393 (1985).
167. A. F. Voronova and B. M. Sefton, *Nature* **319**, 682 (1986).
168. H. T. Adler, P. J. Reynolds, C. M. Kelly and B. M. Sefton, *J. Virol.* **62**, 4113 (1988).
169. F. Laigret, R. Repaske, A. B. Boulukos, A. B. Rabson and A. S. Khan, *J. Virol.* **62**, 376 (1988).
170. L. H. Evans and M. W. Cloyd, *PNAS* **82**, 459 (1985).
171. A. B. Rabson, Y. Hamagishi, P. E. Steele, M. Tykocinski and M. A. Martin, *J. Virol.* **56**, 176 (1985).
172. S. Gattoni-Celli, K. Kirsch, S. Kalled and K. J. Isselbacher, *PNAS* **83**, 6127 (1986).
173. T. I. Bonner, C. O'Connell and M. Cohen, *PNAS* **79**, 4709 (1982).
174. R. Repaske, P. E. Steele, R. R. O'Neill, A. B. Rabson and M. A. Martin, *J. Virol.* **54**, 764 (1985).
175. B. Davis, E. Linney and H. Fan, *Nature* **314**, 550 (1985).
176. P. A. Chatis, C. A. Holland, J. W. Hartley, W. P. Rowe and N. Hopkins, *PNAS* **80**, 4408 (1983).
177. P. A. Chatis, C. A. Holland, J. E. Silver, T. N. Frederickson, N. Hopkins and J. W. Hartley, *J. Virol.* **52**, 248 (1984).
178. Y. Li, E. Golemis, J. W. Hartley and N. Hopkins, *J. Virol.* **61**, 693 (1987).

Structure–Function Relationships in *Escherichia coli* Promoter DNA

MARSHALL S. Z. HORWITZ AND
LAWRENCE A. LOEB

*The Joseph Gottstein Memorial Cancer
Research Laboratory
Department of Pathology
University of Washington
Seattle, Washington 98195*

Among the most important and the most precisely regulated of biological processes is transcription. The enzyme responsible for transcription, RNA polymerase, must identify the beginning of a gene, interact with the accessory activator and repressor DNA-binding proteins, separate the DNA strands, and initiate and terminate RNA synthesis. The simplest definition of a promoter is that it is a sequence of nucleotides that differentiates the start of a gene from other DNA sequences. In this respect, the promoter participates in transcription initiation by serving as a signal for binding by RNA polymerase. Much recent evidence, however, suggests that promoter sequences also assist with RNA polymerase's other functions. Far from being just a punctuation mark, there is reason to suspect that promoter sequences have evolved in such a way that the physical and chemical properties of their DNA sequences contribute to the reactions catalyzed by RNA polymerase. This paper reviews the structure of *Escherichia coli* promoter DNA, emphasizing the aspects of that structure consistent with this notion.

We begin with a general summary of *E. coli* RNA polymerase, its promoter DNA sequences, and the kinetic nature of their interaction, followed by a detailed discussion of promoter structure and what it infers for the structure of RNA polymerase. Features of the transcription cycle in *E. coli* represent fairly well the processes in the Enterobacteriaceae, other eubac-

137

Progress in Nucleic Acid Research
and Molecular Biology, Vol. 38

teria, mitochondria, and chloroplasts, and may also illustrate principles common to archaeobacteria and eukaryotes. There are many reviews of prokaryotic transcription emphasizing different topics, including the general aspects of transcription initiation (1–6), the general principles of protein–DNA interactions (7, 8), RNA polymerases (9–11), inhibitors of RNA polymerase (12), σ factors (13, 14), the positive regulation of transcription by *trans*-acting factors (15), supercoiling and gene regulation (16–18), promoter sequences (19, 20), transcription elongation (21), transcription attenuation (22, 23), and transcription termination (21, 24).

I. RNA Polymerase

The subunit composition of the *E. coli* RNA polymerase core enzyme (EC 2.7.7.6) is $\alpha_2\beta\beta'$, with (deduced) subunit molecular weights of α, 36,512; β, 150,618; and β', 155,613 (9). The occasional presence of ω subunits (approximate molecular weight, 10,000) is of uncertain significance. Subunit α is the product of *rpoA*; β, *rpoB*; and β', *rpoC*. Subunit β is the target of such RNA polymerase inhibitors as the ansamycin antibiotics (e.g., rifampicin), the antibiotic streptolydigin, and the dye Rose Bengal. Rifampicin blocks transcription initiation just after the formation of the initial phosphodiester bonds, while the latter two agents inhibit phosphodiester bond formation noncompetitively during any stage of initiation or elongation. The first few transcribed bases of the template DNA strand may be cross-linked photochemically to the β subunit, further suggesting that this polypeptide may contain the active site for phosphodiester bond formation (25, 26).

The core enzyme is catalytically competent, but binds nonspecifically to DNA. The core enzyme bears some sequence homology with eukaryotic RNA polymerase II (27). Low-resolution structures have been determined by X-ray scattering in solution (28) and, more recently, by X-ray diffraction of two-dimensional crystals adsorbed onto a synthetic lipid bilayer (29).

The association of core enzyme with a σ factor, to form the holoenzyme, confers a 10^4-fold increase in promoter DNA specificity. (The σ factor alone does not bind DNA.) There are approximately 3000 molecules of holoenzyme per cell (30), about half of which are transcriptionally active at any one time (31).

The fidelity of DNA-directed RNA polymerization is about one mispair for every 10^5 ribonucleotides polymerized (32). Unlike *E. coli* DNA polymerase I, RNA polymerase lacks a direct 3′-to-5′ exonuclease (8). Nevertheless, RNA polymerase can remove the terminal nucleotide of the nascent chain in a pyrophosphate-dependent manner (33). To what extent such activity accomplishes "proofreading" and contributes to transcriptional fidelity remains to be seen.

Four separate σ subunits are now known to be encoded by the *E. coli* genome, each acting in combination with the core enzyme to recognize different promoter sequences (*13, 14*). The product of *rpoD*, σ^{70}, is found in most of the holoenzyme molecules purified from normally grown cells.* Three less abundant σ subunits promote the transcription of sets of genes coordinately regulated for growth in unusual conditions. The proportion of holoenzyme containing σ^{32}, the gene product of the *rpoH* locus, increases with heat shock, and holoenzyme containing σ^{54}, the gene product of the *ntrA* locus, increases with growth in limiting concentrations of nitrogen metabolites. An additional factor, σ^{28} (candidate genetic loci *flaI* or *flbB*), has been identified (*34*). Prior to its purification, its existence was inferred by the conservation of an unusual promoter sequence common among the genes involved in motility and chemotaxis (*35*). Yet another σ subunit is found during infection with bacteriophage T4, when σ^{70} is supplanted by phage-specific σ^{23}, the product of T4 gene 55. (T4 infection also induces ADP-ribosylation of the α subunits and phosphorylation of the β and β' subunits.)

Comparison of the sequences of the σ factors reveals some homology (*14, 36*). Both σ^{70} and σ^{32} contain two likely helix–turn–helix DNA-binding domains, whereas σ^{23} contains only one such domain. Interestingly, the number of helix–turn–helix domains of these σ factors equals the number of DNA sequence motifs conserved in the respective promoter (see Section V). σ^{54} is not homologous with other σ factors. In addition to its role in promoter recognition, it has been conjectured that the σ subunit also participates in DNA strand separation, a belief based, in part, on the subunit's possession of a characteristic sequence of aromatic amino-acid residues that form a motif common to other single-stranded binding proteins (*14*).

During transcriptional elongation, core polymerase associates with the NusA (*N* utilization substance) protein, which facilitates the recognition of at least some termination sites in the absence of participation by the termination factor ρ (*21*). Association of core enzyme with σ and NusA is mutually exclusive. A bacteriophage-lambda antitermination factor, N, also associates with elongating core enzyme, but only in the presence of a host factor, most likely NusA (*37, 38*).

In addition to its role in transcription, *E. coli* RNA polymerase participates in the initiation of DNA synthesis. Transcription in the vicinity of the *E. coli* chromosomal origin of replication, *oriC*, creates a short hybrid RNA–DNA "R-loop" that distorts the helix and facilitates the separation of DNA strands by the replication-associated dnaA protein, needed for the assembly of replication forks (*39*). RNA polymerase may also synthesize the primer required for the initiation of replication of some extrachromosomal elements (reviewed in *40*).

* Each subunit is identified as σ^{n}, where *n* is the mass of the subunit in kilodaltons.

II. Promoter Sequences

The promoter consensus sequence for each of the *E. coli* holoenzymes is listed in Table I. With the notable exception of σ^{23}, the promoters recognized by each holoenzyme reveal conservation of two sequence motifs. The spacing of these two motifs is highly conserved, but the spacing of the start site for transcription relative to these motifs varies somewhat. The promoters for the σ^{70}, σ^{32}, σ^{28}, and σ^{23} holoenzymes most commonly initiate transcription at a purine, usually A. The promoters for σ^{54} usually initiate transcription at a pyrimidine. There are often heterogeneous 5′ ends in a given population of RNA molecules, indicating that transcription may be initiated from several adjacent bases, or, in at least one case, that additional 5′ residues, not encoded by the DNA sequence, are occasionally added during initiation (*41*). In any case, the exact sequence of the 5′ end may be temperature-dependent (*42*). The −10 elements of promoters for the σ^{70}, σ^{32}, σ^{28}, and σ^{23} holoenzymes are similar to the highly conserved "TATA" promoter element of eukaryotic RNA polymerase II. In fact, some eukaryotic genes can be expressed in *E. coli* solely because of this fortuitous

TABLE I

E. coli PROMOTER CONSENSUS SEQUENCES[a]

Holoenzyme	Consensus	*n*	*s*	References
σ^{70}	TTGACA----------------TATAAT ↑ −35　　　　　↑ −12	263	6	*19*
σ^{54}	GTGGC-------TTGCA ↑ −26　　↑ −14	8	2	5
σ^{32}	CCCCC----------------TATAAATA ↑ −39　　　　　↑ −16	5	2	5
σ^{23}	TATAATA ↑ −15	4		*227, 228*
σ^{28}	TAAA------------------GCCGATAA ↑ "−35"　　　　↑ "−10"			*14*

[a] *n* is the number of such promoters characterized; *s* is the standard deviation above chance expectations of the indicated consensus sequence. Dashes indicate unspecified spacer sequences (nucleotides).

homology (*43–45*). However, this is the exception, rather than the rule, and a detailed analysis of one such yeast promoter has revealed that promoter mutations produce a divergent effect in each of the two organisms (*44*).

For promoters of σ^{70} holoenzyme, a general rule is that mutations that decrease a promoter's agreement with the consensus decrease the frequency of transcription initiation, and mutations that increase consensus agreement increase initiation frequency (*20*). A prediction of this rule is that the consensus sequence represents the most efficient promoter. The correctness of this rule is demonstrated by the success of an algorithm correlating consensus agreement and promoter strength *in vitro* (*46*). Exceptions to this rule are infrequent, but may be of significance. One example is the promoter for the arabinose operon *araBAD*, in which an A-to-G change at −33 decreases consensus homology while increasing promoter strength (*47*).

The −35 motif apparently has a different function in promoters that are positively regulated by transcription factors. Positively regulated promoters, for the most part, maintain poor conservation with the −35 consensus sequence, and the activator's binding site is typically in the vicinity of this promoter region (*15*). In the case of constitutive mutants of the galactose operon *gal* (*48*) and bacteriophage-lambda repressor establishment p_{RE} (*49, 50*) promoters, mutation of the −35 sequence has only a slight effect on transcription in the absence of the positive regulator, the catabolite activator protein CAP or the lambda protein cII, respectively. Thus, binding of the activator may override the effects of interaction of RNA polymerase with the −35 region.

While mutations that do not affect the −10 sequence, the −35 sequence, or the spacing between them are typically inconsequential for initiation frequency in constitutive promoters (*51*), there are also some exceptions. (A+T)-rich sequences upstream from the −35 element are associated with some strong promoters (*52–55*), and mutation of these sequences decreases promoter strength (*52, 55*). Sequences (in addition to the spacing) within the "spacer" region between the −10 and −35 sites may also contribute to promoter strength (*52, 53, 56*).

It has been established that sequences within the 5′ end of the transcribed portion of a gene, approximately +1 to +25, contribute to promoter strength (*57–59*). Such sequences may be responsible for transcription termination as well. *In vivo*, the efficiency of termination at particular sites at the ends of genes curiously has been demonstrated to vary with the promoter used to initiate transcription (*60*). Recent work using a variety of synthetic promoter constructs now demonstrates that the efficiency of utilization of certain ρ-independent termination signals is a function of the sequences several hundred base-pairs upstream in the vicinity of the 25 or so bases initially transcribed (*61, 62*). The effect occurs *in vivo* and has also been shown *in vitro* using purified holoenzyme without the addition of other factors. It has been proposed that such DNA sequences imprint the transcribing RNA polymerase with a conformational change that allows it to read through termination signals ordinarily recognized (*61*). A related mechanism may be employed by the bacteriophage-lambda antitermination systems N (*38*) and Q (*63*), and a similar phenomenon has been reported in eukaryotes, in which correct termination of transcription by RNA polymerase II of the small nuclear RNA U1 is dependent on transcription initiation from the proper promoter (*64*).

III. Kinetic Analysis of Promoters

The first, simplest, and most enduring model of transcription initiation, the "bipartite" model, involves two kinetic intermediates (*65*),

$$ R + P \underset{k_b}{\rightleftarrows} RP_c \underset{k_f}{\rightarrow} RP_o \rightarrow \rightarrow \rightarrow RNA . $$

RNA polymerase (R) binds the promoter (P) with binding constant k_b (10^6 to 10^9 M^{-1}) to form a "closed" complex (RP_c). With rate constant k_f (10^{-3} to 10^{-1} s^{-1}) the closed complex isomerizes to form a transcriptionally active "open" complex (RP_o) in which there is a separation of the double strands of the DNA for about 12 base-pairs near the start site. Polymerase in open complexes is relatively resistant to inhibition by polyanions (such as heparin) and rifampicin, both of which readily inactivate free polymerase. Binding and isomerization involve noncovalent interactions, while chain elongation proceeds by the hydrolysis of nucleoside triphosphates. After the addition of about two to nine nucleotides, the holoenzyme pauses and either releases the short transcript and reinitiates transcription from the open complex in a sequence known as "abortive cycling," or σ dissociates from the polymerase and the core enzyme continues full-length transcription of the nascent chain [maximum rate, 30–50 nucleotides per second (*66*)] in the process, clearing the promoter for binding with subsequent holoenzyme molecules. For most promoters, it appears that the rate-limiting step is isomerization from the closed to the open complex; however, in at least one case, the *lac*-UV5 promoter, escape from abortive cycling to subsequent chain elongation is rate limiting (*67*). The maximum transcription initiation frequency is about one chain per second.

Additional kinetic intermediates are likely to be accommodated within the simple two-step model. There is evidence for a "preclosed" complex (*68*), an intermediate between closed and open complexes (*69*), distinct forms of open complexes (*70*), and a step between open and initiated complexes (*68*).

Kinetic analysis has afforded significant insight into the mechanism of activation by transcription factors. Bacteriophage-lambda repressor protein cI activates the promoter for repressor maintenance (p_{RM}) by increasing k_f (71), whereas CAP activates transcription from *lac* P1 by increasing k_b (72), and cII activates transcription from three lambda promoters through increases in both k_f and k_b (73). The *lac* repressor simultaneously increases k_b and decreases k_f, decreasing initiation frequency while increasing promoter occupancy, so that, upon induction, repression is rapidly reversed with accelerated transcription (74).

Each of the steps of transcription initiation defined by kinetic criteria may be identified in the "footprints" of RNA polymerase upon template DNA. Low-temperature binding of RNA polymerase to promoters demonstrates that the footprint of the putative closed complex extends from about −55 to −1 (75, 76), and reveals a DNase-I hypersensitivity pattern of about 10 base-pair periodicity, indicating that the polymerase contacts only one face of the DNA molecule. Upon shift of temperature to a physiological range and the presumed formation of the open complex, the polymerase preserves its attachment to one helical face while extending its downstream contacts to about +20 (77–82), in the process unpairing the helix from about −10 to +2 (83–85). At this point, the σ subunit can be photochemically cross-linked to the nontemplate strand in the unpaired region (25), suggesting that this subunit may participate in helical melting. Sequence-specific contacts between the polymerase and the promoter are not broken during abortive cycling (86). Only at the step of σ release and escape from abortive cycling does the polymerase dissociate from the promoter.

A footprint of the elongation complex was obtained by stalling the polymerase during transcription elongation. Further movement of the polymerase was halted both by using an incomplete mixture of ribonucleoside triphosphates complementary to the template DNA (70, 86) or by site-specific placement of a psoralen adduct to cross-link the two strands of the DNA template (87). The elongating polymerase core enzyme protects about 40 bp total, 30 of which are downstream from the 3′ terminus of the complementary nascent transcript, and ten of which are upstream. A DNase-hypersensitive site occurs at the putative junction between the RNA–DNA R-loop and the reformed DNA double helix.

In two cases, the RNA polymerase binds less avidly to a second upstream site near the promoter. Occupancy of the second site of the *tyrT* tRNA promoter, as evidenced by a DNA footprint of twice the normal size and extending upstream to −130, increases *in vitro* transcription rates by up to 10-fold (88). The effect may be mediated by cooperative binding of the two polymerase molecules, thereby increasing local polymerase concentration. In the promoter for the β-lactamase gene (*bla*) of the transposon Tn3, occupancy of the second site, as demonstrated by footprinting (89), gel-retardation assay, and electron microscopy (90), curiously reduces transcription.

IV. Promoter Structure

The primary sequence as well as higher order structures influence the interaction of the promoter with RNA polymerase.

A. Primary Structure

The primary sequence requirements of a promoter are delineated by the promoter consensus, yet considerable deviation from the consensus sequence still is found among functional promoters. For example, among 112 well-characterized *E. coli* promoters, not one contains a perfect consensus sequence match (20). So, how much of, and what in, the DNA primary sequence does RNA polymerase actually recognize?

The number of base-pairs recognized by RNA polymerase has been determined in three ways. The first method, by the compilation of a consensus sequence, implies that at each of the −10 and −35 regions, 6 base-pairs are recognized, as they are conserved to a significant level beyond chance occurrence (Table I). The second method, by ethylation interference (78), reveals that about 4 "base-pairs" (the actual site of ethylation is the phosphoric ester) in the −35 region, and 6 or 7 base-pairs in the −10 region, have the potential to disrupt polymerase binding. The third method, the selection of promoters from random DNA sequences (91–93), directly determines the fraction of DNA sequences with promoter activity from among all possible DNA sequences; from this information, it has been concluded that in the −35 region alone about 8 base-pairs are recognized by RNA polymerase (94). Note that the latter two of these methods reveal that there is not necessarily a correspondence between the extent of bases conserved in the consensus and the requirements for promoter recognition by RNA polymerase. A similar analysis of bacteriophage T7 promoters using random DNA sequences revealed that the consensus phage promoter contains about twice as many base-pairs as are minimally required for polymerase recognition (95). Therefore, promoters may have partially evolved in response to selective pressures that are in addition to those required for RNA polymerase binding.

The substituents on individual nucleotides contacted by RNA polymerase have been studied in some detail by base-analog replacement within the right-hand early promoter p_R of bacteriophage lambda (96). At the −35 site, replacement of thymine with uracil in the nontemplate strand at −34 or −35 reduces promoter strength, suggesting that the RNA polymerase recognizes the 5-methyl groups of pyrimidines at these positions. On the other hand, substitution of 5-methylcytidine for thymine also decreases promoter strength, indicating that other features of T·A pairs at this position also contribute to promoter recognition. At the −10 element, replacement of a T·A at −7 by a C·G or C·I reduces promoter strength. Since C·I and T·A base-pairs present identical minor grooves, it is possible that RNA polymerase detects a unique feature of the major groove at this position.

Other clues of functional group involvement in promoter recognition come from the physiological methylation of the adenine N6 in 5′-GATC-3′ by the deoxyadenosine methylase (Dam). Promoter methylation by Dam regulates transcription by transposase of transposon IS10 (97), phage P1 *cre* (98), *dnaA* (99), and phage Mu *mom* (100). In the IS10 transposase, the methylation sequence overlaps with the −10 sequence. Methylation of both strands strongly inhibits transcription from the promoter. Methylation of either individual strand is less inhibitory. Therefore, DNA replication and a consequent transient delay in methylation of one of the strands could result in an increase in transcription, thereby coupling gene expression to the cell cycle. A similar inhibitory effect of methylation is observed for a Dam site contained within the −35 sequence of the phage pI gene *cre*. In the case of *dnaA*, the promoter is methylated within both the −35 and −10 sequences. Interestingly, methylation enhances transcription from this promoter. Methylation also enhances transcription of the phage Mu *mom* gene, although the Dam site is located upstream from the promoter, presumably within the binding site of a transcriptional repressor.

Whatever the primary chemical group requirements for promoter recognition of RNA polymerase may be, the enzyme can accept many different sequences. The technique of random selection from large DNA sequence populations shows that −35 promoter elements may be constructed that are as divergent in sequence as contiguous runs of all G·C basepairs or all A·T basepairs (92). Thus, the sequence information for promoter recognition may not be contained entirely in the primary structure, but may also be encoded in a higher level of DNA structural organization.

B. Secondary Structure

Indeed, there is evidence to suggest a role for DNA secondary structure in promoter recognition by RNA polymerase. Two extreme examples are illustrated by poly(dA–dT) and the ends of linear DNA. RNA polymerase binds so well to poly(dA–dT) that, as visualized by electron microscopy, it is seen to coat these fibers head-to-tail with enzyme (101). Poly(dA–dT) is among the strongest of "promoters," as judged by the frequency with which it initiates transcription in kinetic assays (102). Curiously, poly(dA–dT) contains an altered helical pitch and, under certain conditions, assumes unusual conformations, including Z-DNA, cruciforms, and triple helices (103). RNA polymerase binds strongly to the ends of linear DNA (104) and initiates transcription from them (105). Nevertheless, these structures are not likely to be physiologically relevant, so if DNA secondary structure is important to promoter recognition, the effect is likely to be rather more subtle.

DNA sequences with the potential to adopt unusual structures may account for the occasional disruptive mutation in the promoter spacer region between the -10 and -35 sequences. Substitution within this sequence of the bacteriophage-lambda p_{RM} promoter by $(dC)_9 \cdot (dG)_9$, or its reverse, $(dG)_9 \cdot (dC)_9$, increases k_b, while decreasing k_f (56). NMR shows that poly(dC)·poly(dG) becomes an A-form helix in solution (106); promoters thus substituted reveal an unusual sensitivity to nucleases and chemical modification (107).

A potential role for structural variation in the -35 promoter element has recently been suggested. A selective strand orientation of A·T base-pairs is observed in the -35 promoter motif (92). While A·T base-pairs need not be present in the vicinity of the -35 region, when they are present, they must be oriented so that at least one such base-pair is positioned with the T in the nontemplate strand. It is speculated that such an orientation could fulfill a requirement of an unusual DNA structure, perhaps "heteronomous DNA" (108), comprised of an A-like poly(dA) strand mating to a B-like poly(dT) strand. Such speculation has been supported by the demonstration that a DNA sequence known to adopt the heteronomous conformation under certain conditions, poly(dA)·poly(dT), has -35 promoter activity (92).

It has been proposed (92) that heteronomous DNA is representative of the promoter–polymerase interaction, as a gross model of either static promoter DNA or a kinetic intermediate of initiation complexes. The attractions of such a structure are 3-fold. First, an asymmetric structure that differentiates strands may assist the RNA polymerase in template strand selection. Second, heteronomous DNA would possess an A-form template strand, and this is a requirement of RNA–DNA hybrids formed during transcriptional elongation (109). Third, the junctions between heteronomous structures and B helix have been proposed as a means of bending DNA (110).

In fact, there is evidence to suggest that DNA bends upon binding of RNA polymerase to promoter regions. Electron microscopy reveals a slight bend in DNA bound to RNA polymerase (111). Sequences likely to bend or that are predicted to assume unusual helical twists are frequently found upstream from (52, 54, 55) and within (112–116) promoter sequences. Promoter mutations have been correlated with altered gel-electrophoretic mobility—taken as evidence of bending—of the DNA alone (117, 118) and of the DNA in complex with RNA polymerase (119). The positive transcription activator CAP induces bending upon binding near promoters of several genes (120, 121). As is true for the promoters of many genes that are activated by transcription factors, the promoters of CAP-activated genes often lack conservation with the −35 consensus and are often indifferent to mutation within this region. Therefore, the function of the −35 sequence in constitutive promoters may involve DNA bending; in promoters that lack discernible −35 elements and are consequently dependent upon activators, the protein factor may substitute for this function.

Helical deviations less overt than frank bends may also participate in promoter recognition by RNA polymerase. Local variations in helical structure, as detected by nuclease sensitivity, have been correlated with promoter elements of the *tyrT* promoter (*122*). In particular, there is evidence that the −10 element assumes an atypical structure. The deviation of the −10 promoter element from the B helix is supported by its hyperreactivity to nucleases (*123*) and hydroxyl radicals (*124, 125*), and NMR studies substantiate that this sequence maintains an unusual helical twist in aqueous solution (*126–128*). The hyperreactivity of nucleases toward the −10 sequences of some promoter DNA, not bound to polymerase, is positively correlated with the strength of a promoter (*129*).

One obvious property of −10 elements is the low melting temperature, resulting from weak interstrand A·T hydrogen bonds and 5′-TA-3′ stacking energies (*130*). The estimated melting temperature of DNA has been correlated with promoter strength (*131*) and may be used, with various degrees of success, to predict the location of promoters in genomic sequences (*132*) and the effect of promoter mutations on initiation frequency (*133*).

How might the helical deformability and the observed bending function in transcription? Bending may directly facilitate the strand separation required in open complex formation. Theoretical molecular modeling indicates that bends in DNA lower the activation energy for the opening of the double helix (*134*). Alternatively, helical deformations may lead indirectly to strand separation through the creation of topologically stressed structures.

C. Superhelix-Dependent Structures

Chemical modification experiments (*83–85*) show that strand separation during open complex formation occurs over a length of 12 base-pairs, but other measurements (*135, 136*) indicate that RNA polymerase topologically unwinds the DNA in open complexes by a linking number change of 1.6 turns. If this change could be accounted for solely by strand separation (a reduction in twist), 17 base-pairs (1.6 turns × 10.6 base-pairs per turn) should be opened, five more than that actually observed. So, some of the linking deficit must be accounted for in another way. There are two possibilities. First, a reduction in twist short of actual strand separation could occur. This untwisting could serve to facilitate, or be facilitated by, a requirement for the steric alignment of the −10 and −35 elements on a common helical face (*137*) (Fig. 1A). The helical stress imposed by the reduction in

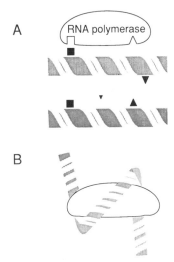

FIG. 1. Helical deviations in promoter DNA. A linking number deficit may be accounted for in the absence of strand separation by either or a combination of the following two mechanisms. (A) The twist component of the linking number is reduced by increasing the number of base-pairs per helical turn. This may serve to facilitate steric alignment of the two promoter sequence motifs on a common helical face [after Stefano and Gralla (137)]. (B) The writhe component of the linking number may be reduced by negative supercoiling of the DNA onto RNA polymerase [after Travers (3)]. The torsional strain may be relieved by ultimate strand separation in open complex formation.

twist could eventually be relieved by strand separation during open complex formation.

Alternatively, the linking number change may be accommodated by a change in "writhe" (i.e., negative supercoiling). An attractive hypothesis (138, 139) is that the DNA winds directly in a left-hand helix (and hence is bent) onto the RNA polymerase, similar to the manner in which nucleosomes restrain supercoils in eukaryotic DNA (Fig. 1B). The pressure to relieve the strain of negative supercoiling may then drive strand separation. This has the advantage of explaining some RNA polymerase–DNA cross-linking results (140), as well as being supported by the observation that a substantial linking deficit (1.25 turns) occurs even in closed complex formation, in which there is no evidence of physical separation of the strands (136). In either case, the overall topology of DNA should profoundly affect transcription.

Transcription from a number of promoters is, in fact, responsive to supercoil-induced changes in DNA topology. That is, the frequency of transcription initiation varies as a function of the superhelical density of the DNA template (141–146). Each promoter tends to respond somewhat uniquely to changes in supercoiling. Mutational analysis indicates that the response of a promoter to supercoiling is dependent on the sequences of both the −10 and −35 elements (*147*), as well as on the spacing between them (*147, 148*).

In general, the effect of negative supercoiling is to increase the isomerization rate, k_f, to the open complex of a promoter. It is likely that negative supercoiling facilitates the helical unwinding that forms the open complex (*149*). This view is supported by the observation that promoters activated by conditions that induce DNA unwinding are also activated by negative supercoiling. For example, the *in vitro* rate of open complex formation of the *rpoH* P2 promoter (which is transcribed by the σ^{70} holoenzyme to produce the message encoding the σ^{32} heat-shock subunit) is increased by both supercoiling and elevated temperature (*150*). The effect is not additive, suggesting that supercoiling and increasing temperature have the same mechanistic effect. A similar relationship holds for promoters that are activated by both supercoiling and decreasing osmolality, which also induces DNA unwinding (*146, 151*).

It should be noted that at exceptionally high negative supercoil densities, well beyond those likely to be physiologically tenable, the overall rate of transcription initiation is actually impaired. A possible explanation for this effect lies in the observation that supercoiling stabilizes many alternative DNA structures (*152*). At such high degrees of supercoiling, a significant proportion of DNA sequences assumes structures distinct from B-form double-helical DNA (*153, 154*). Some of these unusual DNA structures may not be ready templates for RNA polymerase.

1. Z-DNA

The possibility of influencing transcription through specific alternative DNA structures stabilized by levels of supercoiling likely to be encountered under physiological conditions has been addressed. Several studies have evaluated the effect on transcription of Z-DNA. With poly(dC–dG) as a template for *in vitro* reactions, less transcription is observed under ionic conditions that stabilize the Z-form of the sequence relative to the B-form (*155*). Within a gene, transcription by an elongating complex is blocked *in vitro* by supercoil-induced Z-DNA formation within a tract of poly(dC–dG) (*156, 157*). A likely block of transcription by Z-DNA *in vivo* has been reported (*158*). In that study, the insertion of $(dC-dG)_{12}$ into the initially transcribed region of a gene decreased expression, possibly through the formation of Z-DNA.

2. CRUCIFORMS

Cruciforms apparently are unable to block elongating RNA polymerase when situated well within a transcribed portion of a gene (*157, 159*). However, we have found that cruciform extrusion is able to obstruct transcription initiation both *in vitro* and *in vivo* (*160*). We constructed a promoter with the potential to adopt cruciform base-pairing. The promoter contained an inverted repeat extending from -23 to $+27$, and the diad axis of symmetry of the repeat was located near the point of transcription initiation (Fig. 2A). The promoter directed expression of a marker gene (*tet*) conferring resistance to the antibiotic tetracycline. Transcription *in vitro* was repressed as the cruciform was extruded by increasing negative DNA supercoiling. Transcription *in vivo* was induced as supercoiling was relaxed by growth under conditions inhibitory to the enzyme responsible for maintaining DNA supercoiling, DNA gyrase*. A similar promoter mutation (in *bla*) for pBR322 had previously been reported (*161*). In that case, an inverted repeat was formed from the ends of two transposons (one endogenous to the plasmid cloning vector pBR322, the other inserted by recombinant methods). The *in vivo* level of ampicillin resistance was lower than that for a control plasmid containing an oppositely oriented transposon insert. The level of ampicillin resistance conferred by this plasmid was further depressed in host cells bearing a mutation in the enzyme, topoisomerase, that relaxes negative supercoiling. Conversely, hosts with gyrase mutations harboring this plasmid show an increased level of ampicillin resistance. The purified plasmid had a lower negative supercoil density, suggesting that a linking deficit is partially taken up by extrusion of a cruciform.

Although there is still a question of whether cruciforms exist *in vivo*, there is evidence to suggest that cruciforms and other unusual DNA structures do, in fact, form within the cell.

(i)The occurrence *in vivo* of Z-DNA can be inferred by the ability of potential Z-forming sequences to inhibit *in vivo* methylation by the *Eco*RI methylase (EC2.1.1.72) (*162*) as well as by the observation of a negative linking difference in purified plasmid DNA containing such sequences (*163*). This sets a precedent for the occurrence *in vivo* of other unusual DNA structures. While a definitive physiological role of Z-DNA is still elusive, it has been proposed, among other things, to participate in genetic recombination (reviewed in *152*). Two other unusual DNA structures have been recently detected *in vitro* and physiological roles proposed: parallel-stranded quadruple helices (*164*), possibly facilitating synapse formation of sister chromatids during meiosis, and self-paired hairpinned poly(dG), a potential structure for telomeres (*165*).

(ii)Site-specific cleavage at an inverted repeat sequence on a target plas-

---

* DNA topoisomerase (ATP-hydrolyzing), EC 5.99.1.3. Also known as helicase and Type-II DNA topoisomerase [Eds.].

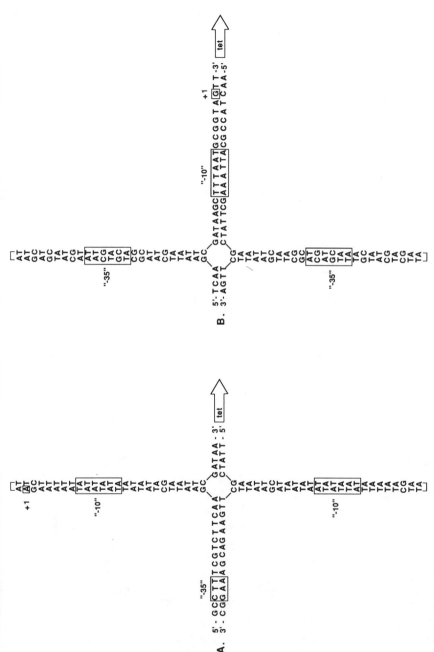

FIG. 2. Cruciform promoters. (A) The *tet* promoter of the pBR322-derived plasmid pX forms a cruciform from an inverted repeat of −10 elements. (B) The promoter of the similarly derived plasmid pX35 is composed of an inverted repeat of −35 elements.

mid has been observed *in vivo* in a host strain expressing a single-strand-specific nuclease at high levels, providing direct evidence for at least transient intracellular cruciform formation (*166*). However, one cannot say from this study whether the cruciform is extruded in a supercoil-dependent manner, or if it results rather from base-pair rearrangements occasioned by transcription or DNA replication.

(iii) Inverted repeat sequences are prone to deletion, presumably a result of a cruciform's resemblance to the Holliday junction intermediate of genetic recombination (*167*).

(iv) The observation of a negative linking difference in inverted repeat-containing plasmid DNA directly isolated from cells grown under conditions that inhibit protein synthesis (*168*), as well as in cells grown under normal conditions (*169*), suggests that intracellular cruciform formation occurs.

(v) Cruciform-specific DNA-binding proteins have been purified (*170*), and single-strand-specific exonucleases that recognize cruciforms, such as bacteriophage T7 endonuclease I (EC3.1.21.2), have long been recognized for their putative role in resolving the Holliday intermediates of genetic recombination (*171, 172*).

The still indeterminate issue of the *in vivo* role of alternate DNA structures notwithstanding, the promoter we constructed has been engineered so that its sequence is likely to form a very unstable double helix, one that should be easily denatured. (i) Of the 50 base-pairs in the cruciform, 44 are A·T. In addition to their low melting temperature, (A+T)-rich sequences have been shown to exist as stably unwound regions in supercoiled DNA (*173*). (ii) The cruciform has been constructed by the repeated inversion of a perfect -10 consensus motif, a sequence of known helical instability, and the site of RNA polymerase-directed strand separation. (iii) Each repeated unit contains a tract of $(dA)_5 \cdot (dT)_5$, a known locus of DNA bending (*110*). [Recall that bending is thought to facilitate helical opening (*134*).]

We have constructed a second cruciform promoter (Fig. 2B) (unpublished). The promoter contains a 50 base-pair inverted repeat of consensus -35 sequences extending from -20 to -69. Compared to a control promoter, this cruciform promoter differs in sequence only by a 22 base-pair insertion between -48 and -69, well upstream from the traditional location of conserved promoter sequence motifs. *In vitro*, this promoter is transcriptionally inactive when the template DNA is supercoiled to a physiological density $(-\sigma \approx 0.03)$, demonstrating that an alternate DNA structure at this more upstream location also has the potential to influence transcription. However, *in vivo*, this promoter is only slightly less active than the control, indicating that this cruciform is not extruded to a significant extent within the cell, most probably as a result of the observed slow kinetics of cruciform extrusion of this inverted repeat sequence.

3. TRANSCRIPTION AS A FORCE FOR SUPERCOILING

Just as DNA topology influences transcription, transcription, in turn, likely influences DNA topology. RNA polymerase locally unwinds DNA during transcription (*135, 174*). It was hypothesized (*175*), and is now experimentally confirmed for both *E. coli* (*176–178*) and yeast (*179*), that this local unwinding partitions the topology of DNA: Without changing the linking number, transcribing RNA polymerase negatively supercoils the DNA that it has passed, while introducing compensatory positive supercoils in the domain ahead that remains to be transcribed (Fig. 3). This local and transient variation in supercoiling is predicted to be greatest at the promoter, and it is perhaps substantial enough to help drive DNA structural transitions. This hypothesis demands that the DNA be fixed relative to the rotational axis of the RNA polymerase; this is probably accomplished by membrane attachment of the DNA, fluid torsional drag of the polymerase and nascent polysomes, or oppositional orientation of transcription units.

Note that if the activities of the type-I (relaxing) topoisomerase and gyrase (type-II topoisomerase) become unbalanced (by either mutation or addition of inhibitors) or if there is differential stabilization of the negatively and

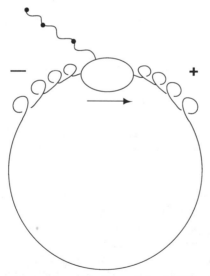

FIG. 3. Transcription-driven supercoiling. Transcription by RNA polymerase partitions the DNA into proximal negatively supercoiled and distal positively supercoiled domains [after Liu and Wang (*175*)]. Nascent polysomes are trailing from the polymerase.

positively supercoiled domains, the transient changes in supercoiling may become fixed, resulting in linking number changes. Exactly the latter situation appears to occur as a normal intracellular routine (177). While one RNA polymerase molecule is transcribing the gene, the next polymerase probably binds to the promoter, thereby reducing negative torsion. Since there are now more positive than negative supercoils, the positive supercoils will be relaxed to a greater extent by gyrase than will the negative supercoils be relaxed by topoisomerase. The net result is that negative supercoils will be introduced into the DNA, and the linking number will decrease. That this is true is suggested by the finding that negative supercoiling of purified pBR322-derived plasmid DNA varies as a function of the strength of one of its promoters (177).

The contributions to supercoiling from transcription may, in fact, be great enough to overshadow the role of the once-heralded gyrase and topoisomerase (180). Since there is a directional component to this supercoiling, the relative orientation of genes may profoundly influence the net effect of transcription-driven supercoiling of the genome. The organization of genes within the genome may therefore be important to the concerted organization of transcription and DNA replication (discussed in 181).

Several genes are probably physiologically regulated by DNA supercoiling (182, 183), most understandably the genes encoding gyrase (184) and topoisomerase (185), whose in vitro and in vivo responses to increased negative supercoiling are repression and induction, respectively. In the case of the gyrase promoter, the DNA sequence responsible for supercoil-induced transcription repression has been defined by deletion analysis (141). The sequence includes the −10 element, the start site, and several transcribed bases. Fusions of that sequence with the galactokinase gene induce in vivo expression of galactokinase (EC 2.7.1.6) activity during growth in the presence of an inhibitor of DNA gyrase (186). It has been hypothesized that the topological regulation of this gene occurs during the transition from abortive cycling to the transcription elongation complex (141): the first few bases of the initial nascent message are paired with the DNA template in an R-loop; DNA relaxation destabilizes the R-loop, enabling the RNA polymerase to escape from abortive cycling.

A number of E. coli genes are differentially regulated by switching between aerobic and anaerobic growth (183, 187, 188). Supercoiling relaxes upon a change from anaerobic to aerobic growth, and this, in turn, probably influences the promoter activity of many genes. Supportive evidence for this phenomenon has come from the in vivo use of gyrase inhibitors, which decrease negative supercoiling and mimic the effects of aerobic growth. The topological state of DNA, and hence gene expression, is also influenced by growth medium osmolarity (142). Increasing extracellular osmolarity increases intracellular negative supercoiling. Therefore, sweeping changes in the physiological regulation of large numbers of genes may be achieved by DNA topological changes in response to environmental conditions.

While it is not known through what mechanism DNA topology responds to changes in oxygen and salt concentration, a simple speculation can be advanced: oxygen forms free radicals within a cell, and oxygen-generated radicals are agents of DNA damage via phosphodiester chain scissions (*189*). Such nicks would have the same effect on relaxing negative supercoiling, as does topoisomerase. In the case of molarity-dependent changes in supercoiling, it is known that helical periodicity varies as a function of salt concentration (reviewed in *190*). *Escherichia coli* intracellular osmolality increases as a function of extracellular osmolality (*191*). Therefore, increasing salt concentration increases helical twist, so that negative supercoiling must increase in order to retain the constancy of the linking number.

4. DNA LOOPS

Another higher level DNA structure that influences transcription is looping, and it is likely to be important to both prokaryotic and eukaryotic transcription regulation. Looping has been invoked as a mechanism to explain the action of transcription-regulating proteins that bind to DNA at sites distant from the promoter (*192–194*). DNA looping has been demonstrated by the cooperative action of multiple protein binding sites *in vivo* using the *lac* repressor (*195*) and the *ara* activator (*196*) and has been demonstrated *in vitro* by DNase footprinting (*197*) of bacteriophage-lambda repressor and electron microscopy (*198*) of lambda cro protein.

DNA looping is greatly influenced by the helical phasing of the protein binding sites; in a relationship that becomes less important with increasing distance of separation, cooperative interaction of *trans*-acting factors by looping requires separation by integral helical turns. Separation by half-turns disfavors cooperation, because the *trans*-acting factors, presumably bound to opposite sides of the helix, are now both a loop and a half of a twist distant. Looping *in vitro* is facilitated by DNA supercoiling (*199*), and supercoiling, in turn, influences the optimal spacing requirements for site separation (*200*). There is an *in vivo* relationship between looping and supercoiling (*201*). Cooperative interaction between two *lac* operator sites is dependent on supercoil-induced DNA looping to allow repressor dimer formation. Relaxation of negative supercoiling by growth in the presence of gyrase inhibitors disfavors cooperation of the two operators, and therefore could influence gene expression. One current explanation of looping suggests it to be a mechanism for increasing the density of transcription factor binding sites in a given genetic regulatory region (*192, 193*).

Recent work with the bacteriophage mu suggests that a novel—and not yet well-characterized—supercoil-dependent DNA structure (perhaps a bend) can, in concert with the *E. coli* protein integration host factor, organize a DNA loop (*202*). Such a loop brings together distant regulatory sequences and may also regulate transcription by impeding the strand separation necessitated by elongating RNA polymerase. Electron microscopy has also revealed that static bends (*203*) and Z-DNA forming tracks (*204*) may similarly serve as sites for supercoil-dependent DNA loop formation.

5. TRIPLE HELICES

Still another example of higher order DNA structure of potential consequence to transcription is eukaryotes. In this case, *in vitro* inhibition of transcription has been demonstrated by site-specific oligonucleotide binding to an upstream region of the human c-*myc* oncogene (*205*). The oligonucleotide apparently forms a triple-stranded helix that interferes with promoter or enhancer recognition. [Note that triple-stranded helices could form in the absence of a complementary oligonucleotide; unimolecular sequence-specific triple-stranded structures form in a supercoil-dependent manner in some plasmid DNAs (e.g., *206*).] It has yet to be determined, however, whether such events occur intracellularly, and whether they are of general significance.

6. TOPOLOGICAL DOMAINS OF THE GENOME

The *E. coli* genome may be divided into as many as 50 independent topological domains (*207*), and so the chromosomal location of an *E. coli* gene may have an effect on its transcriptional activity. As one example, the supercoil-dependent promoter mutation in the leucine operon (*leu-500*) behaves differently when cloned from its chromosomal locus to a multicopy plasmid (*208*), suggesting that the levels of supercoiling of the plasmid may not be comparable to that found on a particular region of the chromosome.

7. TRANSCRIPTIONAL ACTIVITY AS A PROBE OF DNA STRUCTURE *in Vivo*

It is worth noting that the supercoil-dependent transcriptional activity of some operons has been ingeniously exploited to make inferences about the *in vivo* structural features of DNA. For example, the intracellular superhelical density has been estimated by comparing the relative level of expression of two mutant promoters of the lactose operon (*lac*) both *in vivo* and *in vitro* as a function of σ (*147*). The ratio of activities of these two promoters *in vitro* is quite large on relaxed templates, but approaches unity as the template is progressively supercoiled. This relationship between relative *in vitro* activity and superhelical density can be plotted on a curve. By extrapolation from this curve, the ratio of activity of the two promoters observed *in vivo* may be used to predict the *in vivo* superhelical density. Using this method, an estimate of intercellular superhelical density of $\sigma = -0.048$ was determined. This value, in relative agreement with other estimates of *in vivo* superhelical density (*209–212*), is greater than the value of $\sigma \approx -0.065$ that is usually observed for form-I plasmid DNA purified by standard methods. Therefore, about one third of the linking number deficit observed in pure DNA preparations is restrained *in vivo*, possibly through the packaging of DNA into nucleosome-like assemblies.

A similar approach has been employed in order to determine the *in vivo* helical pitch (*213*). The *ara* operon is transcriptionally activated by DNA loop formation mediated by the AraC protein binding to two distant operator sequences. Loop formation, and hence transcriptional activity, varies as a function of the distance of separation of the two operators; when the separation is by integral helical turns, the operator sites reside on the same helical face and loop formation is facile, but when the separation is by fractional turns, the operators are present on opposite faces of the helix, and loop formation is prevented. Using a series of mutants with varying lengths of nucleotides separating the two operators, a plot of transcriptional activity versus distance of separation can be constructed. The plot is sinusoidal, and the frequency equals the helical repeat of the DNA. Using this method, the periodicity of the helical repeat of DNA *in vivo* was found to be 11.1 basepairs per turn. This value is significantly less than the value of 10.5 basepairs per turn determined for linear DNA *in vitro* (*214–216*). Therefore, DNA *in vivo* may be relatively unwound. The driving force for this untwisting could be the negative supercoiling demonstrated by the unrestrained linking-number deficit.

V. Summary and Implications for the Structure of RNA Polymerase

The hypothesis of this review—that promoter DNA does not serve solely as a genomic punctuation mark, but instead directly participates in the reactions of transcription—is supported by several examples. The -10 sequence has an altered helical twist and a low melting temperature, both of which may encourage strand separation. The -35 sequence may be composed of an unusual DNA structure, possibly heteronomous DNA, that could facilitate template strand selection, transition of the template strand into the A-form required for RNA–DNA duplex formation, and perhaps DNA bending as well. The overall topology of the promoter DNA influences the rate of open complex formation, leading to strand separation at the -10 region, and moderates structural transitions, including Z-DNA formation, cruciform extrusion, and looping, all of which may serve to regulate transcription. In turn, transcription changes the promoter topology by supercoiling the DNA template. Lastly, sequences associated with the promoter may direct the utilization of transcription termination signals.

The potential deviation of promoter DNA from the uniform B double helix has provocative implications for the structure of RNA polymerase. A standard feature of prokaryotic site-specific DNA-binding proteins, notably lambda repressor (217), cro (218), and CAP (219), is the helix–turn–helix motif in which the side-chains of the residues in the amino-most α helix site specifically bind, by hydrogen bonds and van der Waals forces, to the edges of the base-pairs in the major groove of the DNA. Recall that the σ subunits of RNA polymerase are predicted, from their primary sequences, to contain helix–turn–helix motifs [one or two, depending on the number of conserved elements of the respective promoter (14, 36)]. A possible model, then, of how RNA polymerase recognizes promoter DNA is one in which the amino-acid side-chains of the enzyme "read" base-pairs in the major groove of the DNA.

This model is supported by the recent isolation of mutations in the gene, rpoD, encoding the σ^{70} subunit (220, 221). In these experiments, rpoD mutations were selected that activated transcription from various promoters containing down-mutations. The rpoD mutations that complemented promoter down-mutations in the −10 region tended to cluster in one of the predicted helix–turn–helix motifs of the polypeptide subunit, while the mutations that enhanced transcription from promoters mutant in the −35 region tended to cluster to the other predicted helix–turn–helix motif of the subunit. Therefore, it appears that one helix–turn–helix motif of the σ subunit recognizes the −10 region and the other such motif recognizes the −35 subunit. A shortcoming of this model, however, is that potential amino-acid/base-pair hydrogen-bonding schemes (222, 223) are unlikely to account for the extraordinary degeneracy of promoter sequences. It is especially difficult to imagine how a limited repertoire of hydrogen-bond-forming side-chains of an α-helix could recognize the divergence of base-pair sequences that function as −35 promoter regions for the σ^{70} holoenzyme. Therefore, it has been proposed (92) that DNA that differs greatly in primary sequence may maintain similar helical conformations and that it is this geometrical similarity that accounts for common recognition as promoters by RNA polymerase.

How then might a helix–turn–helix domain of protein recognize deviations in the helical structure of the DNA phosphodiester backbone? There are at least two possibilities with biological precedent. The first comes from the surprising X-ray structure of the recently resolved trp repressor–operator complex. The trp repressor maintains no direct hydrogen bond or non-polar contacts between α-helix residue side-chains and DNA base-pairs (224). Instead, the α-helix of the repressor indirectly recognizes its operator

DNA through direct and water-mediated hydrogen bonds to the phosphodiester backbone. A different situation holds for the bacteriophage 434 repressor. Like the trp repressor, the 434 repressor binds as a dimer to a palindromic operator sequence, with each monomer contacting one half of the operator. Unlike the trp repressor, however, the crystal structure of the complex of the 434 repressor and operator reveals that the second α-helix of each repressor monomer forms orthodox base-pair-specific hydrogen bonds in the major groove at each half of the operator DNA (*225*). Nonetheless, four central base-pairs (two from each half of the operator) are not contacted by protein, but mutational analysis indicates that they still influence operator affinity for the repressor (*226*). These pairs are apparently responsible for maintaining a unique helical twist that establishes a favorable orientation of protein subunit contacts in repressor dimer formation. Therefore, DNA helical deformations may be recognized by direct protein contact at the level of the phosphate backbone, such as with the trp repressor, or without direct protein–DNA contact by secondarily accommodating protein subunit interactions, such as with the 434 repressor. Thus, the higher order structure of promoter DNA could require the helix–turn–helix of RNA polymerase to contact DNA through a mechanism different than hydrogen bonding to base-pairs through the major groove.

ACKNOWLEDGMENTS

This work was supported by National Institutes of Health Grants R35CA39903 (to L.A.L.) and GM07266 (to the University of Washington Medical Scientist Training Program).

REFERENCES

1. T. Patt, *in* "Genetics of Bacteria" (J. Scaife, D. Leach and A. Galizzi, eds.), p. 255. Academic Press, Orlando, Florida, 1985.
2. W. R. McClure, *ARB* **54**, 171 (1985).
3. A. A. Travers, *CRC Crit. Rev. Biochem.* **22**, 181 (1987).
4. W. S. Reznikoff and W. R. McClure, *in* "Maximizing Gene Expression" (W. Reznikoff and L. Gold, eds.), p. 1. Butterworths, Boston, 1985.
5. B. C. Hoopes and W. R. McClure, *in* "*Escherichia coli* and *Salmonella typhimurium* Cellular and Molecular Biology" (F. C. Neidhardt, ed.), p. 1231. Am. Soc. Microbiol., Washington, D.C., 1987.
5a. A. Ishihama, *Trends Genet.* **4**, 282 (1988).
6. W. S. Reznikoff, D. A. Siegele, D. W. Cowing and C. A. Gross, *ARGen* **19**, 355 (1985).
7. M. T. Record, *in* "Unusual DNA Structures" (R. D. Wells and S. C. Harvey, eds.), p. 237. Springer-Verlag, Berlin and New York, 1988.
8. P. H. von Hippel, D. G. Bear, W. D. Morgan and J. A. McSwiggen, *ARB* **53**, 389 (1984).
9. M. J. Chamberlin, *in* "The Enzymes" (P. D. Boyer, ed.), p. 61. Academic Press, New York, 1982.
10. A. Kornberg, "DNA Replication," Freeman, San Francisco, California, 1980.
11. A. Kornberg, "1982 Supplement to DNA Replication," Freeman, San Francisco, California, 1982.

12. J. S. Krakow and S. A. Kumar, in "International Encyclopedia of Pharmacology and Therapeutics, Section 103: Inhibitors of DNA and RNA Polymerases" (P. S. Sarin and R. C. Gallo, eds.), p. 139. Pergamon, Oxford, 1980.
13. R. H. Doi and L.-F. Wang, Microbiol. Rev. 50, 227 (1986).
14. J. D. Helmann and M. J. Chamberlin, ARB 57, 83 (1988).
15. O. Raibaud and M. Schwartz, Annu. Rev. Genet. 18, 173 (1984).
16. D. M. J. Lilley, in "Regulation of Gene Expression" (I. Booth and C. F. Higgins, eds.), p. 105. Cambridge Univ. Press, London and New York, 1986.
17. G. R. Smith, Cell 24, 599 (1981).
18. G. J. Pruss and K. Drlica, Cell 56, 521 (1989).
19. C. B. Harley and R. P. Reynolds, NARes 5, 2343 (1987).
20. D. K. Hawley and W. R. McClure, NARES 8, 2237 (1983).
21. T. D. Yager and P.H. von Hippel, in "Escherichia coli and Salmonella typhimurium Cellular and Molecular Biology" (F. C. Neidhardt, ed.), p. 1241. Am. Soc. Microbiol., Washington, D.C., 1987.
22. C. Yanofsky, JBC 263, 609 (1988).
23. R. Landick and C. Yanofsky, in "Escherichia coli and Salmonella typhimurium Cellular and Molecular Biology" (F. C. Neidhardt, ed.), p. 1276. Am. Soc. Microbiol., Washington, D.C., 1987.
24. T. Platt, ARB 55, 339 (1986).
25. R. B. Simpson, Cell 18, 277 (1979).
26. C. Jeppesen, K. F. Jensen and P. E. Nielsen, NARes 16, 9545 (1988).
27. D. Sweetser, M. Nonet and R. A. Young, PNAS 84, 1192 (1987).
28. O. Meisenberger, H. Heumann and I. Pilz, FEBS Lett. 122, 117 (1980).
29. S. A. Darst, H. O. Ribi, D. W. Pierce and R. D. Kornberg, JMB 203, 269 (1988).
30. R. R. Burgess, in "RNA Polymerase" (R. Losick and M. Chamberlin, eds.), p. 69. CSHLab, Cold Spring Harbor, New York, 1976.
31. J. C. Ingraham, O. Maaloe and F. C. Neidhardt, "Growth of the Bacterial Cell," p. 370. Sinauer, Sunderland, Massachusetts, 1983.
32. A. Blank, J. A. Gallant, R. R. Burgess and L. A. Loeb, Bchem 25, 5920 (1986).
33. J. D. Kahn and J. E. Hearst, JMB 205, 291 (1989).
34. D. A. Arnosti and M. J. Chamberlin, PNAS 86, 830 (1989).
35. J. D. Helmann and M. J. Chamberlin, PNAS 84, 6422 (1987).
36. M. Gribskov and R. R. Burgess, NARes 14, 6745 (1986).
37. S. Barik, B. Ghosh, W. Whalen, D. Lazinski and A. Das, Cell 50, 885 (1987).
38. W. Whalen, B. Ghosh and A. Das, PNAS 85, 2494 (1988).
39. T. A. Baker and A. Kornberg, Cell 55, 113 (1988).
40. K. J. Marians, J. S. Minden and C. Parada, This Series 33, 111 (1986).
41. C. B. Harley, J. L. Lawrie, M. Betlack, R. Crea, H. W. Boyer and J. Hedgpeth, NARes 15, 7269 (1988).
42. G. Duval-Valentin and R. Ehrlich, NARes 15, 575 (1987).
43. J. W. Kwak, J. Kim, O. J. Yook and M. H. Han, Gene 64, 165 (1988).
44. K. Struhl, JMB 191, 221 (1986).
45. S. A. Mitsialis, J. F. Young, P. Palese and R. V. Guntaka, Gene 16, 217 (1981).
46. M. E. Mulligan, D. K. Hawley, R. Entriken and W. R. McClure, NARes 12, 789 (1984).
47. A. H. Horwitz, C. Morandi and G. Wilcox, J. Bact. 142, 659 (1980).
48. S. Ponnambalam, C. Webster, A. Bingham and S. Busby, JBC 261, 16043 (1986).
49. M.-C. Shih and G. N. Gussin, Cell 34, 941 (1983).
50. S. Keilty and M. Rosenberg, JBC 262, 6389 (1987).
51. P. Youderian, S. Bouvier and M. M. Susskind, Cell 30, 843 (1982).

52. T. Nishi and S. Itoh, *Gene* **44**, 29 (1986).
53. U. Deuschle, W. Kammerer, R. Gentz and H. Bujard, *EMBO J.* **5**, 2987 (1986).
54. R. R. Plaskon and R. M. Wartell, *NARes* **15**, 785 (1987).
55. B. F. Bauer, E. G. Kar, R.M. Elford and W. M. Holmes, *Gene* **63**, 123 (1988).
56. D. T. Auble, T. L. Allen and P.L. deHaseth, *JBC* **261**, 11202 (1986).
57. D. R. Russell, E. A. Auger, P. S. Vermersch and G. N. Bennet, *Gene* **32**, 337 (1984).
58. W. Kammerer, U. Deuschle, R. Gentz and H. Bujard, *EMBO J.* **5**, 2995 (1986).
59. L. E. Maquat, K. Thornton and W. S. Reznikoff, *JMB* **139**, 537 (1980).
60. W. E. Holben and E. A. Morgan, *PNAS* **81**, 6789 (1984).
61. A. P. W. Telesnitsky and M. J. Chamberlin, *JMB* **205**, 315 (1989).
62. J. A. Goliger, X. Yang, H.-C. Guo and J. W. Roberts, *JMB* **205**, 331 (1989).
63. X. Yang, C. M. Hart, E. J. Grayhack and J. W. Roberts, *Genes Dev.* **1**, 217 (1987).
64. N. Hernandez and A. M. Weiner, *Cell* **47**, 249 (1986).
65. M. J. Chamberlin, *ARB* **43**, 721 (1974).
66. M. J. Chamberlin, W. C. Nierman, J. Wiggs and N. Neff, *JBC* **254**, 10061 (1979).
67. J. Stefano and J. D. Gralla, *Bchem* **18**, 1063 (1979).
68. S. Rosenberg, T. R. Kadesch and M. J. Chamberlin, *JMB* **155**, 31 (1982).
69. H. Buc and W. R. McClure, *Bchem* **24**, 2712 (1985).
70. D. C. Straney and D. M. Crothers, *Cell* **43**, 449 (1985).
71. D. K. Hawley and W. R. McClure, *JMB* **157**, 493 (1982).
72. T. P. Malan, A. Kolb, H. Buc and W. R. McClure, *JMB* **180**, 881 (1984).
73. M.-C. Shih and G. N. Gussin, *JMB* **172**, 489 (1984).
74. S. B. Straney and D. M. Crothers, *Cell* **51**, 699 (1987).
75. B. Hofer, D. Muller and H. Koster, *NARes* **13**, 5995 (1985).
76. R. T. Kovacic, *JBC* **262**, 13654 (1987).
77. A. Schmitz and D. J. Galas, *NARes* **6**, 111 (1987).
78. U. Siebenlist, R. B. Simpson and W. Gilbert, *Cell* **20**, 269 (1980).
79. M. M. Becker and J. C. Wang, *Nature* **309**, 682 (1984).
80. J. A. Borowiec and J. D. Gralla, *Bchem* **25**, 5051 (1986).
81. M. D. Kuwabara and D. S. Sigman, *Bchem* **26**, 7234 (1987).
82. C. Jeppesen, O. Buchardt, U. Henriksen and P. E. Nielsen, *NARes* **16**, 5755 (1988).
83. U. Siebenlist, *Nature* **279**, 651 (1979).
84. K. Kirkegaard, H. Buc, A. Spassky and J. C. Wang, *PNAS* **80**, 2544 (1983).
85. A. Spassky, K. Kirkegaard and H. Buc, *Bchem* **24**, 2723 (1985).
86. A. J. Carpousis and J. D. Gralla, *JMB* **183**, 165 (1985).
87. Y.-B. Shi, H. Gamper and J. E. Hearst, *JBC* **263**, 527 (1988).
88. A. A. Travers, A. I. Lamond, H. A. F. Mace and M. L. Berman, *Cell* **35**, 265 (1983).
89. G. Duval-Valentin and R. Ehrlich, *NARes* **16**, 2031 (1988).
90. G. Duval-Valentin, B. Schmitt and R. Ehrlich, *NARes* **16**, 5277 (1988).
91. M. S. Z. Horwitz and L. A. Loeb, *PNAS* **83**, 7405 (1986).
92. M. S. Z. Horwitz and L. A. Loeb, *JBC* **263**, 14724 (1988).
93. A. R. Oliphant and K. Struhl, *NARes* **16**, 7673 (1988).
94. M. S. Z. Horwitz, thesis, University of Washington, Seattle (1988).
95. T. D. Schneider and G. D. Stormo, *NARes* **17**, 659 (1989).
96. J. W. Dubendorff, P. L. deHaseth, M. S. Rosendahl and M. H. Caruthers, *JBC* **262**, 892 (1987).
97. D. Roberts, B. C. Hoopes, W. R. McClure and N. Kleckner, *Cell* **43**, 117 (1985).
98. N. Sternberg, B. Sauer, R. Hoess and K. Abremski, *JMB* **187**, 197 (1986).
99. R. E. Braun and A. Wright, *MGG* **202**, 246 (1986).
100. R. H. A. Plasterk, M. Vollering, A. Brinkman and P. Van de Putte, *Cell* **36**, 189 (1984).

101. R. Williams, *PNAS* **74**, 2311 (1977).

102. W. R. McClure, *PNAS* **77**, 5634 (1980).

103. W. Saenger, "Principles of Nucleic Acid Structure," Springer-Verlag, Berlin and New York, 1984.

104. P. Melancon, R. R. Burgess and M. T. Record, *Bchem* **22**, 5169 (1983).

105. E. Schenborn and R. Mierendorf, *NARes* **13**, 6223 (1985).

106. M. H. Sarma, G. Gupta and R. Sarma, *Bchem* **25**, 3569 (1986).

107. D. T. Auble and P. L. deHaseth, *JMB* **202**, 471 (1988).

108. S. Arnott, R. Chandrasekaran, I. H. Hall and L. C. Puigjaner, *NARes* **11**, 4141 (1983).

109. V. L. Florentiev and V. I. Ivanov, *Nature* **228**, 519 (1970).

110. H. S. Koo and D. M. Crothers, *Bchem* **26**, 3745 (1987).

111. J. Hirsh and R. Schleif, *JMB* **108**, 471 (1976).

112. E. N. Trifonov, *CSHSQB* **17**, 271 (1983).

113. E. N. Trifonov, *CRC Crit. Rev. Biochem.* **19**, 89 (1985).

114. C.-S. Tung and S. C. Harvey, *NARes* **15**, 4973 (1987).

115. R. Nussinov, *JBC* **259**, 6798 (1984).

116. R. Nussinov, *J. Theor. Biol.* **115**, 179 (1985).

117. L. Bossi and D. M. Smith, *Cell* **39**, 643 (1984).

118. R. L. Gourse, H. A. de Boer and M. Nomura, *Cell* **44**, 197 (1986).

119. G. Kuhnke, H.-J. Fritz and R. Ehring, *EMBO J.* **6**, 507 (1987).

120. H.-N. Liu-Johnson, M. R. Gartenberg and D. M. Crothers, *Cell* **47**, 995 (1986).

121. D. Dripps and R. M. Wartell, *J. Biomol. Struct. Dyn.* **5**, 1 (1987).

122. H. R. Drew and A. A. Travers, *Cell*, **37**, 491 (1984).

123. L. G. Sheflin and D. Kowalski, *NARes* **13**, 6137 (1985).

124. D. S. Sigman, A. Spassky, S. Rimsky and H. Buc, *Biopolymers* **24**, 183 (1985).

125. A. Spassky and D. S. Sigman, *Bchem* **24**, 8050 (1985).

126. W. Nerdal, D. R. Hare and B. R. Reid, *JMB* **201**, 717 (1988).

127. D. J. Patel, S. A. Kozlowski and R. Bhatt, *PNAS* **80**, 3908 (1983).

128. J.-F. Lefevre, A. N. Lane and O. Jardetzky, *Bchem* **27**, 1086 (1988).

129. A. Spassky, S. Rimsky, H. Buc and S. Busby, *EMBO J.* **7**, 1871 (1988).

130. O. Gotoh and Y. Tagashira, *Biopolymers* **20**, 1033 (1981).

131. H. Tachibana and A. Ishihama, *NARes* **13**, 9031 (1985).

132. O. Gotoh and Y. Tagashira, *Biopolymers* **20**, 1043 (1981).

133. H. Margalit, B. A. Shapiro, R. Nussinov, J. Owens and R. L. Jernigan, *Bchem* **27**, 5179 (1988).

134. J. Ramstein and R. Lavery, *PNAS* **85**, 7231 (1988).

135. H. B. Gamper and J. E. Hearst, *Cell* **29**, 81 (1982).

136. M. Amouyal and H. Buc, *JMB* **195**, 795 (1987).

137. J. E. Stefano and J. D. Gralla, *PNAS* **79**, 1069 (1982).

138. H. Buc, *Biochem. Soc. Trans.* **14**, 196 (1986).

139. A. A. Travers, *Biochem. Soc. Trans.* **14**, 199 (1986).

140. A. Chenchick, R. Beadealashvili and A. Mirzabekow, *FEBS Lett.* **128**, 46 (1981).

141. R. Menzel and M. Gellert, *PNAS* **84**, 4185 (1987).

142. C. F. Higgins, C. J. Dorman, D. A. Stirling, L. Waddell, I. R. Booth, G. May and E. Bremer, *Cell* **52**, 569 (1988).

143. E. Bertrand-Burggraf, M. Schnarr, J. F. Lefevre and M. Daune, *NARes* **12**, 7741 (1984).

144. R. Ehrlich, A. Larousse, M.-A. Jacquest, M. Marin and C. Reiss, *EJB* **148**, 293 (1985).

145. D. C. Wood and J. Lebowitz, *JBC* **259**, 11184 (1984).

146. A. I. Lamond, *EMBO J.* **4**, 501 (1985).

147. J. A. Borowiec and J. D. Gralla, *JMB* **195**, 89 (1987).

148. T. Aoyama and M. Takanami, *BBA* **949**, 311 (1988).

149. H. R. Drew, J. R. Weeks and A. A. Travers, *EMBO J.* **4**, 1025 (1985).
150. R. Ueshima, N. Fujita and A. Ishihama, *MGG* **215**, 185 (1989).
151. R. A. Dixon, N. C. Henderson and S. Austin, *NARes* **16**, 9933 (1988).
152. R. D. Wells, *JBC* **263**, 1095 (1988).
153. S. K. Bramachari, Y. S. Shouche, C. R. Cantor and M. McClelland, *JMB* **193**, 201 (1987).
154. C. R. Cantor, S. Bondopadhyay, S. K. Bramachari, C.-F. Hui, M. McClelland, R. Morse and C. L. Smith, *in* "Unusual DNA Structures" (R. D. Wells and S. C. Harvey, eds.), p. 73, Springer-Verlag, Berlin and New York, 1988.
155. J. H. van de Sande and T. M. Jovin, *EMBO J.* **1**, 115 (1982).
156. J. G. Brahms, O. Dargouge, S. Brahms, Y. Ohara and V. Vagner, *JMB* **181**, 455 (1985).
157. L. J. Peck and J. C. Wang, *Cell* **40**, 129 (1985).
158. E. Horback and B. Müller-Hill, *JMB* **202**, 157 (1988).
159. N. M. Morales, S. D. Cobourn and U. R. Muller, *FASEB Abstr., Annu. Meet. 72nd*, p. 4252 (1988).
160. M. S. Z. Horwitz and L. A. Loeb, *Science* **241**, 703 (1988).
161. V. Aleixandre and M. Blanco, *MGG* **209**, 56 (1987).
162. A. Jaworski, W.-T. Hsieh, J. A. Blaho, J. E. Larson and R. D. Wells, *Science* **238**, 773 (1987).
163. W. Zacharias, A. Jaworski, J. E. Larson and R. D. Wells, *PNAS* **85**, 7069 (1988).
164. D. Sen and W. Gilbert, *Nature* **334**, 364 (1988).
165. E. Henderson, C. C. Hardin, S. K. Walk, I. Tinoco and E. H. Blackburn, *Cell* **51**, 899 (1987).
166. N. Panayotatos and A. Fontaine, *JBC* **262**, 11364 (1987).
167. D. Lilley, *Nature* **320**, 14 (1986).
168. D. B. Haniford and D. E. Pulleyblank, *NARes* **13**, 4343 (1985).
169. J. A. Blaho, J. E. Larson, M. J. McLean and R. D. Wells, *JBC* **263**, 14446 (1988).
170. K. M. Elborough and S. C. West, *NARes* **16**, 3603 (1988).
171. D. M. J. Lilley and B. Kempter, *Cell* **36**, 413 (1984).
172. B. de Massy, R. A. Weisberg and F. W. Studier, *JMB* **193**, 359 (1987).
173. D. Kowalski, D. A. Natale and M. J. Eddy, *PNAS* **85**, 9464 (1988).
174. J.-M. Saucier and J. C. Wang, *Nature NB* **239**, 167 (1972).
175. L. Liu and J. C. Wang, *PNAS* **84**, 7024 (1987).
176. H.-Y. Wu, S. Shy, J. C. Wang and L. F. Liu, *Cell* **53**, 433 (1988).
177. N. Figueroa and L. Bossi, *PNAS* **85**, 9416 (1988).
178. Y.-P. Tsao, H.-Y. Wu and L. F. Liu, *Cell* **56**, 111 (1989).
179. S. J. Brill and R. Sternglanz, *Cell* **54**, 403 (1988).
180. M. Frank-Kamenetskii, *Nature* **337**, 206 (1989).
181. B. J. Brewer, *Cell* **53**, 679 (1988).
182. R. J. Thompson and G. Mosig, *Cell* **48**, 281 (1987).
183. M. J. Axley and T. C. Stadtman, *PNAS* **85**, 1023 (1988).
184. R. Menzel and M. Gellert, *Cell* **34**, 105 (1983).
185. Y.-C. Tse-Dinh, *NARes* **13**, 4751 (1985).
186. R. Menzel and M. Gellert, *J. Bact.* **169**, 1272 (1987).
187. Y. Zhu and J. E. Hearst, *PNAS* **85**, 4209 (1988).
188. C. J. Dorman, G. C. Barr, N. N. Bhriain and C. F. Higgins, *J. Bact.* **170**, 2816 (1988).
189. Y. W. Kow and S. S. Wallace, *PNAS* **82**, 8354 (1985).
190. W. Bauer, *Annu. Rev. Biophys. Bioeng.* **7**, 287 (1978).
191. B. Richey, D. S. Cayley, M. C. Mossing, C. Kolka, C. F. Anderson, T. C. Farrar and M. T. Record, *JBC* **262**, 7157 (1987).
192. R. Schleif, *Nature* **327**, 369 (1987).
193. R. Schleif, *Science* **240**, 127 (1988).

194. J. C. Wang and G. N. Giaever, *Science* **240**, 300 (1988).
195. M. C. Mossing and M. T. Record, *Science* **23**, 889 (1986).
196. S. Hahn, W. Hendrickson and R. Schleif, *JMB* **188**, 355 (1986).
197. A. Hochschild and M. Ptashne, *Cell* **44**, 681 (1986).
198. J. Griffith, A. Hochschild and M. Ptashne, *Nature* **322**, 751 (1986).
199. J. A. Borowiec, L. Zhang, S. Sasse-Dwight and J. D. Gralla, *JMB* **196**, 101 (1987).
200. H. Kramer, M. Amouyal, A. Nordheim and B. Müller-Hill, *EMBO J.* **7**, 547 (1988).
201. S. Sasse-Dwight and J. D. Gralla, *JMB* **202**, 107 (1988).
202. N. P. Higgins, D. A. Collier, M. W. Kilpatrick and H. M. Krause, *JBC* **264**, 3035 (1989).
203. C. H. Laundon and J. D. Griffith, *Cell* **52**, 545 (1988).
204. H. Castelman, L. H. Hanau, W. Zacharias and B. F. Erlanger, *NARes* **16**, 3977 (1988).
205. M. Cooney, G. Czernuszewicz, E. H. Postel, S. J. Flint and M. E. Hogan, *Science* **241**, 456 (1988).
206. J. C. Harvey, M. S. Shimizu and R. D. Wells, *PNAS* **85**, 6292 (1988).
207. R. R. Sinden and D. E. Pettijohn, *PNAS* **78**, 224 (1981).
208. S. M. H. Richardson, C. F. Higgins and D. M. J. Lilley, *EMBO J.* **7**, 1863 (1988).
209. D. Lilley, *Nature* **320**, 14 (1986).
210. C.-K. J. Shen and W.-S. Hu, *PNAS* **83**, 164 (1986).
211. R. R. Sinden and T. J. Kochel, *Bchem* **26**, 1343 (1987).
212. J. B. Bliska and N. R. Cozzarelli, *JMB* **194**, 205 (1987).
213. D.-H. Lee and R. F. Schleif, *PNAS* **86**, 476 (1989).
214. J. Wang, *PNAS* **76**, 200 (1979).
215. D. Rhodes and A. Klug, *Nature* **286**, 573 (1980).
216. T. D. Tullius and B. A. Dombrowski, *Science* **230**, 679 (1985).
217. C. O. Pabo and M. Lewis, *Nature* **298**, 443 (1982).
218. W. F. Anderson, D. H. Ohlendorf, Y. Takeda and B. W. Mathews, *Nature* **290**, 754 (1981).
219. D. B. McKay and T. A. Steitz, *Nature* **290**, 744 (1981).
220. J. C. Hu and C. A. Gross, *JMB* **203**, 15 (1988).
221. D. A. Siegel, J. C. Hu and C. A. Gross, *JMB* **203**, 29 (1988).
222. N. C. Seeman, J. M. Rosenberg and A. Rich, *PNAS* **73**, 804 (1976).
223. P. H. von Hippel and O. G. Berg, *PNAS* **83**, 1608 (1986).
224. Z. Otwinowski, R. W. Schevitz, R.-G. Zhang, C. L. Lawson, A. Joachimiak, R. Q. Marmorstein, B. F. Luisi and P. B. Sigler, *Nature* **335**, 321 (1988).
225. J. E. Anderson, M. Ptashne and S. C. Harrison, *Nature* **326**, 846 (1987).
226. G. B. Koudelka, S. C. Harrison and M. Ptashne, *Nature* **326**, 886 (1987).
227. A. C. Christensen and E. T. Young, *Nature* **299**, 369 (1982).
228. T. Elliott and E. P. Geiduschek, *Cell* **36**, 211 (1984).

Gene Expression in Seed Development and Germination

J. Derek Bewley* and
Abraham Marcus†

*Department of Botany
University of Guelph
Guelph, Ontario N1G 2W1, Canada
†Fox Chase Cancer Center
Philadelphia, Pennsylvania 19111

In the past decade, there has been a large increase in research into the proteins of seeds, in particular the synthesis of storage proteins during seed development. There is economic justification for such research, as seeds provide the major food source for both humans and domestic animals. From a scientific standpoint, the fact that developing seeds synthesize large quantities of only a few proteins, in a strict temporal sequence and in a tissue-specific manner, has made them an attractive subject for investigations into the control of gene expression. A vast literature now exists, and in this review only certain areas of interest are highlighted. Gene expression during germination has been studied to a far lesser extent, for, unlike in development, there are no proteins synthesized in large amount. Postgerminative physiology, involving the mobilization of stored reserves to provide for seeding growth, requires the expression of genes for hydrolytic enzymes. Studies on this subject, especially in relation to the synthesis of α-amylase in the aleurone layer of the cereal endosperm (1, 2), remain a major part of this aspect of seed biology.

Progress in Nucleic Acid Research
and Molecular Biology, Vol. 38

I. Overview of Seed Development, Germination, and Seedling Establishment

An embryo of a higher plant develops from a single zygotic cell, resulting from the fertilization of an egg nucleus by a pollen nucleus. This cell undergoes extensive division and develops into a mature embryo (often assuming several morphologically distinct shapes in the process). In seeds of dicotyledonous plants (e.g., legumes), the embryo is typically comprised of an axial region (root and shoot) and two large cotyledons. During development, an endosperm is formed from a triploid fusion nucleus. The endosperm may or may not persist in the mature seed, but when present, it usually is the tissue in which the stored reserves are deposited; otherwise, the cotyledons are the major store. In seeds of monocotyledonous plants (e.g., cereals), the embryo contains an axial region, but the cotyledon is modified to form a relatively diminutive scutellum; the endosperm is a large structure at maturity, and is the important storage tissue (3).

Very little storage material is synthesized during the early cell division stage of development. Most of the synthesis of storage proteins, carbohydrates, and lipids occurs during subsequent cell expansion. While the great majority of reserves are sequestered within the cells of the storage tissues (the cotyledons and/or endosperm), some deposition occurs also within the axial regions; such reserves might be important in providing nutrients during germination and early seedling establishment. The final phase of seed development involves loss of water during maturation drying, when reserve synthesis ceases and the seed enters a metabolically inactive state. Drying of the seed converts it to a dispersal structure that is resistant to the vagaries of the environment, and that remains quiescent until conditions are suitable for germination and growth. Seed desiccation also effects a permanent change in metabolism, in that, upon rehydration, synthesis of proteins associated with development ceases, and that associated with germination and seedling establishment commences.

Germination of the seed starts with the imbibition of water, resulting in the rapid resumption of protein synthesis, using those components of the synthetic complex conserved within the dry seed. Upon emergence of the radicle from the seed, germination is complete and the seedling becomes established, with the clearly defined root and shoot regions.

In this review, we concentrate on the regulatory aspects of expression of genes for proteins synthesized during development and germination. We review the synthesis of some important classes of storage proteins during seed development, and discuss the cessation of protein synthesis during maturation drying and the revival of synthesis during germination, leading to seedling establishment.

II. Protein Synthesis during Seed Development

A. Soybean (*Glycine max*): β-Conglycinin

Approximately 15 to 18 × 10^3 genes are expressed during soybean seed development, and most of their messages constitute only 0.001% of the mRNA mass, i.e., there are only a few molecules per cell (4). The expression of most of these genes occurs equally in the vegetative tissues of the mother plant. However, developing seeds at their mid-maturation stage contain 7–10 discrete superabundant mRNAs (about 50,000 mRNA molecules per cell), which together comprise 50–60% of the mRNA mass, but only 0.05% of the sequence complexity. These messages are virtually unique to the developing embryo (5) and encode a spectrum of prevalent seed proteins (7-S and 11-S storage proteins, lectin, and trypsin inhibitor).

The major storage proteins of soybean, which constitute 70% of the seed protein mass, have sedimentation coefficients of 7 S (β-conglycinin) and 11 S (glycinin) and have been characterized in some detail (6–8). Studies of their developmental regulation have progressed most for β-conglycinin, a trimeric protein of approximately 200 kDa comprised of three major subunits: α (76 kDa), α' (72 kDa), and β (53 kDa). The primary translation product of the α and α' subunits is slightly larger than the mature protein and undergoes modifications in length and extent of glycosylation during maturation (9–13). The genes encoding the α and α' subunits are highly homologous and have strong homologies to 7-S (vicilin) storage protein genes in other legumes (12). The α and α' subunits are synthesized initially as a slightly smaller polypeptide than the mature protein, and increase in size by approximately 3 kDa due to posttranslational glycosylation (11). Strong homologies, on the order of 75%, occur at the nucleotide level within the coding sequences of the α' and β subunits, although considerable differences are evident in the 5'-untranslated sequence and the first exon, the α' gene having a 537-base insert therein (10).

Seed storage protein genes are regulated primarily at the transcriptional level; in vegetative tissues they are transcriptionally silent (14). Neither selective gene amplification nor DNA rearrangements play any role in regulating soybean storage protein gene expression; likewise, gene activation and suppression are not correlated with different states of DNA methylation (14).

The seed protein gene families are not regulated in a strict coordinate manner in relation to their expression. The α and α' subunits of β-conglycinin begin to accumulate in the cotyledons during seed development soon after the cell division phase is completed, at 18–20 days after pollination. Accumulation of the β subunit commences some 5–7 days later (15).

Isoforms of α, α′, and β subunits accumulate in a developmentally regulated manner; these are most likely posttranslational modifications of the subunits resulting in alterations of the charges of these proteins (16, 17). mRNA levels for the α and α′ subunits increase concomitantly with their synthesis, indicative of transcriptional control. However, the mRNA for the β subunit is present in a form translatable *in vitro*, for 2–3 days prior to this protein being detectable in the cotyledons (17). It appears that the subunit, although synthesized, is unstable initially and is detectable only after its stability has increased during development (18). The mechanism of this posttranslational stabilization remains to be determined.

Both of the α subunits accumulate in the developing axis in low amounts compared to the cotyledons, but no β subunit accumulates. The reduction in synthesis of the former can be correlated with lower levels of mRNA, and the absence of the latter with both a low frequency of mRNA transcripts and the instability of the product (17).

Genes for the α′ and β subunits have been transferred into petunia and tobacco using the intermediate plasmid pMON200 transferred to *Agrobacterium tumefaciens* carrying a disarmed Ti plasmid (16, 19). Both subunits are expressed exclusively in the developing seed of the transformed plant, although the α′ subunit undergoes some proteolytic cleavage (16); both are present in the different isoforms found in the soybean seed, and assemble to form a 7- to 9-S protein—perhaps in association with the native storage protein of the transformed seed. The temporal regulation of synthesis of the subunits in transformed seed is such that it increases and is processed in the developing seed in parallel with the native storage protein (16, 19, 20), and in the same temporal sequence as in the soybean seed (21).

Transcription of most eukaryotic genes requires a TATA box, CAAT sequence, and other regulatory elements upstream from the transcriptional start site. The best-described of these elements are "enhancers," *cis*-acting regulatory sequences, which strongly stimulate transcription from promoters of nearby genes. Their effect is independent of orientation and rather insensitive to position in relation to the gene. Enhancers control the expression of some genes in a tissue-specific manner; this is considered to be a consequence of the activation of these elements by tissue-specific *trans*-acting factors. Since expression of storage protein genes is primarily under transcriptional control (22), the presence of these types of regulatory elements has been sought.

When the α′ subunit gene, flanked by 159 nucleotides upstream, was transferred into petunia plants (23), its expression in the developing petunia seed was very low, but when nucleotides to −257 were included, expression was increased 20-fold. The TATA and CAAT sequences in the α′ subunit gene lie at −30 and −65, respectively, and thus their presence alone is insufficient to stimulate transcription of the gene. At −560 there is a GTGGATAG sequence, identical to the core enhancer sequence of SV40 and some animal genes; its presence is not essential for expression of the α′ subunit (23). Between −159 and −257 there occur four repeats of a six-basepair (G+C)-rich sequence (ADCCCA),* the importance of which is suggested by experiments in which a 170-bp DNA sequence upstream (−78 to −257) from the α′ subunit was placed in different positions and orientations into a chimeric gene comprised of the 35-S CaMV promoter (a strong constitutive promoter in transgenic plants) linked to a reporter [CAT (chloramphenicol acetyltransferase)] gene (24). When the construct was introduced into tobacco plants, in the absence of the α′ subunit upstream promoter region, CAT was expressed in vegetative (root, leaf, and stem) tissues, and in seeds during early development. The presence of the α′ subunit promoter upstream, whether oriented correctly or in reverse, increased CAT expression in seeds, but not in other plant parts. Some enhancement of CAT-mRNA synthesis also occurred when the promoter region was placed 3′ from the CAT coding region, in either orientation, but not when introduced 3′ from the polyadenylation region.

A lectin gene, expressed during seed development, also has been transferred to tobacco plants. Its expression is predominantly in the seeds during their development, and to a lesser extent in the mature plant root (25). About 0.5 kb of the 5′ upstream sequence is necessary to program this expression. Another developmentally regulated protein, the KTi2 Kunitz trypsin inhibitor, requires only 0.4 kb 5′ to the gene. In a search for trans-acting factors that control seed storage protein synthesis, a 60-kDa DNA-binding protein that promotes expression of the lectin and Kunitz trypsin inhibitor genes was discovered (26). The embryo nuclear protein binds to one or more sites −77 to −217 upstream from the lectin gene; it protects nucleotides −184 to −173 and −165 to −126 from DNase digestion. A seven-nucleotide core motif, ATTWAAT,* is common to the protected regions. The embryo nuclear protein does not bind to pBR322 nor to the 5′ region of the leghemoglobin gene (i.e., nonembryonic genes), but it does bind to the 5′ region of the trypsin inhibitor, which contains the seven-nucleotide core motif, as do other seed protein genes (27). Maximum lectin DNA–protein binding was obtained with nuclear proteins extracted from seeds at the time of maximum synthesis of the lectin (26). The protein(s) are tissue-specific, as no binding complex was formed when leaf, stem, or root nuclear protein was used. No binding of the embryo nuclear proteins to a 3′ lectin probe occurred.

* D = A or G or C; W = A or T.

B. Pea (*Pisum sativum*): Legumin

Two major classes of storage proteins (11-S legumin and 7-S vicilin) and one minor class (2-S albumin) occur in the cotyledons of mature seeds, the former two classes constituting 60–80% of the total protein of the cotyledons. The pea legumin storage proteins and their genes are among the most highly characterized in plants. There are approximately eight genes per haploid genome; variations in the amount of legumin synthesized by different pea lines appear not to be related to gene dosage, which remains relatively constant (28).

The mature legumin protein is a molecule of 360–400 kDa consisting of six subunits, each of which is composed of a 40 kDa acidic polypeptide linked to a 20 kDa basic polypeptide. These polypeptides are synthesized from a single mRNA in which the coding sequence for the acidic polypeptide precedes that of the basic polypeptide (29). The 60-kDa primary translation product is composed of two domains, one acidic and one basic, linked by a peptide bond that is subsequently cleaved posttranslationally, producing two subunits that remain joined by a single disulfide bond.

Little is known about the control of expression of the legumin gene during pea development. In the cotyledon, legumin mRNA accumulation is delayed by 4–6 days compared to vicilin mRNA, and this is reflected in the relative amounts of protein synthesized (30, 31). Thus, while synthesis of these two major proteins is not temporally correlated, it is controlled mainly at the transcriptional level. Some posttranscriptional control has been suggested, however, since the nuclear transcription rates of some legumin genes during development appear to be unrelated to the levels of mRNAs present (32). The evidence is tentative, although there is considerable variation in the expression of the various legumin genes at different stages of development (33).

About 100 nucleotides upstream from the site of transcription in two pea legumin genes, there occurs a conserved region of 28 bases (approximately 50% G+C) (34, 35), that shows strong homologies with legumin genes in *Glycine max* and *Vicia faba* (36). The importance of this region, the "legumin box," in transcriptional control is unknown, and a preliminary study (37) suggests that it is not the regulatory region. Recently, a 3.4-kb legumin gene fragment, including 1.2-kb 5' and 0.4-kb 3' noncoding regions, was successfully transferred into *Nicotiana plumbaginifolia* using the BIN19 binary Ti plasmid system (38); it was expressed in the seed, but not in the leaf. Sequences in the 5' flanking region between bp −97 and −549 contain a positive control element, and other sequences further upstream enhance expression (39). When transferred into yeast, the legumin gene is expressed, but the 60-kDa precursor polypeptide is not processed into the mature protein (32).

C. Barley (*Hordeum* spp.): Hordein

The major storage proteins of barley and most other cereals are pro-lamins, so named because they are rich in proline and amide nitrogen (glu-tamine). They are deficient in lysine. Hordein is the specific name of the prolamin in barley and it accounts for 30–50% of the total grain nitrogen. It consists of three major groups of polypeptides, hordeins B (75–90% of the total) and C and D (much lesser amounts). The B hordeins, the major deter-minants of seed protein quality, are complex polymorphic groups of polypep-tides encoded by a multigene family at a single locus (*Hor 2*) on the short arm of chromosome 5 (*40, 41*). The *Hor 1* locus for the hordein C group is also multigenic, while the *Hor 3* locus for the hordein D protein contains only 1 or 2 genes, both loci also being located on chromosome 5.

Some 10–15 B hordein polypeptides per genotype encoded by the *Hor 2* locus are categorized in relation to their cyanogen bromide peptide maps as members of the B_1, B_2 or B_3 class (*42*). Each polypeptide is specified by a separate mRNA, and presumably by a separate gene (*43*). The hordein genes are expressed in a tissue-specific manner, i.e., only in the endosperm of the developing barley grain. Synthesis of the hordein mRNAs commences sever-al days prior to the appearance of the protein *in vivo* (*44*), but this may be because the methods used for detection of the mRNA are more sensitive than those used for the protein. Although, as already noted, two major subfamilies of B hordein (B_1 and B_3) are encoded by the same multigenic locus, they still are differentially expressed during endosperm development. Thus, mRNAs for B_1 hordeins increase 12- to 15-fold 14–34 days after an-thesis, whereas those for B_3 increase only 3- to 4-fold over the same period. The amount of protein synthesized relates well to the amount of mRNA present, suggestive of transcriptional control, although some discrepancies occur, perhaps due to methodological limitations (*44*).

Expression of hordeins is affected by the *lys 3a* gene of the high-lysine mutant Risø 1508, located on chromosome 7. The homozygous presence of this gene has a differential "*trans*-acting" influence on the expression of the hordein genes: D hordein is unaffected, C hordein is not synthesized, and B_3 synthesis is moderately reduced, while B_1 synthesis is strongly curtailed (*43, 45*). The reduced synthesis of the hordeins can be correlated with reduced abundances of their cognate mRNAs, suggesting that gene *lys 3a* directly or indirectly regulates transcription rates of the hordein gene. Alternatively, the product of gene *lys 3a* may be affecting mRNA stability, the rates turn-over, or protein processing. The high-lysine Risø 56 mutant synthesizes no major hordein B polypeptides, nor their mRNAs, due to a major structural deletion of the *Hor 2* locus. On the other hand, another high-lysine mutant, Risø 1508, which synthesizes reduced amounts of B_1 hordein and its mRNA, suffers no major deletions in this locus (*46, 47*).

The genome for B hordein has been isolated and the complete nucleotide sequence has been determined, including the 5′ and 3′ flanking regions (48, 49). Within 600 bp 5′ from the initiator codon are three conserved sequences with extensive (>80%) homology to sequences present in prolamins in wheat and maize. There is a conventional TATA box, a CATC ("CAAT") box, and at −300 there is a sequence about 33 bp in length, within which the same 29 nucleotides are present in both the B hordein and α-gliadin (the prolamin from wheat) genes, and a zein (21-kDa maize prolamin) gene. That the upstream region of B hordein plays some regulatory role in gene expression has been shown by transformation experiments (50). A segment of the 5′ flanking region (511 bp upstream from, the transcription start site) of the B_1 hordein gene has been linked to the CAT reporter gene and transferred, using *A. tumefaciens*, into tobacco. The CAT protein appears only in the endosperm of the transformed tobacco (not in the embryo or vegetative plant), and its expression occurs only at the time of normal storage protein synthesis within this tissue. Thus, the regulatory elements for the B_1 hordein gene are within the approximately −500 bp transferred and are expressed with high fidelity in the seed of transformed plants.

Two chymotrypsin inhibitors, CI-1 and CI-2, are synthesized during barley development, the latter from a small multigene family (4–6 copies per haploid genome). In the Hiproly mutant of barley, CI-1 and CI-2 content is increased appreciably compared to normal cultivars (51, 52). The abundance of mRNA for this protein, determined by Northern blots, correlates well with the amount of CI-1 and CI-2 synthesized *in vitro* and *in vivo* in both cultivars; this is an indication of transcriptional control and/or differential stability of chymotrypsin mRNA (52, 53). The structural genes for CI-2 are located on chromosome 5, at the *Ica-2* locus (54), and the increased amount of this protein in Hiproly barley is controlled by the single recessive gene *lys* on chromosome 7—another interesting example of the control of gene expression by a "regulatory" gene on a separate chromosome.

D. Maize (*Zea mays*): Zeins

Zeins are the major storage proteins of maize, comprising 50–70% of the proteins of the endosperm of the mature dry seed. The zeins are separable into two major size classes of 19 and 21 kDa (55), and are coded for by a complex multigene family, with a minimum of 100 genes per haploid genome (56–58). The molecular biology of the zein genes has been reviewed recently in detail (59). The zein gene family is made up of several small groups of gene subfamilies, none of which contain intervening sequences (60, 61). The genes are located on three of the ten maize chromosomes, with subfamilies of genes being clustered together on a chromosome.

Synthesis of the zeins occurs exclusively within the endosperm on the rough endoplasmic reticulum during seed development, between 10 and 50 days after pollination (DAP). The mRNAs increase in amount up to the peak of zein synthesis at about 35 DAP, with the transcription of different zein genes commencing at different times during development (63). There is an enormous increase in DNA to over 200 copies in the endosperm nuclei up to the 18–20 DAP stage of endosperm development (62) and this may be responsible in part for the increase in zein mRNA levels. To date, no selective amplification of the genome has been demonstrated, and even zein genes (pseudogenes) that are not expressed are also amplified (59).

The regulatory mechanism for zein synthesis is effected at the level of transcription, with some posttranscriptional modulation (64). For example, while the 21- to 22-kDa zein genes are transcribed at approximately twice the rate of the 19-kDa genes, the relative amount of mRNA from the latter recruited into polysomes is almost three times that of the former. When zein messages are injected into *Xenopus* oocytes, those lacking a poly(A) sequence translate less protein over longer incubation times than do mRNAs containing this 3′ noncoding region. Thus, the presence of the poly(A) tail may confer stability on the mRNA and increase the efficiency or probability of reinitiation events (65). Whether the poly(A) region plays any role in the developing seed in regulating posttranscriptional expression remains to be determined.

Sequencing of the 5′ noncoding region of zein genes has revealed a TATA box at −30 bp from the transcription initiation site (66, 67), a CAAT box, and various o⁺ ₂r sequences that may be related to the high efficiency with which zein genes are ultimately translated. Nucleotide combinations on the mRNA near the start codon may facilitate its binding to the ribosome (59, 68).

There is controversy concerning the number of promoter regions involved in the transcription of zein genes. Feix and co-workers, using maize cultivar A619, claim that zein genes possess two promoters, one (P1) occurring approximately −900 to −1000 bp upstream and another (P2) about −40 to −60 bp upstream from the coding region, giving rise to mRNA transcripts of 1800 and 900 bases, respectively (66, 69, 70). Multiple zein precursor mRNAs occur in the developing maize endosperm (71), and since zein genes are devoid of introns, the variable sizes of their transcription products can come only from the presence of transcribed upstream sequences, which are eventually removed to produce the mature 900-base message (69). That the P1 promoter is active has been demonstrated in experiments where 19-kDa and 21-kDa zein genes were injected into nuclei of the unicellular green alga *Acetabularia:* transcription started only from the P1 promoter (72). Removal of the CAAT and TATA boxes resulted in no zein production. In transformed HeLa cells, the P1 promoter is used exclusively (unless it is disconnected, then P2 is used); on the other hand, *Xenopus* shows a preference for P2 (*66*). When the 19-kDa zein gene is transferred into petunia, tissue (i.e., seed-)-specific expression is very poor and even the zein mRNA synthesized within the petunia seed is barely detectable (*72*). This may mean that there is inefficient regulation of the synthesis of a monocot protein by its own promoter in a dicot plant. In the presence of dicot flanking regions of β-phaseolin, the 15-kDa zein gene is transcribed and translated in transgenic tobacco in a tissue-specific manner (*74*).

Besides sequence homology upstream from the zein genes in the TATA and CAAT box regions, there is also a common 15 bp sequence at approximately −330 (CACATGTGTAAAGGT), which lies 260 bp upstream from the P2 promoter site, and which contains part of the core sequence of viral, animal, and human enhancers (*62, 72, 75*). Upstream deletion experiments show that nucleotides in the region −125 to −337 are necessary for maximum transcription of the 19 kDa zein gene (*67*); within this region are four regions that share imperfect homology with the SV40 virus core enhancer sequence. A 22-bp sequence lying 260 bp upstream from the P1 promoter site has also been identified (*76*); it might bind nuclear proteins and hence play a role in gene expression.

There are interactions between crude nuclear extracts of endosperm and fragments from the 5′ flanking region of a 19-kD zein gene and of specific double-stranded oligonucleotides (*77*). Two binding sites were identified, one between positions −8 and −225, which contains a moderately conserved region (−150 to −223) and the P2 promoter, and a second 22-nucleotide sequence (−318 to −339) containing 14 nucleotides of a 15-bp sequence conserved in all zein genes (*77*). This sequence may be important in the overall binding of *trans*-acting factors, rather than just functioning in the expression of zein genes. A similar sequence is located in the upstream regions of endosperm-specific storage protein genes from other cereals (e.g., B1 hordein and α-gliadin of barley and wheat, respectively) (*48*) and in the gene for another endosperm-specific protein in maize, sucrose synthase (EC 2.4.1.13) (*78*).

A number of maize mutants exhibit reduced zein synthesis, largely because of reduced zein mRNA (*79*). Some genetic mutants reduce the synthesis of both the 19-kDa and 21-kDa zeins, e.g., *fl-2*, *Mc*, and *opaque-6*, while *opaque-2* and *De*-B30* mutants preferentially repress 21-kDa zeins, and *opaque-7* represses the 19-kDa zeins (*80*). How these mutants influence zein production is not known, but because the mutations map to chromosomes different from the zein genes that they affect, there is likely to be an interaction of the products of *trans*-active genes with sequence elements in the flanking regions of zein genes. The *opaque-2* locus on chromosome 7 affects the expression of zein genes located on chromosome 4. A 32-kDa soluble non-storage endosperm protein (b-32) (*81*) is under the control of the *opaque-2* locus, but is not encoded by it: the gene for b-32 protein is located on the *opaque-6* locus. It is proposed (*81*) that the *opaque-2* locus induces the *opaque-6* locus to produce the b-32 protein, which in turn controls the level of zein produced by a battery of zein genes (*82*)—either by transcriptional regulation, or by reducing the efficiency of translation of zein messages. Another protein, b-70, which is overproduced in the presence of the *fl-2* mutation, appears to prevent zein accumulation, not by regulating mRNA levels, but rather by interfering with zein deposition into protein bodies (*83*).

E. Other Storage Proteins

The composition, synthesis, and deposition of many other storage proteins from cereals, legumes, and other species have been studied. For several, the sequences of their genes have been determined and studies on their synthesis and the regulatory mechanisms involved have been initiated, e.g., in wheat (*48, 84*), oat (*85–87*), field bean (*88–90*), cotton (*91*), rapeseed (*92, 93*), sunflower (*94*), Brazil nut (*95*), and French or common bean (*12, 96*). The β-phaseolin gene from the common bean was the first seed protein to be expressed in a "foreign" plant (*97*). This protein has now been expressed in tobacco seeds (*96*), sunflower seeds (*97*), yeast (*98*), *Xenopus oocytes* (*99*), and insect cells (*100*).

The general pattern that emerges from these studies is similar to that outlined for the proteins considered above. The time of maximum synthesis of storage protein coincides with the highest levels of mRNA within the storage tissue of the developing seed, i.e., transcriptional control, with some modulation in expression due to translational, or posttranslational, control.

Many seed storage proteins are glycosylated posttranslationally during their maturation into the final storage form (*101*). Glycosylation and correct targeting of introduced proteins into protein bodies occurs in seeds of transgenic plants (*102, 103*), although glycosylation itself is not an essential part of targeting. Phytohemagglutinin (PHA), a major seed lectin in the common bean, is deposited within vacuoles of transgenic yeast, thus demonstrating that the vacuolar targeting information present on the plant protein is recognized in a very divergent species (*104*). This information appears to be contained within the PHA protein, near the amino-terminal end, and hence is encoded within the gene itself.

F. Factors That Influence Gene Expression

1. Nutritional Status

The expression of some developmentally regulated genes can be altered by environmental factors, such as nutrient stress. For example, certain legumes and cereals grown in suboptimal levels of sulfur show a selective reduction in the proportion of sulfur-containing proteins in their seeds (105–108). There is no decline in the levels of sulfur-free proteins (they often increase), and hence they are in greater proportion in the mature seed than in conditions where sulfur is plentiful.

Under sulfur-deficient conditions, pea seeds synthesize only 15% of the 11-S legumin of those developing under nondeficient conditions, whereas the 7-S vicilin increases by about 50%. There is a parallel reduction (70–90%)in extractable legumin mRNA in sulfur-deficient seeds, and an increase in vicilin message (109, 110). Addition of sulfur to seeds developing under deficient conditions markedly restores legumin synthesis and the amount of legumin mRNA, while vicilin synthesis and the amount of vicilin mRNA gradually decline to normal levels (110).

In the case of legumin mRNA, it appears that the amount present during development under sulfur-deficient conditions is regulated posttranscriptionally (111), i.e., legumin mRNA may be more unstable in sulfur-deficient seeds. In vitro transcription experiments show that within the first 48 hours of recovery from sulfur deficiency, legumin mRNA in pea cotyledons increases more than 20-fold, whereas transcription of the legumin gene increases only 2-fold. On the other hand, vicilin is regulated transcriptionally, for there is a significant decline in the transcription of its genes during recovery from sulfur deficiency, and a slow decline in vicilin mRNA (111).

Pea seeds also synthesize two small sulfur-rich albumins during development. Both are coded for by one gene, whose product (PA1) is cleaved posttranslationally to yield the two albumins (PA1a and PA1b). In seeds developing under normal conditions, expression of the PA1 gene is under transcriptional control, the amount of PA1a and PA1b synthesized being related to the amount of PA1 mRNA transcribed (112). Under sulfur-deficient conditions, there is a greatly reduced accumulation of PA1a and PA1b in the developing seed, due to a decline in the PA1 message; as with legumin, this is due to reduced posttranscriptional stability of the message, rather than an altered rate of transcription of the PA1 gene (112).

Soybean cotyledons grown on culture media synthesize the 7-S and 11-S storage proteins, as normal. In the presence of excess methionine, synthesis of the methionine-less β-subunit of the 7-S (β-conglycinin) protein decreases, whereas synthesis of methionine-containing α and α′ subunits is unaffected, and the proportion of 11-S (glycinin) storage protein increases (113). Extractable mRNA for the β subunit is decreased in cotyledons subjected to excess methionine, and increases again when methionine is lowered, whereas those for the α and α′ subunits remain unchanged (114, 115). It is unclear whether the control by methionine is effected at the level of transcription of the β-subunit gene, or whether stability of the subunit mRNA plays a role.

Sulfur starvation of barley plants results in decreased accumulation in the developing seeds of "sulfur-rich" B hordeins, with little effects on the "sulfur-poor" C-hordein class (116). mRNA levels for the former decline under conditions of sulfur deficiency, but not those of the latter; changes in transcription or mRNA stability could be responsible. Nitrogen nutrition also affects the synthesis of proteins during seed development, with mRNA levels being strongly influenced (117).

2. ABSCISIC ACID AND WATER STRESS

Embryos isolated from their surrounding seed structures during the mid- to late stages of development will often germinate precociously, i.e., will pass into the germinative phase without completing development (118). Incubating the isolated embryos in abscisic acid (ABA) suppresses precocious germination and prolongs normal embryogeny (118, 119). If introduced to abscissate at the correct stage of development (usually between mid-maturation and prior to the onset of drying), embryos will also exhibit prolonged or enhanced synthesis of storage proteins, e.g., glycinin, and of the β-subunit of β-conglycinin in soybean (120, 121). There has also been observed increased synthesis of cruciferin and napin in rapeseed (122), phaseolin in French bean (123), wheat germ agglutinin in wheat (124), and early-methionine-labeled protein in wheat (125), or of non-storage proteins, e.g., malate synthase (126) and some late-embryogenesis-abundant (Lea) proteins (127) in cotton, an embryo in which storage protein synthesis seems not to be affected by ABA. A 15-kDa glycine-rich protein in maize embryos, whose synthesis is enhanced by ABA, is also synthesized in vegetative tissues in response to water stress, an event which increases ABA levels (128). This ABA-induced protein contains a sequence that conforms with the RNP consensus sequence and thus may be a single-stranded RNA-binding protein (129). Determining to which RNA it binds should reveal whether it has an important regulatory role in ABA-sensitive genes.

Recently, a chimeric gene, containing a 650-bp segment of the promoter for the E_m protein from wheat, linked to GUS as the reporter, was transferred into rice protoplasts. The GUS gene is expressed in response to ABA, which is indicative of ABA control of gene expression at the transcriptional level (130). Additional control of E_m protein synthesis at the posttranscriptional level in vivo also may occur (119).

While there are some correlations between ABA levels and protein synthesis within developing intact seeds, the evidence that this hormone is a primary regulatory component is still tenuous (118, 119). Placing rapeseed embryos in solutions of high osmotic potential will maintain them in a developmental mode, and they continue to synthesize cruciferin and its mRNA at near-normal levels (131). While osmotic treatment results in a response which is very similar to that of ABA application, the water-stress effect appears not to be mediated through increasing the amount of this hormone within the developing embryo. Several *Lea* proteins and their mRNAs increase during the natural drying event to which cotton embryos are subjected *in situ* late in development (*132*). Expression of the *Lea* genes is thus enhanced, either by changing embryo water potential, or an event (or series of events) resulting from water stress (*132*).

3. DESICCATION

Maturation drying is the normal terminal event in seed development, at which stage metabolism ceases and the seed passes into a quiescent state. Upon subsequent rehydration, seeds rapidly resume metabolism, but the pattern of protein synthesis, both quantitatively and qualitatively, is very different from that taking place during development. Thus, desiccation acts as a "switch," to suppress the transcription of genes for developmental proteins and allow the induction of expression of those for germinative proteins (*118*). This has been demonstrated in several seeds, including castor bean (*133–135*), soybean (*136*), French bean (*135, 137, 138*), and wheat (*139*). The changes in protein synthesis elicited by desiccation result from identifiable changes in the mRNA population, e.g., gibberillin-inducible α-amylase in wheat (*139*), phaseolin in French bean (*138*), and ricin D (*140*) and various *Lea* proteins (Fig. 1) in castor bean.

The approach to studying the effect of drying on gene expression usually involves subjecting seeds to desiccation prior to the completion of their developmental synthetic events. Upon rehydration, developmental protein synthesis ceases, despite being incomplete at the time of drying, and germinative protein synthesis commences. The factors regulating this dramatic change in gene expression are unknown. Interestingly, a pattern of developmental protein synthesis may continue for several hours during germination prior to the full germinative patterns being expressed (*133–135, 138*). Presumably residual mRNAs for these proteins are present in the dry seed and are utilized during early germination, but are gradually replaced by germinative mRNAs as the developmental ones are degraded and not replenished because their genes are transcriptionally silent.

III. Gene Expression during Germination and Seedling Establishment

A. General Considerations (Including Preformed mRNAs)

As a dry seed imbibes water, it undergoes a rapid transition from quiescence to vigorous metabolism. Numerous biochemical and physiological processes are activated during germination and seedling establishment (*141*,

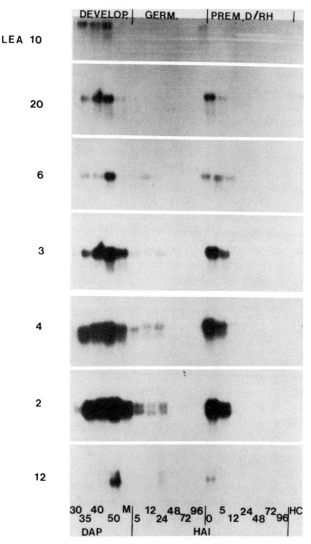

FIG. 1. "Northern" hybridization studies using several *Lea* cDNA clones (127) to demonstrate the expression of *Lea* genes during late development of the endosperm of the castor bean seed [30–50 days after pollination (DAP), and in the mature dry seed (M)]. Only residual mRNA activity is present during the first 24 hours after imbibition (HAI), i.e., during germination, and none thereafter. Premature desiccation of the seeds at 35 DAP results in some *Lea* protein mRNA being present in the dry seed (0HAI, prematurely dried/rehydrated), which is rapidly degraded soon after the start of imbibition (5HAI and later). (Unpublished data of D. W. Hughes, G. A. Galau, A. R. Kermode and J. D. Bewley.)

142). An obvious expectation, therefore, is increased expression of many different genes whose products provide for the higher steady-state metabolic rate achieved during this period. Some of the biochemical events might be unique to this period, whereas the majority would be expected to be associated with normal "growth-maintenance."

Undoubtedly there are genes coding for proteins and metabolic processes that control activation of the genes whose products provide for the higher steady-state metabolic rate. In addition, there are probably a number of genes that code for proteins involved in the more subtle developmental aspects of germination and seedling establishment. Identification of these "growth-regulatory" genes would be a major contribution to the molecular analysis of this stage of plant growth. The expression of these genes must be defined both temporally and spatially, i.e., in which organs and cell types the increased expression occurs.

Seedling establishment requires the mobilization of stored reserves, involving such supporting tissues as the cotyledons and endosperm in dicotyledonous seeds and the aleurone layer and endosperm in seeds of monocots. These tissues will undergo increases in expression of growth-maintenance genes, but there will be major activation of growth-regulatory genes in accord with the role of the tissues in supporting germination and growth, e.g., the postgerminative production of hydrolytic enzymes by storage tissues.

An early event upon rehydration of seed tissues is an increase in protein synthesis and the appearance of cellular organelles. The first consequence of imbibition may be an increase in ATP (*143–145*) to an appropriate threshold amount allowing these basic metabolic processes to commence. Axis germination would then proceed through an initial phase during which substrates and enzymes already present in the dry seed provide the necessary biochemical activity, to a final phase in which the primary interactants are mobilized substrates and proteins synthesized on newly transcribed mRNAs. Preformed mRNAs are present in the dry seed (*146*) and several have been identified by the proteins for which they code. With the possible exception of isocitritase (isocitrate lyase, EC 4.1.3.1) and malate synthase (EC 4.1.3.2), (*147, 148*), all of the preformed mRNAs and their cognate proteins thus far defined (*135, 149–158*) decay rapidly during the first few hours after the start of imbibition, thus behaving essentially as the *Lea* proteins (see Section II,F,2) (*159*). It remains to be ascertained whether there are preformed mRNAs that survive into the stage of seedling establishment, and if so, what role they play. Preformed mRNAs of the growth-maintenance type are expected to be transcribed anew during early germination. The only obvious approach to their identification, therefore, is either through the use of conditional mutants or by tag to distinguish the newly transcribed mRNAs. An example of the latter approach would be to allow newly synthesized mRNAs to incorporate thiouridine, thereby facilitating the separation of the newly synthesized and the preformed mRNAs (*160–162*). Specific probes could then be used to quantitate the levels of specific mRNAs in the two populations, such probes being selected on the basis of their presence in both the dry seed and the germinating seed.

B. Newly Transcribed mRNAs

1. AMYLASES AND PROTEASES DURING SEEDLING GROWTH

A major consideration in studying processes related to early seedling establishment is that they should be of sufficient magnitude to allow biochemical analysis. The accumulation of amylases and proteases that brings about the rapid breakdown of the abundant storage components in the cereal endosperm is an example. Analyses of their control have focused directly on one hormone, gibberellic acid (GA), and have indirectly drawn attention to another hormone, ABA (see also Section II,F,2).

After germination of both wheat and barley, the cells of the aleurone layer (the secretory cells that surround the nonliving starchy endosperm; Fig. 2) synthesize several hydrolytic enzymes, the most prominent being α-

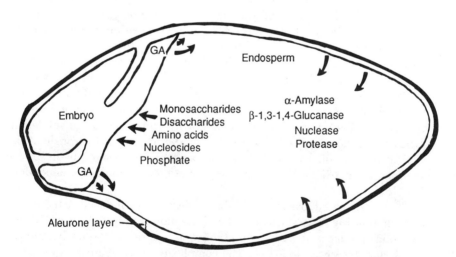

FIG. 2. The germinated barley seed. Shortly after germination, gibberellic acid, released from the embryo, diffuses to the aleurone layer, directing the cells to synthesize and secrete hydrolases. The endosperm reserves are degraded by the hydrolases to produce sugars, amino acid, and nucleosides that are absorbed by the embryo and used to sustain heterotrophic growth. (From *182*, with permission.)

amylase (163, 164). In barley aleurone layer cells, α-amylase is present as two sets of isozymes (type A, low PI; type B, high pI) (165, 166) and cDNA clones corresponding to each have been isolated (166, 167). Type A α-amylase mRNA preexists in the aleurone layer of the unimbibed seed and increases about 20-fold following germination, whereas type B mRNA is present only minimally in the aleurone layer of the dry seed and increases 100-fold after germination (166). Similar data have been obtained from wheat seeds, i.e., the mRNA for the low-pI-amylase isozyme is present in the ungerminated seed and both isozymes increase in the young seedling. The site of accumulation of the mRNAs in wheat, however, appears to be the embryo rather than the aleurone layer (168).

Activation of the aleurone layer cells in barley to produce α-amylase results from the synthesis of GA in the embryo and its release into the endosperm (169–171). After entering the aleurone layer cells, the hormone brings about an accumulation of α-amylase mRNA primarily as a consequence of an increased rate of transcription (1, 172 and references therein), although there are indications of additional translational control (173). An antisense RNA to the α-amylase mRNA is present in barley aleurone layer cells (174); up- or down-regulation of its expression by ABA or GA, respectively, could result in lower and higher amounts of the enzyme being produced.

A number of other hydrolytic activities are induced in the barley aleurone by GA, including nucleases (176), β-glucanases (175), and proteases (177). Two GA-induced cysteine proteases have been characterized at the molecular level. The amino-acid sequence of one of these, aleurain (similar to cathepsin H, EC 3.4.22.16), has been determined via a cDNA clone (178) while the second, a 37-kDa endoprotease (EP-A), exhibits some homologies to papain (EC 3.4.22.2) at the amino terminus (179). In Brassica napus seeds, an mRNA for a similar cysteine protease accumulates after germination. This mRNA was localized by in situ hybridization in the cotyledon, primarily in the vascular tissue and the epidermis, but not throughout the storage parenchymal cells (180). A carboxypeptidase occurs in the barley aleurone layer (181), with its secretion, but not its accumulation, dependent GA (182).

The germinated barley seed, showing some GA-induced activities, is illustrated in Fig. 2. A discussion of enzyme induction by GA, as well as the antagonistic effects of ABA, is presented in a series of essays by Brown, Brodl, and Trewavas (182–184). The complexity of the regulation by GA is indicated in a recent study showing fluctuations in the amount of several mRNAs in response to varying doses of hormone (2). Clearly, this area of research should profit significantly from detailed molecular analyses.

2. THE GROWING AXIS

As noted earlier, studies of genes expressed in the germinating and growing axis have been limited. The rapid growth of the seedling during its early establishment is accompanied by substantial augmentation of many growth-related enzyme activities. Because growth continues throughout the life of the vegetative plant, control of the expression of the genes coding for growth-maintenance enzymes may not be unique to this early stage of establishment. Even if one could select genes that are uniquely expressed at the onset of seedling growth, a further difficulty is to define the functions of the proteins for which they code. Notwithstanding these considerations, a number of studies have identified genes that are expressed in the seedling axis during early growth, and approaches are available to select genes whose expression is unique to seedling growth (growth-regulatory). Sequence analogy may provide clues to the functions of the encoded proteins. Recent studies of gene-specific expression (185) lead to the further possibility that, even with the growth-maintenance genes, specific genes within a family will be selectively expressed only at the early seedling stage.

The first report of a defined mRNA whose expression increases in the axis of the young seedling described a gene coding for a shoot-specific polypeptide (mRNA of 850 nucleotides) that accumulates in 2-day-old pea seedlings (186). From cDNA analysis, the protein contains a sequence of 26 amino acids reiterated four times, a putative signal peptide, and three N-glycosylation sites. The absence of the mRNA from the plumule and the leaf, as well as the lack of an effect of illumination on its accumulation, indicates that the protein is not related to the photosynthetic system. Rather, it seems to be involved with the elongation of the seedling stem.

A number of undefined mRNAs are expressed in soybean (187), pea (188), and *Brassica napus* (189) during seedling establishment. The temporal patterns of accumulation of these mRNAs in the germinated seed differ from each other, suggesting a developmental control of their expression. A similar suggestion follows from the finding that different mRNAs are localized within different regions of the axis. This result has been obtained both by direct analyses of isolated mRNAs (187) and by *in situ* localization with hybridizing mRNA-specific probes (180, 190).

There is a protein that is synthesized in wheat embryonic axes only after the onset of seedling growth (191). This 125-kDa homopentameric protein, called germin (192), has been isolated from germinated wheat embryos in milligram amounts, taking advantage of its indifference to pepsin (193). It contains much (11%) aspartic acid and glycine, and 25% hydrophobic amino acids. Incorporation of radioactive glucosamine, mannose, and fucose identify germin as a glycoprotein, and a shift in gel mobility upon deglycosylation with trifluoromethanesulfonic acid indicates a carbohydrate content of 10% (193). The protein is synthesized in the stem and the root of wheat seedlings and to a lesser extent in the leaves (194). Recently, a full-length germin cDNA clone has been isolated and sequenced, providing both the linear amino-acid sequence of the protein and evidence for a signal peptide and two glycosylation sites (195, 196). This sequence, as well as evidence suggesting that the protein may occur near the cell surface, has been interpreted to suggest that germin may function in sugar uptake, cell wall synthesis, or membrane repair (192, 196).

Another defined mRNA, whose expression increases early in axis growth, occurs in the soybean seedling. The mRNA is novel in that it codes for a protein abundant in proline and hydroxyproline. Figure 3 presents the nucleotide sequence of mRNA 1A10-2 in comparison with a similar but not identical (79% homology) sequence of mRNA SbPRP1 obtained from an auxin-treated soybean cell culture (197). The proteins coded by the mRNAs contain a repeat of the basic pentamer Pro-Pro-Val-Tyr-Lys. In SbPRP1, there is an occasional replacement of tyrosine by glutamate, while in 1A10-2, there is an alternation of tyrosine and glutamate in the fourth position of each

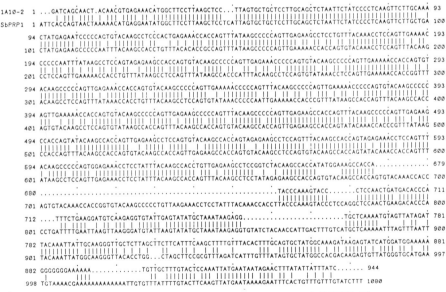

FIG. 3. Nucleotide sequence comparison of cDNAs 1A10-2 and SbPRP1. The sequences are aligned to give the best fit (K. Datta, A. Schmidt and A. Marcus, unpublished data) and have a similarity of 79%.

succeeding repeat, generating the decamer Pro-Pro-Val-Tyr-Lys-Pro-Pro-Val-Glu-Lys (Fig. 4). Since plant cell walls are rich in hydroxyproline (198), it seems reasonable to conclude that these mRNAs are coding for cell wall proteins, a conclusion supported by the recent isolation of a wall protein from soybean cells in culture that has a similar amino-acid composition (199). More recently, a second protein (28 kDa) that also corresponds in amino-acid content to the 1A10-2 cDNA sequence has been resolved from the walls of cultured soybean cells (Table I).

The gene for phytochrome also increases in expression in germinated pea axes (200, 201). The amount of phytochrome mRNA, and that of the mRNA for glutamine synthetase (glutamate-ammonia lyase EC 6.3.1.2) (clone 2A2; 187), peaks shortly after the onset of increased embryo fresh weight, suggesting that these mRNAs can be regarded as functioning primarily in the maintenance of steady-state growth (growth-maintenance). Glutamine synthetase mRNA is also abundant in soybean seedling root tips (where the predominant activity is cell division and early elongation) and in a rapidly growing soybean cell culture (where little or no differentiation occurs), a conclusion again consistent with the idea that this mRNA is predominantly involved in

```
SbPRP-1....MetArgAsnMetAla SerLeuSerSerSer LeuValLeuLeuLeu AlaAlaLeuIleLeu
1A10-2.....       Met -      -   -   -   -   -   -   -   -   -   -   -   -   -   -
SbPRP-1....SerProGlnValLeu AlaAspTyrGluLys ProProIleTyrLys ProProValTyrThr
1A10-2..... -   -   -   -   -   - Asn -   - Asn  -   - Val  -   -   -   - ThrGluLys
SbPRP-1....ProProValTyrLys ProProValGluLys ProProValTyrLys ProProValTyrLys
1A10-2..... -   -   -   -   -   -   -   -   -   -   -   -   -   -   - GluAsn
SbPRP-1....ProProValGluLys ProProValTyrLys ProProValTyrLys ProProIleTyrLys
1A10-2..... -   - IleTyr -   -   -   - Glu -   -   -   -   -   -   - ValGlu -
SbPRP-1....ProProValTyrLys ProProValGluLys ProProValTyrLys ProProValTyrLys
1A10-2..... -   -   -   -   -   -   -   -   -   -   -   -   -   - Glu -
SbPRP-1....ProProValTyrLys ProProValTyrLys ProProIleGluLys ProProValTyrLys
1A10-2..... -   -   -   -   -   -   - Glu -   -   - ValTyr -   -   -   - Glu -
SbPRP-1....ProProValTyrLys ProProValTyrLys ProProValTyrLys ProProValTyrLys
1A10-2..... -   -   -   -   -   -   - Glu -   -   -   -   -   -   - Glu -
SbPRP-1....ProProValTyrLys ProProValGluLys ProProValTyrLys ProProValTyrLys
1A10-2..... -   -   -   -   -   -   -   -   -   -   -   -   -   - Glu -
SbPRP-1.... ProProValTyrLys ProProValTyrLys ProProValGluLys ProProValTyrLys
1A10-2..... -   -   -   -   -   -   - Glu -   -   - Tyr -   -   -   - Glu -
SbPRP-1....ProProValTyrLys ProProValTyrLys ProProValTyrLys ProProValGluLys
1A10-2..... -   -   -   -   -   -   - Glu -   -   -   -   -   -   -   -
SbPRP-1....ProProIleTyrLys ProProValTyrLys ProProIleGluLys ProProValTyrLys
1A10-2..... -   -   -   -   -   -   - Glu -   -   - ValTyr -
SbPRP-1....ProProValTyrLys ProProValTyrLys ProProValTyrLys ProProValLysLys
1A10-2.....
SbPRP-1....ProProIleTyrLys ProProTyrProLys TyrProProGlySer Asn
1A10-2..... -   - TyrGly -   -   -   -   -   -   -   - ThrAsp AspThrHisPhe
```

FIG. 4. The predicted amino acid sequences encoded by mRNAs 1A10-2 and SbPRP1. The sequences are aligned to give the maximal amino-acid match (K. Datta, A. Schmidt and A. Marcus, unpublished data).

TABLE I

AMINO-ACID COMPOSITION OF SOYBEAN PROTEINS RICH
IN REPEATED PROLINES

	Extensin (mol %)	33 kDa (mol %)	28 kDa (mol %)	1A10-2 cDNA[a] (mol %)
Asp	—	1.2	1.2	2.5
Glu	—	8.9	9.8	9.1
Pro	15.6	21.5	21.6	38.9
Hyp	32.5	20.0	20.3	—
Tyr	10.8	11.5	8.1	11.1
Val	4.9	17.3	15.8	16.4
Ile	—	1.1	3.1	1.0
Leu	—	—	1.1	—
Lys	11.9	17.3	17.1	18.3
Thr	1.1	0.4	0.8	1.4
Ser	9.1	—	—	—
His	10.6	—	—	0.5

[a] 1A10-2 cDNA is composed of 208 amino acids (23.8 kDa).

growth-maintenance. In contrast, two soybean seedling mRNAs have been identified (clones 4D7 and 2E2; 187) that are not expressed in seedling root tips, nor in growing cells in culture, and thus are presumably involved in more subtle aspects of seedling development. Of particular interest is the mRNA for 2E2, in that it accumulates maximally in soybean seedling axes only at 31 hours after the onset of germination. Figure 5 presents the nucleotide sequence of this mRNA and the predicted amino-acid sequence. There is a probable signal sequence (cleaving between residues 19 and 20) and two glycosylation signals (residues 223 and 259). Possibly the 2E2 gene product is a protein that is secreted either into the cell wall or into the intercellular spaces.

C. Concluding Remarks

Research into the control of expression of specific genes during seed development is quite advanced, especially those for storage proteins. At the same time, relatively few such studies have been carried out with genes that are expressed during germination and early seedling establishment. Ultimately, it will be necessary to define both the cis-regulatory elements in their genome and the protein factors that function to activate them.

With regard to the genes of the growing axis, we have distinguished between "growth-regulatory" and "growth-maintenance," the latter referring primarily to those genes whose products maintain the metabolic activity common to most vegetative cells. First considerations suggest that only the

```
1                                                    ACAAATCTTTCGCTAACACTCATTAATTGCAAGA    34

35  ATG GCA CTT CGT TGC TTG GTG ATG TCC CTT TCT GTT CTC TTC ACT CTT GGT CTT GCG AGA GAA AGC CAT GCC AGA    109
1   Met Ala Leu Arg Cys Leu Val Met Ser Leu Ser Val Leu Phe Thr Leu Gly Leu Ala Arg Glu Ser His Ala Arg    25

110 GAC GAA GAT TTT TGG CAT GCT GTT TGG CCA AAC ACT CCC ATT CCA AGT TCA TTG CGA GAT CTT CTA AAG CCT GGC    184
26  Asp Glu Asp Phe Trp His Ala Val Trp Pro Asn Thr Pro Ile Pro Ser Ser Leu Arg Asp Leu Leu Lys Pro Gly    50

185 CCT GCA AGT GTT GAA ATC GAT GAT CAC CCT ATG CAA ATT GAA GAA ACA CAG TAC CCG AAA ACC TTC TTC TAT AAA    259
51  Pro Ala Ser Val Glu Ile Asp Asp His Pro Met Gln Ile Glu Glu Thr Gln Tyr Pro Lys Thr Phe Phe Tyr Lys    75

260 GAA GAC CTT CAT CCA GGC AAA ACA ATG AAA GTA CAA TTC AGC AAG CCT CCC TTT CAA CAA CCA TGG GGT GTT GGT    334
76  Glu Asp Leu His Pro Gly Lys Thr Met Lys Val Gln Phe Ser Lys Pro Pro Phe Gln Gln Pro Trp Gly Val Gly    100

335 ACA TGG TTA AAG GAA ATT AAA GAC ACT ACT AAA GAA GGA TAT AGT TTT GAA GAG CTA TGC ATC AAG AAA GAA GCC    409
101 Thr Trp Leu Lys Glu Ile Lys Asp Thr Thr Lys Glu Gly Tyr Ser Phe Glu Glu Leu Cys Ile Lys Lys Glu Ala    125

410 ATT GAG GGA GAA GAG AAG TTT TGT GCA AAA TCC TTG GGA ACA GTA ATT GGT TTT GCC ATT TCA AAG CTG GGA AAG    484
126 Ile Glu Gly Glu Glu Lys Phe Cys Ala Lys Ser Leu Gly Thr Val Ile Gly Phe Ala Ile Ser Lys Leu Gly Lys    150

485 AAC ATT CAA GTA CTT TCA AGT TCC TTT GTC AAT AAG CAA GAC CAA TAC ACT GTG GAA GGA GTG CAG AAT CTT GGA    559
151 Asn Ile Gln Val Leu Ser Ser Ser Phe Val Asn Lys Gln Asp Gln Tyr Thr Val Glu Gly Val Gln Asn Leu Gly    175

560 GAC AAA GCA GTG ATG TGT CAT AGG CTA AAT TTC AGA ACT GCA GTA TTT TAC TGC CAT GAA GTC CGT GAA ACA ACA    634
176 Asp Lys Ala Val Met Cys His Arg Leu Asn Phe Arg Thr Ala Val Phe Tyr Cys His Glu Val Arg Glu Thr Thr    200

635 GCT TTC ATG GTT CCA TTG GTG GCT GGT GAT GGA ACC AAA ACT CAG GCA CTT GCT ATT TGC CAC TCA AAT ACT TCT    709
201 Ala Phe Met Val Pro Leu Val Ala Gly Asp Gly Thr Lys Thr Gln Ala Leu Ala Ile Cys His Ser Asn Thr Ser    225

710 GGA ATG AAT CAT CAA ATG CTT CAT CAA CTT ATG GGA GTT GAT CCT GGA ACT AAC CCT GTT TGC CAT TTC CTT GGA    784
226 Gly Met Asn His Gln Met Leu His Gln Leu Met Gly Val Asp Pro Gly Thr Asn Pro Val Cys His Phe Leu Gly    250

785 AGC AAG GCC ATT TTA TGG GTA CCC AAT TTA TCT GTG GAC ACT GCC TAT CAG ACC AAC ATT GTT GCT TAA TTA GTC    859
251 Ser Lys Ala Ile Leu Trp Val Pro Asn Leu Ser Val Asp Thr Ala Tyr Gln Thr Asn Ile Val Ala  •          272

854 CATGCATCTTGAGCACCATGAGAATGAGATTGTGTATAAAATAAATTATCATGTGCTGTGTGTTGTGCAAGTACTACCTTCTCTAGCTAGATTGCTAGA    958

959 GCTAGAATTTCAACCTACCTATGTGTACTGATAAGATCTGCTTCCCTACTTAAAGAGAGCATCATCCTGTGATCAGTGTGCTTCGTATTCTCTCTCTCT    1057

1058 ATATATATATGGTAAAAAGTGGTT                                                                              1081
```

FIG. 5. The nucleotide sequence and the predicted amino-acid sequence of cDNA 2E2 (K. Datta, A. Schmidt and A. Marcus, unpublished data).

growth-regulatory genes will be of interest in providing a molecular definition of early seedling growth. However, as mentioned briefly earlier (Section III,B,2), it remains possible, indeed probable, that different growth-maintenance genes within a given gene family will be expressed at different stages of the life cycle of the vegetative plant. Furthermore, it is known that some seeds fail to complete germination because of inherent dormancy. While it is probable that the expression of specific growth-regulatory genes is being suppressed in these seeds, the analysis should be facilitated by identifying the growth-maintenance processes that are affected by dormancy. Consideration of these questions will be possible only with the identification of the full range of genes that are expressed in the early establishment of the seedling.

REFERENCES

1. J. V. Jacobsen and L. R. Beach, *Nature* 316, 275 (1985).
2. R. C. Nolan and T.-H. D. Ho, *Planta* 174, 551 (1988).
3. J. D. Bewley and M. Black, "Seeds. Physiology of Development and Germination." Plenum, New York, 1985.
4. R. B. Goldberg, G. Hoschek, S. H. Tam, G. S. Ditta and R. W. Breidenbach, *Dev. Biol.* 83, 201 (1981).
5. R. B. Goldberg, G. Hoschek, G. S. Ditta and R. W. Breidenbach, *Dev. Biol.* 83, 218 (1981).

188 J. DEREK BEWLEY AND ABRAHAM MARCUS

6. J. E. Hill and R. W. Breidenbach, *Plant Physiol.* **53**, 742 (1974).
7. M. A. Moreira, M. A. Hermodson, B. A. Larkins and N. C. Nielsen, *JBC* **254**, 9921 (1979).
8. V. H. Thanh and K. Shibasaki, *BBA* **490**, 370 (1977).
9. C. Sengupta, V. Deluca, D. S. Bailey and D. P. S. Verma, *Plant Mol. Biol.* 1, 19 (1981).
10. N. E. Tumer, B. H. Thanh and N. C. Nielsen, *JBC* **256**, 8756 (1981).
11. R. N. Beachy, N. P. Jarvis and K. A. Barton, *J. Mol. Appl. Genet.* 1, 19 (1981).
12. J. J. Doyle, M. A. Schuler, W. D. Godette, V. Zenger, R. N. Beachy and J. L. Slightom, *JBC* **261**, 9228 (1986).
13. M. L. Tierney, E. A. Bray, R. D. Allen, Y. Ma, R. F. Drong, J. Slightom and R. N. Beachy, *Planta* **172**, 356 (1987).
14. L. Walling, G. N. Drews and R. B. Goldberg, *PNAS* **83**, 2123 (1986).
15. D. W. Meinke, J. Chen and R. N. Beachy, *Planta* **153**, 130 (1981).
16. R. N. Beachy, Z.-L. Chen, R. B. Horsch, S. G. Rogers, N. J. Hoffman and R. T. Fraley, *EMBO J.* 4, 3047 (1985).
17. B. F. Ladin, M. L. Tierney, D. W. Meinke, P. Hosangadi, M. Veith and R. N. Beachy, *Plant Physiol.* **84**, 35 (1987).
18. D. M. Shuttuck-Eidens and R. N. Beachy, *Plant Physiol.* **78**, 895 (1985).
19. E. A. Bray, S. Naito, N.-S. Pan, E. Anderson, P. Dube and R. N. Beachy, *Planta* **172**, 364 (1987).
20. S. J. Barker, J. J. Harada and R. B. Goldberg, *PNAS* **85**, 458 (1988).
21. S. Naito, P. H. Dube and R. N. Beachy, *Plant Mol. Biol.* **11**, 109 (1988).
22. R. B. Goldberg, *Philos. Trans. R. Soc. London, Ser.* B 314, 343 (1986).
23. Z.-L. Chen, M. A. Schuler and R. N. Beachy, *PNAS* **83**, 8560 (1986).
24. Z.-L. Chen, N.-S. Pan and R. N. Beachy, *EMBO J.* 7, 297 (1988).
25. J. K. Okamuro, K. D. Jofuku and R. B. Goldberg, *PNAS* **83**, 8240 (1986).
26. K. D. Jofuku, J. K. Okamuro and R. B. Goldberg, *Nature* **328**, 734 (1988).
27. R. B. Goldberg, S. J. Barker, L. Perez-Grau, *Cell* **56**, 149 (1989).
28. C. Domoney and R. Casey, *NARes* **13**, 687 (1985).
29. R. R. D. Croy, G. W. Lycett, J. A. Gatehouse, J. N. Yarwood and D. Boulter, *Nature* **295**, 76 (1982).
30. J. A. Gatehouse, I. M. Evans, D. Bown, R. R. D. Croy and D. Boulter, *BJ* **208**, 119 (1982).
31. I. M. Evans, J. A. Gatehouse, R. R. D. Croy and D. Boulter, *Planta* **160**, 559 (1984).
32. R. R. D. Croy, I. M. Evans, J. N. Yarwood, N. Harris, J. A. Gatehouse, A. H. Shirsat, A. Kang, J. R. Ellis, A. Thompson and D. Boulter, *Biochem. Physiol. Pflanz.* 183, 183 (1988).
33. C. Domoney and R. Casey, *Planta* **170**, 562 (1987).
34. G. W. Lycett, R. R. D. Croy, A. H. Shirsat and D. Boulter, *NARes* **12**, 4493 (1984).
35. J. A. Gatehouse, I. M. Evans, R. R. D. Croy and D. Boulter, *Philos. Trans. R. Soc. London, Ser.*, B 314, 367 (1986).
36. H. Baumlein, V. Wobus, J. Pustell and F. C. Kafatos, *NARes* **14**, 2707 (1986).
37. I. M. Evans, J. A. Gatehouse, R. R. D. Croy and D. Boulter, *Planta* **160**, 559 (1984).
38. J. R. Ellis, A. H. Shirsat, A. Hepher, J. N. Yarwood, J. A. Gatehouse, R. R. D. Croy and D. Boulter, *Plant Mol. Biol.* **10**, 203 (1988).
39. A. Shirsat, N. Wilford, R. Croy and D. Boulter, *MGG* **215**, 326 (1989).
40. R. N. Oram, H. Doll and B. Koie, *Hereditas* **80**, 53 (1975).
41. B. G. Forde, M. Kreis, M. S. Williamson, R. P. Fry, J. Pywell, P. R. Shewry, N. Bunce and B. J. Miflin, *EMBO J.* 4, 9 (1985).
42. A. J. Faulks, P. R. Shewry and B. J. Miflin, *Biochem. Genet.* **19**, 841 (1981).
43. M. Kreis, S. Rahman, B. G. Forde, J. Pywell, P. R. Shewry and B. J. Miflin, *MGG* **191**, 194 (1983).

44. S. Rahman, M. Kreis, B. G. Forde, P. R. Shewry and B. J. Miflin, *BJ* **223**, 315 (1984).
45. M. Kreis, P. R. Shewry, B. G. Forde, S. Rahman, M. B. Bahramian and B. J. Miflin, *Biochem. Genet.* **22**, 231 (1984).
46. H. E. Hopp, S. K. Rasmussen and A. Brandt, *Carlsberg Res. Commun.* **48**, 201 (1983).
47. M. Kreis, P. R. Shewry, B. G. Forde, S. Rahman and B. J. Miflin, *Cell* **34**, 161 (1983).
48. B. G. Forde, A. Heyworth, J. Pywell and M. Kreis, *NARes* **13**, 7327 (1985).
49. M. Kreis, M. S. Williamson, J. Forde, D. Schmutz, J. Clark, B. Buxton, J. Pywell, C. Harris, J. Henderson, N. Harris, P. R. Shewry, B. G. Forde and B. J. Miflin, *Philos. Trans. R. Soc. London Ser. B* **314**, 355 (1986).
50. C. Marris, P. Gallois, J. Copley and M. Kreis, *Plant Mol. Biol.* **10**, 359 (1988).
51. S. Borsen, C. Y. Andersen and J. Hejgaard, *Physiol. Plant* **52**, 167 (1981).
52. M. S. Williamson and J. Forde, *Plant Mol. Biol.* **10**, 521 (1988).
53. M. S. Williamson, J. Forde, B. Buxton and M. Kreis, *EJB* **165**, 99 (1987).
54. J. Hejgaard, S. E. Bjorn and G. Nielsen, *Theor. Appl. Genet.* **68**, 127 (1984).
55. E. Gianazza, P. G. Righetti, F. Pioli, E. Galante and C. Soave, *Maydica* **21**, 1 (1976).
56. G. Hagen and I. Rubenstein, *Gene* **13**, 239 (1981).
57. A. Viotti, D. Abildsten, N. Pogna, E. Sala and V. Pirrotta, *EMBO J.* **1**, 53 (1982).
58. B. Burr, F. A. Burr, T. P. St. John, M. Thomas and R. W. Davis, *JMB* **154**, 33 (1982).
59. G. Heidecker and J. Messing, *Annu. Rev. Plant Physiol* **37**, 439 (1986).
60. N.-T. Hu, M. A. Peifer, G. Heidecker, J. Messing and I. Rubenstein, *EMBO J.* **1**, 1337 (1982).
61. K. Pedersen, J. Devereux, D. R. Wilson, E. Sheldon and B. A. Larkins, *Cell* **29**, 1015 (1982).
62. M. D. Marks, J. S. Lindell and B. A. Larkins, *JBC* **260**, 16445 (1985).
63. R. V. Knowles and R. I. Phillips, *PNAS* **82**, 7010 (1985).
64. R. C. Boston, R. Kodrzycki and B. A. Larkins, *In* "Molecular Biology of Seed Storage Proteins and Lectins" (L. M. Shannon and M. J. Chrispeels, eds.), p. 117. Am. Soc. Plant Physiol., Bethesda, Maryland, 1986.
65. G. Galili, E. E. Kawata, L. D. Smith and B. A. Larkins, *JBC* **263**, 5764 (1988).
66. P. Langridge and G. Feix, *Cell* **34**, 1015 (1983).
67. D. L. Rousell, R. S. Boston, P. B. Goldsbrough and B. A. Larkins, *MGG* **211**, 209 (1988).
68. M. Kozak, *NARes* **9**, 5233 (1981).
69. J. S. Brown, U. G. Maier, M. Schwall, L. Schmitz, C. Wandelt and G. Feix, *Biochem. Physiol. Pflanz.* **183**, 99 (1988).
70. P. Langridge, H. Eibel, J. W. S. Brow and G. Feix, *EMBO J.* **3**, 2467 (1984).
71. P. Langridge, J. A. Pintor-Toro and G. Feix, *MGG* **187**, 432 (1982).
72. J. S. Brown, C. Wandelt, G. Feix, G. Neuhaus and H.-G. Schweiger, *Euro. J. Cell Biol.* **42**, 161 (1986).
73. P. Ueng, G. Galili, V. Sapanara, P. B. Goldsbrough, P. Dube, R. N. Beachy and B. A. Larkins, *Plant Physiol.* **86**, 1281 (1988).
74. L. M. Hoffman, D. D. Donaldson, R. Bookland, K. Rashka and E. M. Herman, *EMBO J.* **6**, 3213 (1987).
75. J. C. Kridl, J. Vieira, I. Rubenstein and J. Messing, *Gene* **28**, 113 (1984).
76. U.-G. Maier, J. W. S. Brown, L. M. Schmitz, M. Schwall, G. Dietrich and G. Feix, *MGG* **212**, 241 (1988).
77. U.-G. Maier, J. W. S. Brown, C. Toloczyki and G. Feix, *EMBO J.* **6**, 17 (1987).
78. W. Werr, W.-B. Frommer, C. Maas and P. Starlinger, *EMBO J.* **4**, 1373 (1985).
79. J. M. Chandlee and J. G. Scandalios, *Adv. Genet.* **24**, 73 (1987).
80. C. Soave and F. Salamini, *Dev. Genet.* **5**, 1 (1984).
81. N. DiFonzo, L. Manzocchi, F. Salamini and C. Soave, *Planta* **167**, 587 (1986).

82. C. Soave, L. Tardani, N. DiFonzo and F. Salamini, *Cell* 27, 403 (1981).
83. E. Galante, A. Vitale, L. A. Manzocchi, C. Soave and F. Salamini, *MGG* 192, 316 (1983).
84. J. A. Rafalski, K. Scheets, M. Metzler, D. M. Peterson, C. Hedgcoth and D. G. Soll, *EMBO J.* 3, 1409 (1984).
85. G. Walburg and B. A. Larkins, *Plant Mol. Biol.* 6, 161 (1986).
86. S. Fabijanski, S.-C. Chang, S. Dukiandjiev, M. B. Bahramian, P. Ferrara and I. Altosaar, *Biochem. Physiol. Pflanz.* 183, 143 (1988).
87. M. A. Shotwell, C. Afonso, E. Davies, R. S. Chesnut and B. A. Larkins, *Plant Physiol.* 87, 698 (1988).
88. H. Baumlein, U. Wobus, I. Pustell and F. C. Kafatos, *NARes* 14, 2707 (1986).
89. H. Baumlein, A. J. Miller, J. Schiemann, D. Helbing, R. Manteuffel and U. Wobus, *Biol. Zentralbl.* 106, 569 (1987).
90. W. Weschke, R. Bassumer, N. V. Hai, A. Czihal, H. Baumlein and U. Wobus, *Biochem. Physiol. Pflanz.* 183, 233 (1988).
91. C. A. Chlan, J. B. Pyle, A. B. Legocki and L. Dure III, *Plant Mol. Biol.* 7, 475 (1986).
92. A. E. Simon, K. M. Tenbarge, S. R. Scofield, R. R. Finkelstein and M. L. Crouch, *Plant Mol. Biol.* 5, 191 (1985).
93. S. E. Radke, B. M. Andrews, M. M. Moloney, M. L. Crouch, J. C. Kridl and V. C. Knauf, *Theor. Appl. Genet.* 75, 685 (1988).
94. R. D. Allen, E. A. Cohen, R. A. Vonder Haar, C. A. Adams, D. P. Ma, C. L. Nessler and T. L. Thomas, *MGG*, 210, 211 (1987).
95. S. B. Altenbach, K. W. Pearson, F. W. Leung and S. S. M. Sun, *Plant Mol. Biol.* 8,239 (1987).
96. C. Sengupta-Gopalan, N. A. Reichert, R. F. Barker, T. C. Hall and J. D. Kemp, *PNAS* 82, 3320 (1985).
97. N. Murai, D. W. Sutton, M. G. Murray, J. L. Slightom, D. J. Merlo, N. A. Reichert, C. Sengupta-Gopalan, C. A. Stock, R. F. Barker, J. D. Kemp and T.C. Hall, *Science* 222, 476 (1983).
98. J. H. Cramer, K. Lea and J. L. Slightom, *PNAS* 82, 334, (1985).
99. R. Bassumer, A. Huth, R. Manteuffel and T. A. Rapoport, *EJB* 133, 321 (1983).
100. M. M. Bustos, V. A. Luckow, L. R. Griffing, M. D. Summers and T. C. Hall, *Plant Mol. Biol.* 10, 475 (1988).
101. E. M. Herman, L. M. Shannon and M. J. Chrispeels *in* "Molecular Biology of Seed Storage Proteins and Lectins" (L. M. Shanon and M. J. Chrispeels, ed.), p. 163. Am. Soc. Plant Physiol., Bethesda, Maryland, 1986.
102. J. S. Greenwood and M. J. Chrispeels, *Plant Physiol.* 79, 65 (1985).
103. T. A. Voelker, E. M. Herman and M. J. Chrispeels, *Plant Cell* 1, 95 (1988).
104. B. W. Tague and M. J. Chrispeels, *J. Cell Biol.* 105, 1971 (1987).
105. P. J. Randall, J. A. Thomson and H. E. Schroeder, *Aust. J. Plant Physiol.* 6, 11, (1979).
106. P. R. Shewry, J. Franklin, S. Parmar, S. J. Smith and B. J. Miflin, *J. Cereal Sci.* 1, 21 (1983).
107. C. W. Wrigley, D. L. du Cros, M. J. Archer, P. G. Downie and C. M. Roxburgh, *Aust. J. Plant Physiol.* 7, 755 (1980).
108. J. H. Skerritt, P. Y. Lew and S. L. Castle, *J. Exp. Bot.* 39, 723 (1988).
109. P. M. Chandler, T. J. V. Higgins, P. J. Randall and D. Spencer, *Plant Physiol.* 71, 47 (1983).
110. P. M. Chandler, D. Spencer, P. J. Randall and T. J. V. Higgins, *Plant Physiol.* 75, 651 (1984).
111. L. R. Beach, D. Spencer, P. J. Randall and T. J. V. Higgins, *NARes* 13, 99 (1985).

112. T. J. V. Higgins, P. M. Chandler, P. J. Randall, D. Spencer, L. R. Beach, R. J. Blagrove, A. A. Kortt and A. S. Inglis, *JBC* **261**, 11124 (1986).
113. L. P. Holowach, J. F. Thompson and J. T. Madison, *Plant Physiol.* **74**, 584 (1984).
114. G. L. Creason, L. P. Holowach, J. F. Thompson and J. T. Madison, *BBRC* **117**, 658 (1983).
115. L. P. Holowach, J. T. Madison and J. F. Thompson, *Plant Physiol.* **80**, 561 (1986).
116. S. Rahman, P. R. Shewry, B. G. Forde, M. Kreis and B. J. Miflin, *Planta* **159**, 366 (1983).
117. H. Giese and H. E. Hopp, *Carlsberg Res. Commun.* **49**, 365 (1984).
118. A. R. Kermode, M. Y. Oishi and J. D. Bewley, *Spec. Publ.—Crop Sci. Soc. Am.* **14**, 23 (1989).
119. R. S. Quatrano, *Oxford Surv. Plant Mol. Biol.* **3**, 467 (1986).
120. E. A. Bray and R. N. Beachy, *Plant Physiol.* **79**, 746 (1985).
121. A. J. Eisenberg and J. P. Mascarenhas, *Planta* **166**, 505 (1985).
122. R. R. Finkelstein, K. M. Tenbarge, J. E. Shumway and M. L. Crouch, *Plant Physiol.* **78**, 630 (1985).
123. S. R. Long, R. M. K. Dale and I. M. Sussex, *Planta* **153**, 405 (1981).
124. B. A. Triplett and R. S. Quatrano, *Dev. Biol.* **91**, 491 (1982).
125. J. D. Williamson, R.S. Quatrano and A. C. Cuming, *EJB* **152**, 501 (1985).
126. J. S. Choinski Jr., R. N. Trelease and D. C. Doman, *Planta* **152**, 428 (1981).
127. G. A. Galau, D.W. Hughes and L. Dure III, *Plant Mol. Biol.* **7**, 155 (1986).
128. J. Gomez, D. Sanchez-Martinez, V. Stiefel, J. Rigau, P. Puigdomenech and M. Pages, *Nature* **334**, 262 (1988).
129. E. Mortenson and G. Dreyfuss, *Nature* **337**, 312 (1989).
130. W. R. Marcotte, Jr., C. C. Bayley and R. S. Quatrano, *Nature* **335**, 454 (1988).
131. R. R. Finkelstein and M. L. Crouch, *Plant Physiol.* **81**, 907 (1986).
132. G. A. Galau, N. Bijaisoradat and D.W. Hughes, *Dev. Biol.* **123**, 198 (1987).
133. A. R. Kermode and J. D. Bewley, *J. Exp. Bot.* **36**, 1916 (1985).
134. A. R. Kermode, D. J. Gifford and J. D. Bewley, *J. Exp. Bot.* **36**, 1928 (1985).
135. J. D. Bewley, A.R. Kermode and S. Misra, *Ann. Bot.* **63**, 3 (1989).
136. L. A. Rosenberg and R. W. Rinne, *Plant Physiol.* **87**, 474 (1988).
137. J. Dasgupta and J. D. Bewley, *Plant Physiol.* **70**, 1224 (1982).
138. S. Misra and J. D. Bewley, *Plant Physiol.* **78**, 876 (1985).
139. C. A. Cornford, M. Black, J. M. Chapman and D. C. Baulcombe, *Planta* **169**, 420 (1986).
140. A. R. Kermode, S. K. Pramanik and J. D. Bewley, *J. Exp. Bot.* **40**, 33 (1989).
141. A. Marcus and S. Rodaway, in "Molecular Biology of Plant Development" (H. Smith, ed.), p. 337. Univ. of California Press, Berkeley, 1982.
142. J. D. Bewley and M. Black, "Physiology and Biochemistry of Seeds in Relation to Germination," Vol. 1. Springer-Verlag, Berlin and New York, 1978.
143. A. Pradet, A. Narayanan and J. Vermeersch, *Bull. Soc. Fr. Physiol Veg.* **14**, 107 (1968).
144. R. L. Obendorf and A. Marcus, *Plant Physiol.* **53**, 779 (1974).
145. D. E. Moreland, G. G. Hussey, C. R. Shriner and F. S. Farmer, *Plant Physiol.* **54**, 560 (1974).
146. P. I. Payne, *Biol. Rev.* **51**, 329 (1976).
147. E. M. Weir, H. Reizman, J. M. Grienenberger, W. M. Becker and C. J. Leaver, *EJB* **112**, 469 (1980).
148. S. S. Smith and C. J. Leaver, *Plant Physiol.* **81**, 762 (1986).
149. B. G. Lane and E. W. Thompson, *JBC* **255**, 5965 (1980).
150. A. R. Carlier, A. Manickam and W. J. Peumans, *Planta* **149**, 227 (1980).
151. W. J. Peumans, B. M. Delaney, A. Manickam and A. R. Carlier, *Planta* **150**, 286 (1980).
152. W. J. Peumans, H. M. Stinnisen and A. R. Carlier, *Planta* **156**, 41 (1982).

153. Z. F. Grzelczak, M. H. Sattolo, L. K. Hanley-Bowdoin, T. D. Kennedy and B. G. Lane, *Can. J. Biochem.* **60**, 389 (1982).
154. A. C. Cuming, *EJB* **145**, 351 (1984).
155. J. C. Litts, G. W. Colwell, R. L. Chakerin and R. S. Quatrano, *NARes* **15**, 3607 (1987).
156. L. Hanley-Bowdoin and B. G. Lane, *EJB* **135**, 9 (1983).
157. B. G. Lane, R. Kajioka and T. D. Kennedy, *Biochem. Cell Biol.* **65**, 1001 (1987).
158. M. Laroche-Raynal, L. Aspart, M. Delseny and P. Penon, *Plant Sci. Lett.* **35**, 139 (1984).
159. J. Baker, C. Steele and L. Dure III, *Plant Mol. Biol.* **11**, 277 (1988).
160. H. Shibata, H. Ochiai and I. Uchida, *FEBS Lett.* **119**, 85 (1980).
161. G. L. Stetler and J. Thorner, *PNAS* **81**, 1144 (1984).
162. C. L. Cramer, T. B. Ryder, J. N. Bell and C. J. Lamb, *Science* **227**, 1240 (1985).
163. D. T. H. Ho and J. E. Varner, *PNAS* **71**, 4783 (1974).
164. D. C. Baulcombe and D. Buffard, *Planta* **157**, 493 (1983).
165. J. V. Jacobsen and T. J. V. Higgins, *Plant Physiol.* **70**, 1647 (1982).
166. J. C. Rogers, *JBC* **260**, 3731 (1985).
167. C. M. Lazarus, D.C. Baulcombe and R. A. Martienseen, *Plant Mol. Biol.* **5**, 13 (1985).
168. K. Saitoh, S. Mitsui, K. Uchida and K. Ishikawa, *Plant Cell Physiol.* **29**, 1069 (1988).
169. M. J. Chrispeels and J. E. Varner, *Plant Physiol.* **42**, 398 (1967).
170. R. L. Jones, *Planta* **88**, 73 (1969).
171. T. J. V. Higgins, J. V. Jacobsen and J. A. Zwar, *Plant Mol. Biol.* **1**, 191 (1982).
172. J. A. Zwar and R. Hooley, *Plant Physiol.* **80**, 459 (1986).
173. J. Deikman and R. L. Jones, *Plant Physiol.* **80**, 672 (1986).
174. J. C. Rogers, *Plant Mol. Biol.* **11**, 125 (1988).
175. P. H. Brown and T. H. D. Ho, *EJB* **168**, 387 (1987).
176. I. M. Stuart, L. Loi and G. B. Fincher, *Plant Physiol.* **80**, 310 (1986).
177. N. O. Sundblom and J. Mikola, *Physiol. Plant.* **27**, 281 (1972).
178. J. C. Rogers, D. Dean and G. R. Heck, *PNAS* **82**, 6512 (1985).
179. S. Koehler and T. H. D. Ho, *Plant Physiol.* **87**, 95 (1986).
180. R. A. Dietrich, D. J. Maslayar, R. C. Heupel and J. J. Harada, *Plant Cell* **1**, 73 (1989).
181. R. Hammerton and T. H. D. Ho., *Plant Physiol.* **80**, 692 (1986).
182. P. H. Brown and M. R. Brodl, *Bioessays* **8**, 199 (1988).
183. A. J. Trewavas, *Bioessays* **9**, 213 (1988).
184. P. H. Brown and M. R. Brodl, *Bioessays* **9**, 214 (1988).
185. M. Rocha-Sosa, U. Sonnewald, W. Frommer, M. Strattman, J. Schell,; and L. Willmitzer. *EMBO J.* **1**, 23 (1989).
186. S. C. DeVries, W. M. Devos, M. C. Harmsmen and J. G. H. Wessels, *Plant Mol. Biol.* **4**, 95 (1985).
187. K. Datta, H. Parker, V. Averyhart-Fullard, A. Schmidt and A. Marcus, *Planta* **170**, 209 (1987).
188. L. Lalonde and J. D. Bewley, *Planta* **167**, 504 (1986).
189. J. H. Harada, R. A. Dietrich, L. Comai and C. S. Baden, *in* "Temporal and Spatial Regulation of Plant Genes" (D. P. S. Verma and R. Goldberg, eds.), p. 27. Springer-Verlag, Berlin and New York, 1988.
190. J. H. Harada, C. S. Baden and L. Comai, *MGG* **212**, 466 (1988).
191. Z. F. Grzelczak and B. G. Lane, *Can. J. Biochem. Cell Biol.* **61**, 233 (1983).
192. B. G. Lane, *in* "Roots of Modern Biochemistry" (H. Klienkauf, H. Von Dohren and L. Jaenicke, eds.), p. 457. de Gruyter, Berlin, 1988.
193. B. G. Lane, Z. Grzelczak, T. Kennedy, C. Hew and S. Joshi, *Biochem. Cell Biol.* **65**, 354 (1987).

194. Z. F. Grzelczak, S. Rahman, T. D. Kennedy and B. G. Lane, *Can J. Biochem. Cell Biol.* **63**, 1003 (1985).
195. S. Rahman, Z.F. Grzelczak, T. Kennedy and B. G. Lane, *Biochem. Cell Biol.* **66**, 100 (1988).
196. E. Dratewka-Kos, S. Rahman, Z. F. Brzelczak, T. D. Kennedy, R. K. Murray and B. G. Lane, *JBC*, in press (1989).
197. J. C. Hong, R. T. Nagao and J. L. Key, *JBC* **262**, 8367 (1987).
198. G. I. Cassab and J. E. Varner, *Annu. Rev. Plant Physiol.* **39**, 321 (1988).
199. V. Averyhart-Fullard, K. Datta and A. Marcus, *PNAS*, **85**, 1082 (1988).
200. N. Satoh and M. Furuya, *Plant Cell Physiol.* **26**, 511 (1985).
201. K. Konomi, H. Abe and M. Furuya, *Plant Cell Physiol.* **28**, 1443 (1987).

Transcriptional and Translational Regulation of Gene Expression in the General Control of Amino-Acid Biosynthesis in *Saccharomyces cerevisiae*

ALAN G. HINNEBUSCH

Unit on Molecular Genetics of Lower
Eukaryotes
Laboratory of Molecular Genetics
National Institute of Child Health and
Human Development
National Institutes of Health
Bethesda, Maryland 20892

I. General Amino-Acid Control in *Saccharomyces cerevisiae*

The expression of more than 30 genes encoding enzymes in ten different amino-acid biosynthetic pathways is co-regulated in the yeast *Saccharomyces cerevisiae* (Table I). In response to starvation for any one of at least ten amino acids, transcription of these genes is stimulated 2- to 10-fold, the exact amount depending on the gene in question and the particular amino acid that is limiting. The cross-pathway characteristics of this response have led to its designation as "general amino-acid control." As shown in Table I, not every enzyme belonging to a given biosynthetic pathway is subject to this general control. Moreover, the degree of derepression can be greater for certain enzymes in the pathway than for others. For example, those enzymes that catalyze the rate-limiting steps in the pathway generally exhibit the largest derepression ratios (reviewed in *1*). Some pathways appear to have no enzymes whose expression is subject to general amino-acid control, such as the methionine pathway (Table I).

Progress in Nucleic Acid Research
and Molecular Biology, Vol. 38

TABLE I

ENZYMES SUBJECT TO GENERAL AMINO-ACID CONTROL

Pathway	Enzyme	Gene	Derepression observed in response to		References
			Amino-acid starvation	gcd mutation	
Trp	Anthranilate synthase (EC 4.1.3.27)	TRP2	+	+	(4, 22, 118, 119)
	Anthranilate PRib-transferase (EC 2.4.2.18)	TRP4	+	+	(118, 119)
	Indoleglycerol-P synthase (EC 4.1.1.48)	TRP3	+	+	(102, 118, 119)
	Tryptophan synthase (EC 4.2.1.20)	TRP5	+	+	(34, 118)
	PRib-anthranilate isomerase	TRP1	−	−	(15, 118)
Trp⎫ Phe⎬ Tyr⎭	DHAP synthase[a] (4.1.2.15)	ARO3	+	+	(32, 120)
		ARO4	+		
Arg	Argininosuccinate synthase (EC 6.3.4.5)	ARG1	+		(107)
	Acetylglutamate synthase	ARG2	+		(121)
	Acetylglutamate kinase (EC 2.7.2.8)	ARG6	+		(122)
	Acetylglutamyl-P reductase (EC 1.2.1.38)	ARG5	+		(122)
	Acetylornithine aminotransferase (EC 2.6.1.11)	ARG8	+		(119)
		ARG7	+		(121)
	Ornithine carbamoyltransferase (OTCase) (EC 2.1.3.3)	ARG3	+	+	(4, 11, 22, 119, 122, 123)
	Arginosuccinate lyase (EC 4.3.2.1)	ARG4	+		(4, 11, 30, 123)
	Carbamoyl-P synthase (EC 6.3.5.5)	CPA1	+		(5, 124)
		CPA2			(5, 123, 124)
His	ATP PRib-transferase (EC 2.4.2.17)	HIS1	+		(4, 22, 120)
	PRib-AMP cyclohydrolase (EC 3.5.4.19)	HIS4A	+	+	(22, 30, 35, 123, 125)
	Histidinol dehydrogenase (EC 1.1.1.23)	HIS4C	+	+	(22, 30, 35, 119, 123, 125)
	Imidazolegycerol-P dehydratase (EC 4.2.1.19)	HIS3	+	+	(38, 39)
	Histidinol-P aminotransferase (EC 2.6.1.9)	HIS5	+		(46, 119)

	Enzyme	Gene			
Lys	Histidinol-phosphatase (EC 3.1.3.15)	HIS2	+	+	(22, 119)
	Homocitrate synthase (EC 4.1.3.21)	LYS1		+	(6)
	Saccharopine dehydrogenase (EC 1.5.1.7, —.8)	LYS9		+	(4, 6, 126)
	Saccharopine dehydrogenase (EC 1.5.1.9, —.10)	LYS2	+	+	(6, 126)
	2-Aminoadipate reductase (EC 1.2.1.31)	LYS5		+	(6, 22, 126)
	Homoaconitase			+	(126)
	Homoisocitrate dehydrogenase (EC 1.1.1.155)			+	(126)
	Lysyl-tRNA synthetase (EC 6.1.1.6)	KRS1		+	(108)
Ile–Val	Transaminase B (EC 2.6.1.42)		+	+	(4, 8)
	Threonine dehydratase (deaminase) (EC 4.2.1.16)	ILV1	+	+	(8)
	Acetolactate synthase (EC 4.1.3.18)	ILV2		+	b
	Acetohydroxyacid reductoisomerase (EC 1.1.1.86)	ILV5	+	+	(8, 112)
Leu	Isoleucyl-tRNA synthetase (EC 6.1.1.15)	ILS1	+	+	(127)
	α-Isopropylmalate synthase (EC 4.1.3.12)	LEU4		+	(128)
	α-Isopropylmalate isomerase	LEU1		−	(128)
	β-Isopropylmalate dehydrogenase (EC 1.1.1.85)	LEU2		−	(128)
	Transcriptional activator protein	LEU3		+	(129)
Gln	Glutamine synthetase (EC 6.3.1.2)	GLN1		+	(9)
	NAD-Glutamate dehydrogenase (EC 1.4.1.2, —.3)		+	+	(4, 9)
Glu	NADP-Glutamate dehydrogenase (EC 1.4.1.3, —.4)	GDH1		−	(4, 22)
Met	Sulfite reductase (EC 1.8.99.1)	MET10 MET5 MET18 MET19 MET20		−	(22)
Thr	Aspartate kinase (EC 2.7.2.4)	HOM3		−	(130)

[a] Phospho-2-dehydro-3-deoxyheptonate (DHAP) aldolase.
[b] S. C. Falco (personal communication).

197

Enzyme derepression mediated by the general control system is usually produced in the laboratory by treating wild-type cells with inhibitors of amino-acid biosynthesis, such as 3-aminotriazole, a competitive inhibitor of the histidine biosynthetic enzyme encoded by *HIS3*. An alternative method is to culture a strain containing a leaky mutation in an amino-acid biosynthetic gene on minimal medium. The important feature of both approaches is that cells remain capable of growth and division, albeit at reduced rates, under the starvation conditions imposed. Partial derepression can also be achieved by growing cells in minimal medium containing amino-acid imbalances, most notably leucine provided in the absence of isoleucine and valine, or phenylalanine and tyrosine provided in the absence of tryptophan. Derepression occurs in these instances because the amino acids provided in the medium reduce the biosynthesis or utilization of those amino acids that were omitted (2). A mutation in the structural gene for isoleucyl-tRNA synthetase (*ils1-1*) is lethal at 37°C but causes derepression of enzymes subject to the general control when mutant cells are grown at the permissive temperature of 23°C (3). The latter result suggests that uncharged tRNA or the rate of protein synthesis is a more direct signal for enzyme derepression than actual depletion of an amino-acid pool.

Many amino-acid biosynthetic genes are subject to pathway-specific regulatory mechanisms in addition to general amino-acid control. The arginine pathway is a well-studied example of such dual regulation. Addition of arginine to minimal medium results in repression of several arginine biosynthetic enzymes, and this response can dampen the magnitude of general-control-mediated derepression of these enzymes when cells are starved for amino acids other than arginine (4, 5).

General-control-mediated derepression of certain lysine biosynthetic enzymes is also partially overridden by a lysine-specific repression mechanism when lysine is not limiting (6). The same phenomenon may apply to certain leucine biosynthetic enzymes that are subject to leucine-specific repression (reviewed in 7). By contrast, multivalent repression of enzymes in the isoleucine–valine pathway by a mixture of isoleucine, valine, and leucine does not interfere with their derepression by the general control system in response to starvation for other amino acids. In fact, the magnitude of derepression observed in response to tryptophan starvation is greater in the presence of leucine, isoleucine, and valine than in the absence of these supplements (8). Similarly, derepression of glutamine synthetase in response to histidine starvation is only observed under conditions of glutamine-specific repression of this enzyme (9).

There appears to be no amino-acid-specific repression of enzyme expression in the histidine and tryptophan pathways, since addition of these amino acids to minimal medium does not alter the levels of the corresponding enzymes. However, it was recently discovered that expression of the *HIS4* gene is controlled by a second cross-pathway regulatory system involving the *BAS1* and *BAS2* gene products. In addition to being required for normal basal expression of *HIS4*, these two factors are needed for a wild-type level of adenine biosynthesis and, in the case of *BAS2*, for derepression of acid phosphatase under conditions of limiting inorganic phosphate (*10*). The latter regulatory system and the general amino-acid control appear to be additive in their effects on *HIS4* expression.

As would be expected, derepression of enzyme synthesis under the general control system results in 2- to 10-fold increases in the pool sizes of several amino acids, including histidine, lysine, arginine, tyrosine, and phenylalanine. Smaller increases have been observed for the leucine and glutamate pools (*4, 11*). It is not obvious why S. *cerevisiae* responds to limitation for a single amino acid by increasing the size of many different amino-acid pools. Perhaps single amino-acid limitation occurs rarely in nature, so that multiple-pathway derepression is generally a simple and effective response to starvation conditions, with specific repression mechanisms operating to override derepression of those pathways for which no amino-acid limitation exists. Alternatively, it has been suggested that accumulation of certain amino acids in the vacuole under starvation conditions may drive other limiting amino acids from the vacuole into the cytoplasm, where they can be utilized in protein synthesis (*12*).

II. *trans*-Acting Regulatory Factors in General Amino-Acid Control

A. Positive and Negative Effectors of Amino-Acid Biosynthetic Gene Expression

Mutations have been isolated in multiple unlinked genes that impair the regulation of enzymes subject to general amino-acid control. Based on their phenotypes, these mutations fall into two classes. A recessive mutation in any one of nine *GCN** genes (*GCN1–GCN9*) impairs enzyme derepression under conditions of amino-acid starvation. This Gcn⁻ phenotype is illustrated in Table II for several *gcn* mutants using a *HIS4–lacZ* fusion to model *HIS4* expression. Because *gcn* mutations are recessive, their nonderepressible phenotype formally suggests that *GCN* gene products are positive effectors of gene expression. All nine *GCN* genes regulate enzyme synthesis by controlling mRNA abundance (reviewed in *7, 13*). Because of their derepression defect, *gcn* mutants are more sensitive than wild-type strains to

---

* GCN (gcn): General control nonderepressible; GCD (gcd): general control derepressed.

TABLE II
EXPRESSION OF HIS4–lacZ AND GCN4–lacZ FUSIONS UNDER NORMAL
AND AMINO-ACID STARVATION CONDITIONS IN WILD-TYPE
AND GENERAL CONTROL REGULATORY MUTANTS[a]

| | Units of β-galactosidase activity | | | | | |
| | HIS4–lacZ | | GCN4–lacZ | | GCN4(ΔuORFs)–lacZ | |
Strain	R	DR	R	DR	R	DR
Wild-type	280	2000	10	105	550	470
gcn2-1	200	160	2	4	1000	1900
gcn3-102	230	260	5	15	420	630
gcn4-101	100	300	40	120	850	1200
gcd1-101	2000	3000	360	270	1600	1000
gcn2-1 gcd1-101	ND	ND	250	240	1100	940

[a] All three fusion constructs are integrated in single copy at the URA3 locus. GCN4(ΔuORFs)–lacZ differs from the conventional GCN4–lacZ fusion by deletion of about 240 bp in the mRNA leader region containing the four uORFs. R and DR refer, respectively, to repressing conditions (minimal medium) or derepressing conditions (minimal medium supplemented with 10 mM 3-aminotriazole to cause histidine starvation). (Data taken from 1.)

various culture conditions in which amino-acid biosynthesis is inhibited, including: (i) growth in the presence of amino-acid analogues; (ii) growth on minimal medium in strains containing a leaky mutation in a structural gene for a biosynthetic enzyme; (iii) growth in the presence of amino-acid imbalances. The last of these conditions is probably closest to the situation in natural environments where general amino acid control plays an important role in determining the growth rate.

A recessive mutation in any one of twelve GCD* genes (GCD1, GCD2=GCD12, GCD3–GCD11, GCD13) results in elevated expression of enzymes subject to the general control under nonstarvation conditions (reviewed in 7). (See Table II for the effect of gcd1-101 on HIS4 expression.) This Gcd⁻ phenotype formally suggests that GCD gene products are negative regulators of gene expression. As mentioned above, enzyme derepression also occurs in the presence of leaky mutations that interfere with amino-acid biosynthesis or aminoacylation of tRNA; however, these conditions are unlikely to explain the derepressed phenotype of most gcd mutants for the following reasons. First, many gcd mutations derepress enzyme levels even when cells are grown in media containing all necessary amino acids (reviewed in 7). Second, levels of all 20 aminoacylated tRNAs are normal in a gcd1-101 strain (14). Third, the derepressing effect of the ils1-1 tRNA synthetase mutation is reversed by a gcn1 mutation (15), whereas most gcd mutations are not suppressed by inactivation of GCN1 (see Section II,B). These observations suggest that the majority of GCD gene products do not function in amino-acid biosynthesis or tRNA aminoacylation; rather, they appear to play a more direct role in regulating gene expression.

Mutations in GCD1, GCD2, GCD7, and GCD10–GCD13 lead to constitutive derepression of enzymes subject to the general control by elevating the steady-state levels of the mRNAs from which these enzymes are made. Thus, like GCN1–GCN9, these GCD factors control amino-acid biosynthetic gene expression at the transcriptional level (7). By contrast, GCD8 appears to regulate expression of genes for amino-acid biosynthesis posttranscriptionally (16), making it unlikely that this factor functions in general amino-acid control. gcd9 mutations (formerly gcd4; 17) lead to increased mRNA levels for certain amino-acid biosynthetic genes; however, these transcripts still derepress to a normal extent in response to amino-acid starvation in gcd9 mutants. This phenotype suggests that GCD9 might also function in a regulatory system distinct from the general control.

B. A Hierarchy of Regulatory Factors Controls GCN4 Expression

GCN genes were divided into two classes based on their interactions with gcd mutations. All gcn4 gcd double mutants examined thus far have a Gcn⁻ phenotype, being unable to derepress enzymes that are subject to the general control in response to starvation (17–21). This result implies that positive regulation by GCN4 is required for enzyme derepression even in the absence of functional GCD negative regulatory factors. Because the derepression associated with gcd mutations is completely dependent on GCN4 function, it has been suggested that GCD factors act as negative effectors by antagonism or repression of the GCN4 product (Fig. 1). This epistatic relationship was demonstrated for all combinations of gcn4 gcd mutations, with the exception of gcd5 and gcd8. The gcn4 gcd5 double mutation appears to be lethal (21); the gcn4 gcd8 double mutant was not examined.

In contrast to the interaction observed between gcn4 and gcd mutations, the nonderepressible phenotypes associated with gcn1, gcn2, and gcn3 mutations are suppressed by mutations in GCD1, GCD2, GCD3, GCD4, GCD6, GCD7, and GCD10–GCD13 (18–22). These interactions suggest that the products of GCN1, GCN2, and GCN3 function indirectly as positive regulators by antagonism or repression of GCD factors (Fig. 1). Mutations in GCN6–GCN9 suppress the gcd8-201 mutation and thus exhibit the same interaction seen between mutations in GCN4 and gcd mutations (16); however, the epistasis relationships between gcn6–gcn9 mutations and mutations in other GCD genes have not been determined. Therefore, it is unclear whether the products of GCN6–GCN9 function more directly than GCD

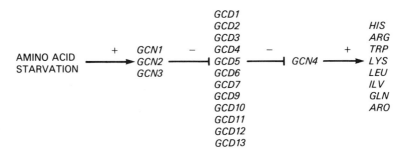

FIG. 1. Hierarchy of regulatory factors involved in general amino-acid control. *GCN1–GCN3* encode positive-acting factors; *GCD1–GCD13*, negative ones. [*GCD2* and *GCD12* were shown recently to be the same gene (94).] *ILV* products are involved in Ile and Val biosynthesis; *ARO* encodes enzymes common to the synthesis of the aromatic amino acids. Arrows marked with plus signs indicate stimulatory interactions; bars marked with minus signs indicate repressing interactions.

factors other than *GCD8*. Moreover, it is possible that the phenotype of *gcd8-201* can be suppressed by any *gcn* mutation.

The genetic observations summarized in Fig. 1 suggest that *GCN4* encodes the most direct positive regulator of structural genes subject to the general control, and that *GCN1*, *GCN2*, and *GCN3* act indirectly as positive effectors by activation or derepression of the *GCN4* gene product (19). This conclusion is supported by several lines of evidence. First, increased *GCN4* gene dosage partially overcomes the requirement for *GCN1*, *GCN2*, and *GCN3* for enzyme derepression (19, 23). Second, expression of β-galactosidase activity from a *GCN4–lacZ* translational fusion is derepressed about 10-fold in response to amino-acid starvation in wild-type cells (24, 25), and this derepression is impaired by *gcn2* and *gcn3* mutations (26) (Table II). The latter results indicate that GCN2 and GCN3 are positive regulators of *GCN4* at the level of gene expression. In addition, *gcd1*, *gcd2*, and *gcd10–gcd13* mutations result in constitutively derepressed expression of *GCN4–lacZ* enzyme activity, showing that the corresponding *GCD* gene products are repressors of *GCN4* expression. As expected, these *gcd* mutations derepress *GCN4–lacZ* expression in *GCN*, *gcn2*, or *gcn3* strains (see Table II for *GCN4–lacZ* expression in the *gcd1-101 gcn2-1* double mutant) (18, 26).

The third line of evidence supporting the model shown in Fig. 1 is the finding that *GCN4* encodes a DNA-binding protein that specifically interacts with regulatory sequences located upstream from structural genes that are subject to the general control (27, 28). This result strongly suggests that the

GCN4 protein acts directly to stimulate transcription of the amino-acid biosynthetic genes that are under its control.

C. The Role of GCN4 in Basal Expression of Amino-Acid Biosynthetic Genes

Mutations in *GCN4* reduce expression significantly from a number of amino-acid biosynthetic genes when cells are cultured in minimal medium containing no amino-acid supplements. Because Saccharomyces can synthesize all of the amino acids, growth in unsupplemented minimal medium is not a starvation condition; consequently, it appears that the GCN4 protein is required for normal basal expression of amino-acid biosynthetic genes, in addition to their derepression in response to starvation. The reduction in *HIS4* basal expression seen in a *gcn4-101* mutant grown on minimal medium is shown in Table II (*1*). Similar reductions in basal expression were reported for *HIS3* (*29*), *ARG4* (*30*), *ARG3* (*31*), and *ARO3* (*32*); however, this phenomenon is not universal, as *ARO4* basal expression is unaffected by a *gcn4* mutation even though its derepression under severe starvation conditions is completely *GCN4*-dependent (*32*).

The reduction in *HIS4* basal expression that occurs in *gcn4* mutants is not great enough to produce histidine auxotrophy unless combined with a mutation in the *BAS1* or *BAS2* genes, encoding positive effectors of *HIS4* basal expression that function independently of *GCN4* (*10*). By contrast, *gcn4* mutations result in weak arginine auxotrophy, and in fact, the first known *gcn4* mutation was designated *arg9* (*19*). *gcn1*, *gcn2*, and *gcn3* mutations do not lower basal expression of amino-acid biosynthetic genes, because these factors are required only for derepression of *GCN4* expression under severe starvation conditions. Presumably, the low level of GCN4 protein that exists in these mutants under nonstarvation conditions is sufficient to support the basal level of expression of amino-acid biosynthetic genes that requires GCN4 function.

Wild-type Saccharomyces may be slightly limited for leucine, isoleucine, or valine when grown on minimal medium, since provision of all three amino acids lowers *HIS4* expression by about 25%. The same degree of repression was observed under identical conditions for the *ILV1* gene. The increased *ILV1* expression that occurs when leucine, isoleucine, and valine are withdrawn from the medium was attributed to GCN4-mediated derepression because it was impaired by a *gcn1* mutation. These observations suggest that part of the reduction in enzyme expression seen in *gcn4* mutants on minimal medium is not the result of a GCN4 requirement for basal expression; rather, it results from impaired GCN4-mediated derepression of amino-acid biosynthetic genes under conditions of slight amino-acid starvation (*8*).

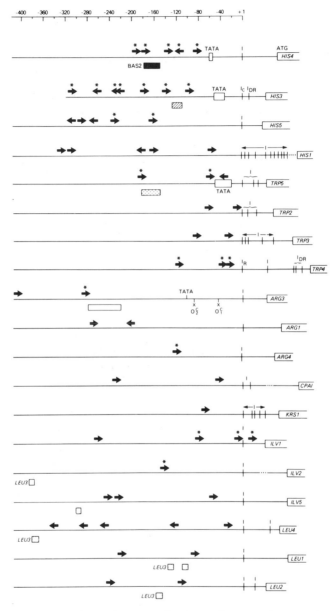

Fig. 2. *cis*-acting regulatory elements in the 5′ noncoding DNA of structural genes subject to general amino-acid control. The involvement of the general control in governing *LEU1* and *LEU2* expression is conjectural (see 7); however, all other genes listed are known to be regulated by GCN4. The scale at the top gives the distance (in base-pairs) from the 5′-proximal transcription initiation sites at each gene. The labeled boxes designate the beginnings of the protein-

III. cis-Acting Regulatory Elements in General Amino-Acid Control

A. GCN4 Binding Sites and Basal Control Elements at Amino-Acid Biosynthetic Genes

The steady-state amounts of mRNAs encoded by genes subject to the general control increase under starvation conditions by an amount sufficient to account for the observed derepression of the corresponding enzyme activities. In the case of *TRP3* and *TRP4*, two genes encoding enzymes in tryptophan biosynthesis, the increase in mRNA levels under starvation conditions takes place without any change in the mRNA half-life, implying that transcription initiation is the sole regulated parameter at these genes (33). This conclusion was demonstrated directly for *TRP5* mRNA by measuring the instantaneous rates of mRNA synthesis under normal and starvation conditions by pulse-labeling cells with radioactive RNA precursors (34). In accord with these results, mutational analyses of 5' noncoding sequences at *HIS4*, *HIS3*, *TRP5*, and *ARO3* show that a short nucleotide sequence of about 12 base-pairs, containing a conserved hexanucleotide core of (5') TGACTC (3'), is both necessary and sufficient for transcriptional activation of these genes in response to amino-acid starvation. As discussed below, this sequence is the binding site for GCN4 protein. In Fig. 2 it can be seen that TGACTC-related sequences (arrows) are present in one or more copies upstream from every structural gene examined thus far whose expression is regulated by GCN4, thus accounting for the co-regulation of these dispersed genes.

---

coding sequences and I's mark the transcription initiation sites. I_C and I_{DR} at *HIS3* designate constitutive and GCN4-derepressible transcription start sites, respectively. TATA boxes are indicated for those genes in which a small sequence interval containing a TATA sequence is required for normal transcription. Arrows symbolize TGACTC sequences; asterisks indicate those for which evidence exists that the sequence is required for normal derepression of gene expression *in vivo*, or the GCN4 protein binds to the sequence *in vitro*. Boxes beneath the lines designate regulatory sequences other than GCN4 binding sites. These include the recognition sequence at *HIS4* for the *BAS2* gene product required for efficient basal expression, the T-rich sequence basal control element at *HIS3*, and undefined basal control sequences at *TRP5* and *ARG3*. The boxes at *ILV2*, *LEU4*, *LEU1*, and *LEU2* are binding sites for the positive regulatory protein LEU3, required for leucine-specific regulation of these genes. Oc's at *ARG3* indicate the positions of *cis*-dominant mutations that impair arginine-specific repression of this gene. *KRS1* encodes lysyl-tRNA synthetase; *CPA1*, the small subunit of carbamoyl-P synthetase. This figure is based on data from the following sources: *HIS4* (10, 23, 28, 35–37, 99), *HIS3* (27–29, 38–40, 48, 100), *HIS5* (46), *HIS1* (19), *TRP5* (34, 44, 45), *TRP2* (101), *TRP3* (101, 102), *TRP4* (32, 33, 103), *ARG3* (31), *ARG1* (107), *ARG4* (27, 104), *CPA1* (105, 106), *KRS1* (108), *ILV1* (28, 109) *ILV2* (28, 110, 111), *ILV5* (112), *LEU4* (111, 113), *LEU1* (111, 114), *LEU2* (111, 115–117).

The importance of the TGACTC repeat was first established by deletion analysis of the *HIS3* and *HIS4* genes. For *HIS4*, deletions of a segment containing the 5′-proximal three copies of the repeat reduced basal expression to very low levels and also impaired *HIS4* derepression in response to starvation. A yeast strain containing this *his4* deletion allele in place of the wild-type gene is auxotrophic for histidine. Prototrophic revertants of the *his4* deletion strain were isolated, and there were two in which derepression of *HIS4* expression by the general control system was restored; both revertants contain point mutations that regenerated a copy of the TGACTC sequence at or near the original deletion junction at position −136. These results suggested that the TGACTC sequence is critical for derepression of *HIS4* expression under starvation conditions (23, 35). The revertant strains also showed partial restoration of *HIS4* basal expression, suggesting that the TGACTC sequence is additionally required for efficient *HIS4* transcription under nonstarvation conditions. However, it was subsequently shown that most of the reduction in *HIS4* basal expression caused by the aforementioned deletions resulted from removal of an additional positive control site located between the second and third copies of the TGACTC repeat (between −180 and −154; Fig. 2). This basal control element is the binding site for the BAS2 protein (*10*).

Small deletions at *HIS4* that remove only the third copy of the TGACTC sequence at position −136 significantly reduce the magnitude of *HIS4* derepression under starvation conditions, but do not completely abolish this response. This fact suggests that the additional copies of the TGACTC sequence at *HIS4* are functional as positive control sites but are insufficient for a wild-type regulatory response in the absence of the −136 repeat (*36*). The same conclusion was reached from experiments in which different segments of the *HIS4* upstream control region were tested for their ability to confer general amino-acid control upon transcription of the *CYC1* gene, which encodes iso-1-cytochrome *c*. When inserted upstream from the *CYC1* "TATA" box, a synthetic fragment of 14 bp (base-pairs) containing the *HIS4* −136 TGACTC sequence was sufficient to confer a 5-fold increase in *CYC1–lacZ* enzyme activity in response to histidine starvation. Two copies of the 14-bp fragment inserted in tandem gave a much greater derepression of *CYC1–lacZ* expression, and in both cases the increased expression was *GCN4*-dependent. By contrast, a 25-bp fragment containing the first and second TGACTC sequences from *HIS4* (located at −192 and −180) gave a much lower derepression than that seen for the −136 doublet (*37*) (Fig. 3). All three repeats contain the TGACTC core; therefore, it appears that nucleotides flanking the core can have an important influence on the efficiency of transcriptional activation mediated by these sequences. Also, a TGACTC element stimulates *CYC1–lacZ* transcription when present in either orienta-

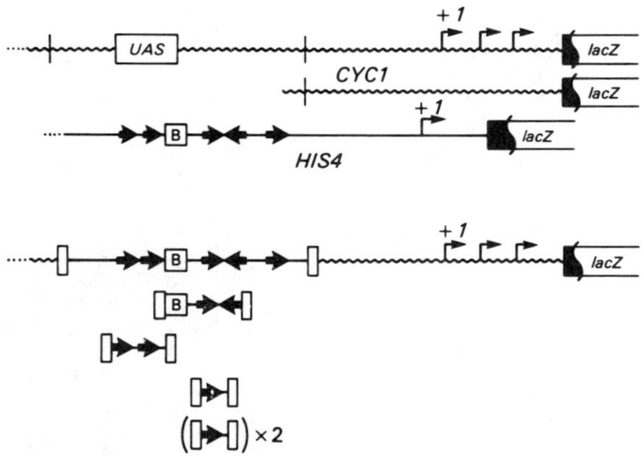

Fusion Enzyme Activity (U)

	wt	
	R	DR
	200	100
	20	10
	1400	2400

	wt		gcn4⁻		gcd1⁻	
	R	DR	R	DR	R	DR
	3300	5900	1400	1500	12,000	9700
	1200	4100	720	870	11,000	8200
	120	400	210	140	300	430
	60	300	70	100	950	1500
	110	2200	35	35	5800	9800

= 5' TCG ACTGACTCACGT TTTT G3'

FIG. 3. GCN4 regulation of HIS4–CYC1 promoter fusions. The 5' noncoding sequences of the various constructs are shown schematically on the left. Thin straight lines represent HIS4 sequences; the wavy lines designate sequences from the CYC1 gene of S. cerevisiae, encoding iso-1-cytochrome c. UAS is the upstream transcriptional activation site identified at CYC1. Arrows mark start sites of transcription. The HIS4 TGACTC sequences are indicated by arrows, as in Fig. 2. The open rectangles represent linker sequences used in making the fusions. The open box labeled "B" designates the BAS2 binding site at HIS4. The first construct is the wild-type CYC1 promoter driving a CYC1–lacZ translational fusion on a high copy-number plasmid. This construct exhibits no derepression when cells are shifted from minimal medium (R) to medium containing 10 mM 3-aminotriazole, an inhibitor of histidine biosynthesis (DR). The second construct is a derivative of the first, lacking the CYC1 UAS; its expression is low and unregulated. The third construct is a HIS4–lacZ fusion on a high copy-number plasmid that shows approximately 2-fold derepression in response to histidine starvation. The remaining constructs contain different segments of HIS4 5' noncoding sequences inserted in place of the UAS-containing fragment in the CYC1–lacZ construct. (The last construct contains two tandem insertions of the sequence shown at the bottom, with the consensus GCN4 binding site boxed.) The HIS4–CYC1 hybrid constructs derepress in wild-type cells in response to starvation, and this derepression is GCN4 dependent. In addition, their expression is constitutively derepressed in gcd1 transformants in which GCN4 expression is expected to be constitutively elevated.

tion, and at variable distances upstream from the *CYC1* mRNA start sites (37).

The requirement for particular nucleotides within and surrounding the TGACTC core for efficient derepression was studied by saturation mutagenesis of the 3′-proximal repeat at *HIS3*. Small deletions of this TGACTC sequence (located at −99) completely abolish *HIS3* derepression, showing that the −99 repeat is absolutely required for positive regulation of *HIS3* expression even in the presence of other TGACTC-related sequences at this gene (29, 38) (Fig. 2). Exploiting this fact, saturation mutagenesis of the −99 repeat was conducted, with the result that 15 out of 18 possible single substitutions in the TGACTC core either severely impair or completely abolish *HIS3* derepression. In addition, certain mutations in nucleotides flanking the core reduced *HIS3* derepression almost as severely as core-sequence substitutions (39) (Fig. 4A). Based on these results, and a compilation of naturally occurring TGACTC sequences, the following consensus was proposed for an efficient positive regulatory site for general amino acid control: (5′) RRTGACTCATTT (3′), where R designates a purine nucleotide.[1] The three positions immediately 3′ to the core sequence appear to be the most important of the flanking nucleotides in determining the extent of derepression conferred by the *HIS3* −99 repeat. In fact, a mutation that alters this sequence from GATGACTCTTTT to GATGACTCATTT was the only alteration that led to greater *HIS3* derepression than that given by the parental wild-type allele (Fig. 4A). This substitution increases the 2-fold rotational symmetry of the −99 repeat, prompting the suggestion that GCN4 protein binds as a dimer to two half-sites of ATGA (39). As discussed in Section IV,A, there is also biochemical evidence that GCN4 binds to DNA as a dimer.

Using the DNase-I-protection assay (footprinting) and GCN4 protein prepared by *in vitro* translation of *GCN4* mRNA, it was shown that GCN4 specifically binds to the *HIS3* −99 repeat, protecting from DNase I digestion the TGACTC sequence and two nucleotides on either side of the core (27). Using a gel electrophoretic-mobility-shift assay for DNA binding and the same preparations of GCN4 protein, a good correlation was established between the ability of mutant derivatives of the *HIS3* −99 repeat to activate transcription *in vivo* and their ability to bind GCN4 protein *in vitro* (39). These results provide strong support for the idea that GCN4 is directly responsible for stimulating *HIS3* transcription under starvation conditions by interacting with the −99 TGACTC sequence.

The binding affinity of GCN4 protein for different naturally occurring copies of the TGACTC repeat at *HIS4*, *HIS3*, *ILV1*, and *ILV2* was also compared using a partially purified preparation of GCN4 protein synthesized

[1] See list of abbreviations in frontmatter of this volume.

A

his3 Allele	Sequence			HIS3 Derepression Ratio
-162	GGA	TGACTC	TTTTTT	5.9
-163	GTA	TGACTC	TTTTTT	5.9
-164	GGG	TGACTC	TTTTTT	4.6
-165	GGA	AGACTC	TTTTTT	1.0
-166	GGA	TTACTC	TTTTTT	1.1
-157	GGA	TGCCTC	TTTGAG	0.8
-190	GGA	TGAGTC	TTTTTT	1.6
-168	GGA	TGACGC	TTTTTT	1.5
-169	GGA	TGACTA	TTTTTT	1.2
-188	GGA	TGACTC	GTTTTT	1.5
-189	GGA	TGACTC	ATTTTT	8.6
-172	GGA	TGACTC	TGTTTT	2.1
-173	GGA	TGACTC	TTATTT	5.0
-186	GGA	TGACTC	TTGTTT	2.1
-Δ83	TTC	TGACTC	TTTTTT	1.0
-145	GGA	TGACTC	TTTGAG	3.8
-161	GGA	TGACTC	GAGCTC	0.9

B

Gene	Position	Sequence			GCN4 Binding Affinity
HIS4	-136	CAG	TGACTC	ACGT	1.00
HIS3	-99	GGA	TGACTC	TTTT	0.75
ILV2	ca. -150	CGA	TGATTC	ATTT	0.50
ILV1	-88	AGA	TGACTC	TTTT	0.40
HIS4	-113	GAA	TGACTG	ATAA	0.30
HIS4	-85	ATA	TGACTA	TGAA	0.15
HIS3	-258	CAG	TGACTC	CTAG	0.12
HIS4	-192	AAC	TGACTC	TAAT	0.08
HIS4	-180	TAG	TGACTC	CGGT	0.08
HIS3	-225	CCC	TGACTA	ATGC	0.07
HIS3	-216	TTA	TGACTT	CCCT	0.07
HIS3	-310	AGA	TGACGA	CTTT	0.05
ILV1	+23	AAT	TGACTT	AGTT	0.04
ILV1	-9	GTG	TGAGTG	CTAC	0.03
HIS3	-181	CTA	TTACTC	TTGG	0.02

FIG. 4. (A) Selected mutant alleles obtained from saturation mutagenesis of the *HIS3* −99 TGACTC sequence element. Base changes from wild-type are underlined. The derepression ratio given for each allele is the ratio of +12 (GCN4-regulated) to +1 (constitutive) *HIS3* transcripts in a constitutively derepressed *gcd1* mutant. (B) Relationship between the binding affinity of GCN4 protein for various TGACTC sequence elements at different genes under the general control and their agreement with the consensus sequence: (5′)-RRTGACTCATTT-(3′), where R is a purine nucleotide. The position of each sequence in the 5′ noncoding DNA is indicated by the location of the 5′-proximal T residue in the TGACTC sequence relative to the start site of transcription at each gene. Deviations from the consensus sequence are underlined. Relative binding affinities were measured by quantitative DNase-I-protection analysis and normalized to the *HIS4* −136 TGACTC sequence, which shows the greatest affinity for GCN4 protein in this assay.

in *Escherichia coli*. DNase-I footprinting analysis was used to measure the extent of DNA binding at different relative concentrations of GCN4. The results of these experiments (Fig. 4B) are in general accord with the conclusions mentioned above regarding the sequence requirements for efficient GCN4 binding to DNA. The poorest binding was seen for copies of the repeat that lack a perfect TGACTC hexanucleotide, consistent with the predominance of the core sequence in determining the degree of *HIS3* derepression. In two out of three cases in which tight binding occurred to a repeat lacking a perfect core, there was only one mismatch with the TGACTC sequence and an A residue immediately following the core. (Recall that introduction of an A residue at this position in the *HIS3* −99 sequence increases *HIS3* transcription.) The binding affinity varied by an order of magnitude among different copies of the repeat that contain a perfect core but that differ in the flanking nucleotides, supporting the idea that the latter make an important contribution to GCN4 binding. Moreover, the sequences in this group with the lowest binding affinity all contain nonconsensus nucleotides at the two positions immediately preceding or following the core sequence (*28*).

Although the −99 repeat at *HIS3* is required for derepression, it is not sufficient for a wild-type regulatory response. Deletion of the first five TGACTC-related sequences at *HIS3*, leaving the 3′-proximal copies at −142 and −99 intact, has no effect on *HIS3* expression. However, additional removal of the −142 repeat TATGCCTCGTGA reduces *HIS3* derepression from 5-fold to 2-fold (*29*). Curiously, the −142 repeat is a poor match to the GCN4 consensus binding site, and no GCN4 binding to this sequence has been detected *in vitro* (*27*, *28*). Based on the latter observation, it has been proposed that a protein other than GCN4 interacts at the −142 sequence and contributes to *HIS3* transcriptional activation when GCN4 is bound at the −99 repeat (*29*). As discussed below, DNA-binding proteins distinct from GCN4 have been detected in Saccharomyces that recognize sequences very similar to the GCN4 binding site. Whether or not such proteins contribute to *HIS3* derepression remains to be determined.

As in the case of *HIS4*, a sequence element completely unrelated to the GCN4 binding site is required for normal *HIS3* basal expression. This sequence, located between −130 and −110 (Fig. 2), is rich in thymine nucleotides and bears no close similarity to the aforementioned BAS2 binding site identified at *HIS4*. Deletion of the poly(dT) element lowers expression to about one-fifth without impairing the magnitude of *HIS3* derepression in response to starvation. Transcription of *PET56* (the product of which functions in respiration), located adjacent to and transcribed divergently from *HIS3*, is also reduced by deletion of the poly(dT) sequence, suggesting that this element functions bidirectionally to stimulate transcription of both genes (*40*). Similar sequences have been implicated as upstream activation sites for several other Saccharomyces genes (40–42); however, it is not known whether any of these control elements bind activator proteins.

It was recently suggested that poly(dT) sequences stimulate transcription nonspecifically by increasing the accessibility of DNA in chromatin to proteins in the transcriptional machinery. This proposal was based on the observation that a poly(dT)-containing sequence can stimulate transcription when inserted upstream from a T7 promoter in yeast cells expressing T7 RNA polymerase (43).

Deletion analysis of the *TRP5* regulatory region led to the conclusion that at least two TGACTC-related sequences at −189 and −62 are required for efficient derepression of this gene under starvation conditions. A different sequence element, located between −183 and −149, that has not been precisely defined, is required for normal *TRP5* basal expression. The latter appears to be unrelated in sequence to either of the basal control elements identified at *HIS4* and *HIS3* (44, 45); however, like these other elements, the basal control sequences at *TRP5* are located between functional copies of the TGACTC repeat (Fig. 2). A similar arrangement of regulatory sequences also seems to occur at *HIS5* (46) and ARG3 (31) (Fig. 2).

The *ARO3* gene, which encodes an enzyme common to the Trp, Phe, and Tyr pathways, contains only a single sequence closely related to the TGACTC element in its 5′ noncoding DNA. A single base-pair change in the hexanucleotide core, changing it from TGACTA to T̲T̲ACTA, was sufficient to completely abolish *ARO3* derepression in response to histidine starvation and to lower *ARO3* basal expression by the same amount observed in response to a *gcn4* mutation (to about one-half) (32). This indicates that a single TGACTC-like sequence is both necessary and sufficient for transcriptional control of *ARO3* by GCN4 protein. *ARO3* is one of three amino-acid biosynthetic genes subject to the general control that contains only a single TGACTC sequence in the 5′ noncoding DNA. The magnitude of *ARO3* derepression is comparable to that of many other genes containing multiple TGACTC sequence elements, making it unclear to what extent repeated GCN4 binding sites are required for efficient derepression. At least in the case of the *HIS4–CYC1* hybrid constructs shown in Fig. 3, tandem copies of the TGACTC sequence clearly led to much greater derepression than that given by a single copy of the element.

B. The Role of the TATA Box in Transcriptional Activation by GCN4

In addition to the GCN4 binding site, it appears that transcriptional activation by GCN4 requires an additional promoter element located close to the start site of transcription. Deletions in the region between −70 and −23 at *HIS4* lower basal expression considerably and abolish its derepres-

sion under starvation conditions. In addition, transcripts with the correct 5'
end are not produced by these *his4* alleles. All of these deletions remove the
sequence TATATA at −60, closely related to the TATA element that functions
in mRNA 5' end selection in mammalian cells.

Replacement of the deleted *HIS4* sequences by an oligonucleotide containing the sequence TATAAA restored efficient transcription, with initiation
occurring close to the normal *HIS4* mRNA start site at +1. Positive regulation by GCN4 was likewise restored by insertion of the TATAAA sequence.
When the deleted sequences were instead replaced by TATAA, *HIS4* transcription was increased several-fold from that given by the parental deletion
allele; however, transcripts with discrete 5' ends were undetectable. Presumably, the transcripts produced by the latter allele have many different 5'
ends, such that no predominant mRNA species can be identified. Interestingly, although significant transcription occurs when the TATAA element is present, GCN4 is unable to derepress transcription from this allele
in response to starvation (*36*) (Fig. 5). These results suggest that a requirement exists for specific TATA-like sequence elements downstream from the
GCN4 binding site for both efficient basal *HIS4* expression and transcriptional activation by GCN4.

These conclusions are consistent with the deleterious effects of deleting
TATA-related sequences in the downstream portions of the *HIS3* regulatory

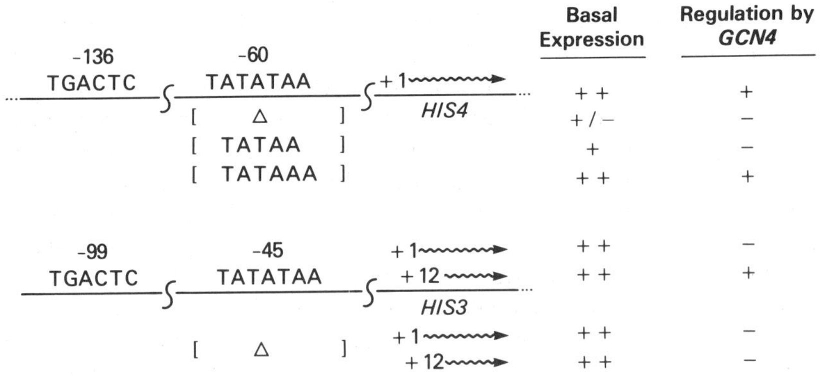

FIG. 5. The effects of TATA-box deletions at *HIS4* and *HIS3* on basal expression and GCN4-
mediated derepression. The 5' noncoding sequences of the two genes are depicted schematically, showing TATA-related sequences, the key GCN4-binding sites, and the distances of these
sequence elements (in base-pairs) upstream from the start sites of transcription. The deltas in
brackets indicate small deletions of the TATA elements at these genes that leave significant basal
expression intact but abolish transcriptional derepression by GCN4. (For *HIS3*, only the +12
transcript is normally GCN4 responsive.) Sequences inserted in place of the normal TATA
element at *HIS4*, one of which restores GCN4 control, are also shown in brackets.

region. A 10-bp deletion that removes a TATATAA sequence beginning at −47 impairs *HIS3* derepression under starvation conditions without affecting basal expression. Deletion of an additional 38 bp just upstream completely abolishes *HIS3* expression; however, deletion of the upstream region alone had no effect (38). These results suggest that either of two elements in the −83 to −35 interval is sufficient for *HIS3* basal expression, but the 3'-proximal element is uniquely required for regulation of *HIS3* transcription by GCN4 (Fig. 5).

Two major transcripts are produced from *HIS3*, at +1 and +12, and the latter shows a much greater derepression response to starvation than does the former (47, 48). Interestingly, small deletions of the TATA element at −47 have little effect on expression of the +1 mRNA but greatly reduce derepression of the +12 transcript under starvation conditions (48) (Fig. 5). The +12 transcript is also preferentially activated by the heterologous transcriptional activator GAL4, that mediates induction of galactose catabolic enzymes' when the binding site for GAL4 protein is inserted upstream from the two *HIS3* TATA regions (49). These results have been interpreted to indicate that two different types of TATA elements occur at *HIS3*, and only the 3'-proximal element at −45 can interact with GCN4 (or GAL4) to stimulate transcription initiation at +12. The TATA element between −53 and −83 can function in start-site selection (at least in the absence of the 3'-proximal TATA element), but is incapable of responding to increased binding by GCN4 or GAL4.

The functional distinction between the constitutive and regulated TATA elements at *HIS3* could reflect the fact that different types of proteins bind to these two sites, only one of which can productively interact with GCN4 to stimulate transcription initiation (48). Most single base-pair substitutions in the −45 *HIS3* TATA sequence seriously reduce its ability to mediate transcriptional activation by GAL4 protein, consistent with sequence-specific binding of a protein factor to the TATA element (50). Presumably, the same type of factor interacts with the multiple TATA sequences in the *CYC1* promoter (51), and that of the yeast transposable element Ty, because insertion of GCN4 binding sites upstream from each of these genes leads to increased transcription from the normal mRNA start sites under starvation conditions (37, 52).

The *TRP4* gene provides an interesting variation on the theme of selective activation of different transcriptional initiation sites by GCN4 protein. Under normal growth conditions, the major *TRP4* mRNAs begin about 125 and 76 bp upstream from the ATG initiation codon. Under starvation conditions, or in a constitutively derepressed *gcd2* mutant, transcription from these sites is repressed and the majority of the mRNAs initiate between positions −31 and −12. Interestingly, GCN4 binding sites are located in the vicinity of the −125 transcription site used predominantly under nonstarvation conditions (*32, 33*) (see *TRP4* in Fig. 2), raising the possibility that GCN4 binding blocks initiation in this region and shifts transcription to the downstream start sites.

IV. Functional Domains of the GCN4 Protein

A. The Carboxyl-Terminal Domain of GCN4 Mediates DNA Binding and Dimerization

The amino-acid residues in the GCN4 protein that mediate sequence-specific binding to DNA and transcriptional activation have been identified by functional analysis of *gcn4* deletion derivatives. Interestingly, these two functions depend largely on different portions of the GCN4 protein. GCN4 polypeptides synthesized by *in vitro* transcription and translation that retain 60 or more carboxyl-terminal amino acids of GCN4 can bind to DNA fragments containing a TGACTC sequence in a fairly specific fashion. Derivatives containing 114 or more carboxyl-terminal residues are identical to the full-length protein in the degree of sequence specificity observed in DNA binding (*53*) (Fig. 6).

The 60 carboxyl-terminal amino acids of GCN4 also mediate the formation of homodimers, and dimer formation appears to be required for DNA binding. These latter conclusions were reached by showing that a mixture of full-length GCN4 and truncated polypeptides containing only the last 60 amino acids gives rise to three DNA–protein complexes with different electrophoretic mobilities. The fastest- and slowest-migrating complexes contain only full-length or truncated GCN4 protein, respectively. The complex with intermediate mobility contains both large and small species. The molar ratios of the three complexes (fast : intermediate : slow, 1 : 2 : 1) are consistent with the idea that GCN4 normally binds to DNA as a dimer (*54*). These results suggest a close relationship between the amino acids at the carboxyl terminus that mediate dimer formation and those responsible for DNA binding (Fig. 6).

Interestingly, the carboxyl-terminal sequence of GCN4 is homologous to that of several polypeptides encoded by animal cell viruses that cause oncogenic transformation. The highest degree of homology occurs between GCN4 and the *jun* protein, with 44% identity seen over the approximately 70 carboxyl-terminal residues of GCN4. The *fos* protein exhibits 28% identity to the same GCN4 sequences (*55*). Remarkably, the coding sequences for the homologous segment of the *jun* oncoprotein partially substitute for the carboxyl terminus of the *GCN4* coding region and restore efficient *HIS3* transcription in a *gcn4* deletion mutant. The stimulatory effect of the *GCN4*–

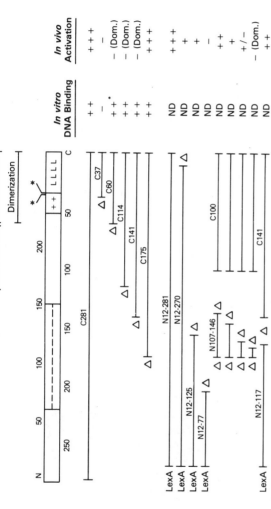

FIG. 6. Functional domains of GCN4 protein. The GCN4 amino-acid sequence is designated by the open rectangle, with residues numbered from the amino terminus (N) on top, from left to right, and from the carboxyl terminus (C) below, from right to left. The segment containing minus signs is an acidic domain involved in transcriptional activation; a basic domain at the carboxyl terminus (marked with plus signs) is a good candidate for the residues that contact DNA; L's indicate four leucine residues that occur every seventh amino acid in a carboxyl-terminal segment that is sufficient for GCN4 dimerization. The regularly spaced Leu residues may function as a "leucine zipper" to mediate dimer formation. Beneath the schematic of the GCN4 sequence are several deletion derivatives; their abilities to bind to DNA and activate transcription are given on the right. Residues missing in the deletion derivatives are indicated by blanks marked with deltas. The amino acids that remain in these constructs are designated by their positions relative to the amino terminus (N) or the carboxyl terminus (C) of GCN4. In the first group of constructs, DNA binding by the C60 construct is designated as "++*" because it is less sequence-specific than that seen for larger derivatives. The " – (Dom.)" activation response indicates a dominant Gcn4⁻ phenotype in vivo. In the second set of constructs, the coding sequences for the lexA DNA-binding domain were joined to the beginning of the GCN4 coding sequences, and the ability of these fusion proteins to activate transcription from a LexA binding site in vivo was measured. ND, in vitro DNA-binding activity was not determined.

jun hybrid on *HIS3* expression was dependent on the exact nucleotides present at the *GCN4* binding site located at position −99 in a fashion similar to that observed for the wild-type *GCN4* gene. These results suggest that the *jun* protein normally binds to DNA sequences that are closely related to GCN4 binding sites in Saccharomyces. [Actually, the GCN4–jun hybrid proteins were unable to derepress *HIS3* expression unless they contained a portion of the *lexA* repressor protein of *E. coli* at their amino termini. Because the *lexA* domain shows no affinity for the GCN4 binding site and is unable to activate transcription in Saccharomyces when bound to a *lexA* operator, it was proposed that the *lexA* amino acids are required to promote dimerization of the GCN4–jun hybrid proteins (56).]

It was subsequently established that the protein product of the proto-oncogene c-*jun* is identical to or closely related to the mammalian transcription factor AP-1, first identified by its selective binding to transcriptional control elements present in the SV40 genome and a human metallothionein gene. In fact, AP-1 binds to a DNA sequence that is very similar to that bound by GCN4 and the c-*jun* protein. In addition, antisera raised against *jun*-encoded peptides cross-react with a major polypeptide present in purified preparations of AP-1 (57; reviewed in 58). These results indicate that the carboxyl-terminus of GCN4 represents a structural motif for DNA binding that was highly conserved during the evolution of eukaryotic organisms. The same motif is encoded in the *cpc-1* gene of *Neurospora crassa* that mediates general amino-acid control in this fungus (59, 60).

Interestingly, DNA-binding factors distinct from GCN4 have been identified in *S. cerevisiae* that interact with a sequence (GCTGACTAATT) recognized in mammalian cells by AP-1 (61, 62). In one study, the Saccharomyces AP-1 factor (yAP-1) was shown to bind to the AP-1 recognition sequence much better than to the *HIS3* −99 repeat, whereas GCN4 interacted with either sequence equally well (61). By contrast, it has been suggested that GCN4 binds very poorly to the optimum AP-1 recognition sequence (62). The AP-1 binding site functions as a relatively weak transcriptional activation site in Saccharomyces cells, comparable in degree to a GCN4 binding site under nonstarvation conditions. A *gcn4* deletion has no effect on transcriptional activation mediated by the AP-1 recognition sequence, suggesting that GCN4 protein does not interact with this site *in vivo*, at least under nonstarvation conditions in which GCN4 is expected to be present at low levels (61).

Recently, the gene encoding the major AP-1-like DNA-binding activity in Saccharomyces (*YAP1*) was cloned and characterized. The deduced sequence of YAP1 protein is 650 amino acids in length and contains a stretch of 50 residues at the amino terminus related in sequence to the carboxyl-terminal

DNA-binding domain of GCN4. Moreover, this homologous sequence occurs in a roughly 90 amino-acid segment of YAP1 that is sufficient for *in vitro* binding to the AP-1 recognition site when the YAP1 fragment is expressed in *E. coli*. Neither this fragment nor a much larger one representing most of the YAP1 protein binds to a GCN4 recognition sequence, confirming that YAP1 is specific for the AP-1 binding site. A *yap1* disruption has no obvious phenotype except that transcription from a construct containing an AP-1 recognition sequence as the sole upstream activation site is abolished. Again, GCN4 seems to make no contribution to transcriptional activation of such a construct, even in the absence of functional YAP1 (*63*).

The *yap1* deletion eliminates most, but not all, AP-1-like binding activity in Saccharomyces extracts, raising the possibility that additional factors related to YAP1 exist in yeast. Moreover, disruption of *YAP1* leads to reduced amounts of other proteins, distinct from GCN4, that bind to an oligonucleotide containing a GCN4 recognition sequence (*63*). The fact that a *gcn4* deletion abolishes transcriptional depression of genes subject to general control (Table II) suggests that neither YAP1 nor any related binding activity can substitute for GCN4 under starvation conditions. However, one or more of these factors could participate with GCN4 in transcriptional activation of amino-acid biosynthetic genes.

The carboxyl-terminal residues of GCN4, jun, and fos proteins are each predicted to be α helix-permissive domains (*55*). When each amino-acid sequence was displayed on an idealized α helix, it was noted that a periodic repetition of leucines occurs at every seventh residue over a span of 28 amino acids. The same structural characteristic was found for segments of the *myc* oncoprotein, and the C/EBP ("CCAAT" box) enhancer binding protein from rats, even though no primary sequence homology exists between the latter two proteins and GCN4, jun, or fos. It was proposed that these polypeptide segments exist as α helices with their leucine side-chains extending from one face of the helix, and that protein dimerization can occur through end-to-end juxtaposition of the α helices mediated by interdigitation of the protruding leucine side-chains in a sort of "leucine zipper" (*64*). In fact, the periodic leucine residues occur in the last, roughly 60, amino acids of GCN4, a domain of the protein known to be sufficient for dimerization (Fig. 6).

Recently, mutational evidence supporting a protein–protein interaction mediated by periodic leucine residues was obtained for the jun and fos proteins. These proteins exist together in a complex *in vivo* (reviewed in *58*), and about 100 amino-acid segments of each polypeptide containing the periodic leucines are sufficient for the formation of jun–fos heterodimers *in vitro*. These heterodimers are capable of binding to a jun/fos recognition sequence under conditions in which neither protein alone binds to DNA.

Mutations that eliminate two of the five periodic leucine residues in fos abolished both heterodimer formation and DNA binding, suggesting that efficient DNA binding by these proteins requires complex formation (65).

Another feature shared by jun, fos, C/EBP, and GCN4 is the occurrence of a basic segment immediately upstream from the leucine zipper region. In the case of GCN4, this segment lies within the 66 carboxyl-terminal amino acids required for DNA binding (Fig. 6). If the portion of GCN4 containing the periodic leucines is involved primarily in dimerization, the adjacent basic domain of the protein would be expected to make contact with DNA. In accord with this hypothesis, substitution of a pair of arginines in the basic domain of fos (corresponding to the arginine and lysine residues at 245–246 in the basic domain of GCN4; see Fig. 6) abolished DNA binding by the jun–fos complex without affecting heterodimer formation (65). In addition, substitution of one of the periodic leucine residues close to the basic domain in fos considerably reduced the efficiency of DNA binding without noticeably affecting the efficiency of heterodimer formation, suggesting that subtle changes in the binding energy or conformation of the helices that participate in dimerization might have a large effect on the affinity of the adjacent basic domain for DNA. If so, heterodimer formation involving different partners could lead to differences in DNA binding strength or specificity. For example, a heterodimer between GCN4 and YAP1 might interact with a set of genes distinct from those recognized by either protein alone.

B. Amino-Acid Residues in GCN4 That Are Required for Transcriptional Activation

As mentioned above, the 114 carboxyl-terminal amino acids of the GCN4 protein are sufficient for highly sequence-specific binding to a TGACTC sequence *in vitro;* however, this polypeptide segment is insufficient for transcriptional activation of genes under GCN4 control *in vivo*. At least 175 carboxyl-terminal residues are required for derepression of *HIS3* expression to the same extent observed for full-length GCN4 protein. A smaller carboxyl-terminal segment of 163 amino acids gives rise to only partial derepression, and segments containing 141 or fewer amino acids are completely defective for derepression. In fact, the latter seem to inhibit expression of *HIS3* and that of other amino-acid biosynthetic genes in a dominant fashion (Fig. 6). To explain this dominant negative phenotype, it was proposed that amino-terminally truncated GCN4 polypeptides containing 141 or fewer residues can bind to TGACTC sequences, but are incapable of productive interaction with the transcriptional machinery; consequently, they reduce the level of transcriptional activation by competing with wild-type GCN4 protein for binding sites (53).

Attaching the coding sequences for the DNA-binding domain of the *lexA* protein to the amino terminus of the *GCN4* coding region provides an alternative means of identifying the residues in GCN4 that are required for positive regulation of transcription. Removal of the coding sequences for the ten carboxyl-terminal residues of GCN4 lowered transcriptional activation by the resulting *lexA–GCN4* hybrid to about one-fifth: however, considerable activity remained intact. (This reduction might result from the failure of the shortened LexA–GCN4 hybrid proteins to dimerize efficiently.) No further reduction in the activation function was observed until roughly 160 amino acids were eliminated from the carboxyl terminus of the GCN4 moiety of the hybrid (Fig. 6). These results indicate that the 125 amino-terminal residues of GCN4 are sufficient for transcriptional activation when attached to a DNA-binding domain (53).

The results of the experiments summarized thus far suggested a critical role for the 19 amino acids located between residues 107–125 (numbering from the amino terminus) in transcriptional activation by GCN4; however, subsequent studies revealed that these residues are not sufficient for the activation function. A variety of other deletions in the *GCN4* coding sequences show that 10–20 amino acids immediately adjacent to the 107–125 residues are additionally required for efficient transcriptional activation. Acidic amino acids are abundant in the 107–146 interval, leading to a net negative charge of -11 for this segment of the protein. Progressive elimination of amino acids from the carboxyl terminus of the 107–146 interval yielded a continuous decline in GCN4 transcriptional activation and also lowered the net negative charge in this segment to about -2 (66) (Fig. 6). The progressive loss of transcriptional activation associated with these deletions supports the previous suggestion (53) that no specific amino-acid sequences are required for this function; rather, the net negative charge of the activation domain may be a more important parameter. Because the correlation between negative charge and efficiency of transcriptional activation is not precise among the deletion mutations, it was further proposed that a particular arrangement of acidic residues in a repeated structure (e.g., an α helix) might be a critical feature of the GCN4 activation domain (66). The GAL4 activator protein of Saccharomyces also contains acidic activating domains distinct from the polypeptide segments that mediate DNA binding (67), suggesting that this functional organization may be common to many transcriptional activators in Saccharomyces.

There appears to be considerable functional redundancy in the GCN4 activation domain. Amino acids 1–106 are dispensable for positive regulation when the rest of the GCN4 protein is intact. In addition, the 126–146 residues are dispensable when residues 12–125 are present. In fact, the last eight residues in the critical 107–125 interval are also largely dispensable in the presence of the amino acids 12–117 (66). It has not been determined how much of the 1–117 segment is required to bypass the need for amino acids in the 118–144 interval for transcriptional activation.

The most important unanswered question regarding the GCN4 activation domain is: With what component(s) of the transcriptional machinery does it interact in order to stimulate transcription initiation? It could associate with a subunit of RNA polymerase itself or, as mentioned above, a TATA-binding factor. Obtaining the answer to this question, and learning the biochemical details of the activation process, should be a major goal of future research on the general control system.

V. Translational Control of GCN4 Expression

A. GCN4 Expression Is Regulated by Amino-Acid Availability

Analysis of GCN4–lacZ fusions suggest that the rate of GCN4 protein synthesis is regulated by amino-acid availability, occurring at low levels under nonstarvation conditions and increasing 10- to 50-fold upon starvation for a single amino acid (24, 25). This derepression requires the products of the positive regulatory genes GCN2 and GCN3 that, as shown in Table II, are also needed for derepression of structural genes subject to GCN4-positive control (26). Negative regulatory factors in this system encoded by GCD2, GCD1, GCD10, GCD11, and GCD13 function as repressors of GCN4 expression under nonstarvation conditions (26, 68) (Table II).

Regulation of GCN4 expression has a large translational component. One piece of evidence leading to this conclusion is that gcn2 and gcn3 mutations impair the derepression of GCN4–lacZ enzyme activity under starvation conditions without reducing the steady-state amount of the fusion transcript (24, 26). A second indication is that regulation of GCN4–lacZ enzyme expression by GCN and GCD factors remains intact following replacement of the GCN4 promoter with that of the GAL1 gene (26, 68). (GAL1 transcription is not subject to general amino-acid control.)

Insight into the mechanism of GCN4 translational control came with the finding that GCN4 mRNA has a long leader containing four AUG codons, each initiating an upstream open-reading-frame (uORF or URF) of two or three codons (24, 25) (Fig. 7A). Upstream AUG codons are rare in Saccharomyces mRNA, as in mammalian transcripts (69, 70), and insertion of extra AUG codons into the leader regions of yeast and mammalian transcripts generally has a large inhibitory effect on the translation of downstream protein-coding sequences (71–78). The strong preference for initiation at 5′-proximal AUG codons in eukaryotic mRNAs is an important piece of evidence in favor of the scanning hypothesis for translation initiation, according to which a preinitiation complex containing a 40-S ribosomal subunit attaches to the capped 5′

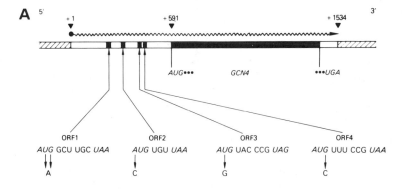

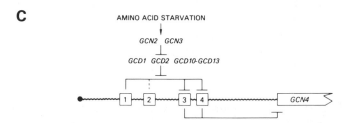

B

		GCN4-lacZ Enzyme Activity (U)					
GCN4		wt		gcn2		gcd1	
UPSTREAM ORFs		R	DR	R	DR	R	DR
		10	80	5	6	280	340
		740	470	1300	1300	1400	700
		240	390	560	310	580	790
		13	30	52	60	59	104
		5	12	6	11	15	16
		110	290	150	190	370	520
		23	88	26	35	290	360
		14	97	9	21	325	380

FIG. 7. Regulation of *GCN4* expression by upstream open reading frames (uORFs) in *GCN4* mRNA. (A) Schematic of the *GCN4* transcription unit (wavy arrow) shown above the protein-coding sequences (large solid rectangle) and the four short uORFs in the leader region (small solid boxes, uORFs 1–4). The sequences of the uORFs are given below, along with the point mutations constructed in their ATG codons. (B) The effects of point mutations in the upstream ATG codons (X's) on expression of *GCN4–lacZ* fusion enzyme activity in wild-type (wt), *gcn2*, and *gcd1* mutant cells in the repressing (R) and derepressing (DR) growth conditions described in Table II and Fig. 3. (C) Model summarizing the functional interactions among the uORFs in the *GCN4* mRNA leader that are required for translational control. uORFs 3 and 4 are needed for efficient repression of *GCN4* expression under nonstarvation conditions. In response to starvation, uORF1, and to a lesser extent uORF2, overcomes the barrier to initiation downstream exerted by uORFs 3 and 4, leading to increased *GCN4* expression. The GCD factors prevent this interaction between the uORFs under nonstarvation conditions; the GCD factors are antagonized or repressed under amino-acid starvation conditions by the products of *GCN2* and *GCN3*.

end of the mRNA and advances in the 3' direction until an AUG codon is encountered (79). The fact that upstream AUG codons generally inhibit translation even when an in-frame "stop" codon occurs before the second initiation site indicates that reinitiation following a termination event is relatively inefficient (71, 76, 77); however, the molecular basis for the low frequency of reinitiation remains to be elucidated.

In view of these considerations, it was of great interest to find that internal deletions removing all four uORFs in the *GCN4* mRNA leader lead to constitutive derepression of *GCN4–lacZ* enzyme expression (Table II). As expected, amino-acid biosynthetic enzymes under GCN4 control were derepressed when the same deletions were introduced upstream from the authentic *GCN4* protein-coding sequences. These mutations have little or no effect on the steady-state levels of *GCN4* or *GCN4–lacZ* mRNAs, showing that the deleted leader sequences affect *GCN4* expression at the translational level (24–26).

Mutations in *GCD* genes cause little additional increase in *GCN4–lacZ* enzyme expression once the uORFs are removed, suggesting that the *GCD* factors mediate the inhibitory effects of the leader sequences under nonstarvation conditions. In *gcn2* and *gcn3* mutants, deletion of the uORFs produces the same high levels of *GCN4* expression as it does in wild-type cells, implying that GCN2 and GCN3 function to overcome the inhibitory effects of the leader sequences under amino-acid starvation conditions (24–26, 68) (Table II). The target of the *GCN* and *GCD* regulatory factors was narrowed down to the small sequence interval in *GCN4* mRNA containing the four uORFs, by showing that translational control by these factors could be conferred upon a heterologous yeast mRNA by insertion of only this small segment of the *GCN4* mRNA leader into the 5' end of the heterologous transcript (68).

B. mRNA Sequence Requirements for GCN4 Translational Control

Direct proof that the upstream AUG codons are responsible for translational control of *GCN4* came from the fact that removal of these sequences by point mutations leads to the same high constitutive *GCN4–lacZ* enzyme activity as deletions of the four uORFs (Fig. 7B). In addition, by constructing alleles containing different combinations of upstream ATG codons, it became clear that the various uORFs play different roles in the translational control mechanism. The third or fourth ATG codon (counting from the 5' end) is necessary for efficient repression of *GCN4* expression under normal growth conditions. By contrast, the first and second ATG codons are relatively weak negative elements when present alone in the mRNA leader. In fact, when ATG codon 3 or 4 is present, the first ATG codon acts as a positive control element, being required for efficient *GCN4* expression under starvation conditions. (The second ATG codon also acts as a positive element in this situation, but to a lesser degree.) Only when ATG codon 1 is present upstream from ATG codons 3 or 4 is there a strong requirement for *GCD* gene products to repress *GCN4* expression efficiently. These findings led to the suggestion, summarized in Fig. 7C, that: (i) recognition of the first (and second) AUG codons overcomes the inhibitory effects of the third and fourth AUG codons; (ii) this interaction is prevented from occurring under nonstarvation conditions by the *GCD* regulatory factors (*68, 80*).

In large part, deletions that remove a subset of the four uORFs have the same phenotype as point mutations in the corresponding ATG codons: (i) deletions of uORFs 3 and 4 increase *GCN4–lacZ* expression under repressing conditions but have much less effect under derepressing conditions, as expected for removal of a *cis*-acting negative element (*81*) (Fig. 8A, A + C); (ii) deletions of uORF1 alone, or a combination of uORFs 1 and 2, reduces *GCN4–lacZ* expression only under derepressing conditions, as expected for removal of positive control sites (*81, 82*) (Fig. 8A, D). In addition, deletion of sequences upstream from uORF1 had little effect on *GCN4* expression (Fig. 8A, S/G construct), suggesting that leader sequences 5' to the four uORFs are largely dispensable for regulation (*81*).

Deletions of uORFs 2 and 3 had greater effects on *GCN4* expression than removal of ATG codons 2 and 3 by point mutations. In the most extreme case, in which all but about 25 base-pairs that normally separate uORFs 1 and 4 were removed, the derepression ratio was reduced to about 5, compared to a value of about 25 given by the construct with point mutations in ATG codons 2 and 3. Despite its low derepression ratio, removal of the uORF1 ATG codon from this deletion allele reduced *GCN4* expression under derepressing conditions, showing that uORF1 was functioning as a positive control element (*81*) (Fig. 8A, E + F and E' + F). Thus, nucleotides located between uORFs 1 and 4 make an important quantitative contribution to the derepression ratio but are dispensable for regulation per se.

Much of the leader region between uORF4 and the *GCN4* start site was deleted without any effect on the derepression ratio; however, the inhibitory effect of the uORFs was increased by this deletion, resulting in lower absolute levels of *GCN4* expression under repressing and derepressing conditions (Fig. 8A, construct B/X). Similarly, when present alone in the mRNA leader, uORF1 becomes more inhibitory when moved closer to the *GCN4* start site (*81, 83*), and uORF4 is less inhibitory to *GCN4* expression when moved into the position normally occupied by uORF1 (*131*). These observations are reminiscent of those in which the inhibitory effect of an uORF on preproinsulin synthesis progressively decreased as the uORF was moved farther upstream from the preproinsulin start site. To explain this trend, it was suggested that the probability of reinitiation following translation of the

GCN4-lacZ
Enzyme Activity (U)

		R (gcn2)	DR (gcd1)
A	wt*	6	170
	A + C	64	220
	D	5	13
	E + D	19	190
	E + F	28	140
	E' + F	25	43
	S/G	7	120
	B/X	2	62
B		18	300
		40	220
		41	65
		5	30
		5	3
C	E + D	18	190
	P + D	6	58
	T + D	7	35
	T' + D	4	10
D	D + A	5	10
	pM98	8	20

FIG. 8. Sequence and positional requirements of the uORFs for *GCN4* translational control. *GCN4–lacZ* enzyme activity was measured in *gcn2* (repressed conditions, R) or *gcd1* transformants (derepressed conditions, DR) containing the indicated constructs. (A) The uORFs (and point mutations in their ATG codons, X's) are shown in the leader as in Fig. 7B, with deletions of leader sequences shown as gaps marked with deltas. Vertical lines in the leader indicate restriction sites introduced to facilitate construction of deletions. The constructs are named as in the original literature. (B) 4-EL designates an elongated version of uORF4, 46 codons in length, constructed by a single base-pair insertion into the uORF stop codon. uORF5 (hatched portions) is a 43-codon uORF constructed by insertion of a linker containing an ATG codon just downstream from the normal location of uORF4 in alleles lacking uORFs 1–4 or 2–4. uORF6 (stippled portions) is an eight-codon uORF contained in a roughly 100-bp fragment from a sea urchin tubulin cDNA inserted in place of uORFs 1–4, or 2–4, the uORFs being removed by deletions, end-points of which are indicated by wavy lines. (C) P and T designate three-codon uORFs containing the −1 to −7 nucleotides found at the *Saccharomyces PGK1* and *TRP1* initiation sites, respectively, inserted on 20-bp fragments in place of uORF1, the latter being removed by a deletion (end-point indicated by a wavy line). T' is identical to the T sequence, except that it contains a point mutation in the ATG codon of the T uORF. (D) D + A is a rearrangement that places a roughly 60-bp segment containing uORF1 downstream from uORFs 3 and 4; in pM98, an approximately 50-bp segment containing uORF1 was substituted with a sequence of the same size containing uORF4.

uORF increased with greater separation between the uORF stop codon and the preproinsulin start codon (84). An alternative explanation is that ribosomes translating the uORF sterically hinder initiation at the second start site, when the two AUG codons are very close together. The latter mechanism is improbable for *GCN4* mRNA because the effects of uORF proximity on *GCN4* expression have been observed with separations between the two initiation sites of about 100 nucleotides or more. Thus, reinitiation probably does occur on *GCN4* mRNA following translation of the uORFs.

C. Translational Control with Heterologous uORFs

Replacement of the *GCN4* leader segment containing the four uORFs with a heterologous nine-codon uORF led to constitutively repressed *GCN4* expression. A similar result was obtained for an inversion that substitutes for the wild-type uORFs two short uORFs of eight or 12 codons (82). These heterologous uORFs supply the repressing function characteristic of authentic *GCN4* uORFs 3 and 4, but their repressing effects cannot be overcome under starvation conditions to permit increased *GCN4* expression.

More recently, the *GCN4* uORFs were replaced by heterologous short coding sequences without destroying the qualitative features of *GCN4* translational control. The stop codons of uORFs 3 or 4 were eliminated, lengthening these elements from 3 to 52 or 43 codons, respectively, with little or no effect on *GCN4* expression (e.g., see Fig. 8B). In addition, a completely heterologous 43-codon uORF (uORF5) was inserted in place of uORFs 3 and 4, which, when present alone, reduced *GCN4–lacZ* expression to a low constitutive level. Introduction of uORF1 upstream diminished the inhibitory effect of uORF5 and increased *GCN4–lacZ* expression about 5-fold in derepressing conditions (Fig. 8B). In the same circumstances, uORF1 overrides the inhibitory effect of authentic uORF3 to about the same extent (85). Similar results were obtained with a nine-codon heterologous uORF (uORF6 in Fig. 8B) inserted downstream from uORF1 (83).

The positive regulatory function of uORFs 1 and 2 was also reconstituted with heterologous ORFs (81). A segment containing uORFs 1 and 2 was deleted and replaced by a synthetic oligonucleotide containing an uORF with the first three codons and −1 to −7 nucleotides found at the highly-expressed *PGK1* gene, corresponding to the consensus sequence of initiation regions from highly expressed yeast genes (86). (*PGK1* encodes an enzyme involved in glycolysis.) As expected, this heterologous uORF greatly reduced *GCN4* expression in repressing conditions (by 95%); more importantly, it mimicked uORF1 and stimulated *GCN4* expression in derepressing conditions when inserted upstream from uORFs 3 and 4 (compare P + D with D in Fig. 8).

A different three-codon uORF derived from the *TRP1* gene (containing a

−1 to −7 sequence that deviates from the consensus initiation sequence) was a weaker translational barrier when present singly in the mRNA leader, and it also functioned less effectively than the *PGK1*-related uORF as a positive control site when inserted upstream from uORFs 3 and 4 (Fig. 8C, T + D). The relative ineffectiveness of the *TRP1*-related uORF in stimulating *GCN4* expression suggests that efficient initiation is required for the 5′-proximal uORF to overcome the translational barrier at uORFs 3 and 4. The fact that heterologous uORFs can mimic the regulatory functions of the authentic *GCN4* uORFs supports the idea that the latter function in the regulatory mechanism as translated coding sequences. It also implies that the interactions between 5′- and 3′-proximal uORFs important for this regulatory mechanism occur without strict requirements for the primary sequences or secondary structures of the uORFs involved. Rather, the regulation appears to be a more general consequence of the translation of two uORFs in the mRNA leader. On the other hand, the *GCN4* derepression ratio varies considerably for different combinations of uORFs, showing that particular nucleotides associated with these elements are very important in determining the efficiency of *GCN4* translational control.

D. Different Roles for uORFs 1 and 4 in GCN4 Translational Control

The importance of sequence differences between the uORFs was confirmed by the fact that the 5′- and 3′-proximal uORFs are not functionally interchangeable. Inserting a segment containing uORF1 downstream from uORFs 3 and 4 resulted in low constitutive *GCN4* expression, indistinguishable from a deletion of uORF1 (*81*) (compare D + A with D in Fig. 8). Similarly, replacement of a segment containing uORF1 with a segment of the same length containing uORF4 (producing an allele with two uORF4 sequences) reduced *GCN4* expression to the low constitutive level observed when uORF4 is present alone in the leader (*131*) (Fig. 8D, pM98). The simplest explanation for these results is that 40-S subunits cannot scan past uORFs 3 and 4 or reinitiate following their translation, when these elements are present in the mRNA as the 5′-proximal start sites. By contrast, uORF1 is a leaky translational barrier, reducing *GCN4* expression by only about 50% when present singly in the mRNA leader, compared to 95–99% inhibition seen when uORFs 3 and 4 are present as solitary uORFs. Presumably, many 40-S subunits either scan past uORF1 or reinitiate following uORF1 translation, and this characteristic is important for the ability of uORF1 to regulate translational events at uORFs 3 and 4.

The deleterious effects on derepression of *GCN4* expression seen for mutations that remove the uORF1 stop codon supports the idea that a leaky translational block at uORF1 is essential for its role as a positive control element. Removing the stop codon and elongating uORF1 from 3 to 10, 12, or 17 codons (depending on the reading-frame used after the stop-codon mutation) increased the efficiency of uORF1 as a translational barrier when present singly in the mRNA leader. In fact, the ten-codon uORF1 functions almost as well as uORF4 in blocking translation initiation events downstream (S-ORF1, Fig. 9, bottom). Correlated with their increased ability to inhibit translation initiation downstream when present as solitary uORFs, the elongated-uORF1 sequences have a reduced ability to stimulate GCN4 expression when situated upstream from uORFs 3 and 4 (85) (Fig. 9, top). To explain these results, it was proposed that most scanning ribosomes translate uORF1 and are able to reinitiate at downstream start sites. The mutations in the uORF1 stop codon reduce the fraction of ribosomes (or 40-S subunits) than can resume scanning and reassemble an initiation complex following uORF1 translation.

Because the mutations in the stop codon impair the ability of uORF1 to overcome the translational barrier at uORFs 3 and 4, it was proposed that only those ribosomes that translate uORF1 and resume scanning can advance beyond the 3′-proximal uORFs. According to this model, prior translation of uORF1 alters the complement of translational factors that are associated with the ribosome from that present during primary initiation events at uORF1. For example, factors that normally associate with the 40-S subunit

URFs	R	DR	gcd1/
1 2 3 4	(gcn2)	(gcd1)	gcn2
⌷ ▌X X▌ ▬	16	390	24
⌷ ▌X X▌ ▬ (F)	10	100	10
⌷ ▌X X▌ ▬ (G)	5	29	6
⌷ ▌X X▌ ▬ (S)	4	13	3
⌷ X X X▌ ▬	11	21	2
⌷ ▌X XX ▬	440	710	2
⌷ ▌X XX ▬ (F)	210	600	3
⌷ ▌X XX ▬ (G)	40	150	4
⌷ ▌X XX ▬ (S)	44	50	1
⌷ X X XX ▬	1300	1100	1

FIG. 9. Elongation of uORF1 by removing its stop codon makes it more inhibitory, when present singly in the mRNA leader, and reduces its ability to overcome the inhibitory effect of uORF4 and stimulate GCN4–lacZ expression in derepressing conditions. The GCN4 mRNA leader is depicted as in Fig. 7B. F, G, and S designate elongated versions of uORF1 produced by mutations in the uORF1 stop codon that are 12, 17, or 10 codons in length, respectively. Each uses a different translational reading-frame downstream from the normal uORF1 stop codon. GCN4–lacZ expression was measured under repressing (R, gcn2 cells) and derepressing (DR, gcd1 cells) conditions.

only at the mRNA 5′ cap might be removed from the ribosome during translation of uORF1. The absence of these factors during the reinitiation process, coupled with reduced GCD function under starvation conditions, would alter the translational behavior of reinitiating ribosomes when they reach uORFs 3 and 4, allowing a certain fraction to scan past AUG codons 3 and 4 or to reinitiate again more efficiently following translation of uORFs 3 and 4 (85) (Fig. 10). The important requirement for uORF1 function in this model are efficient translation and a high probability for resumed scanning

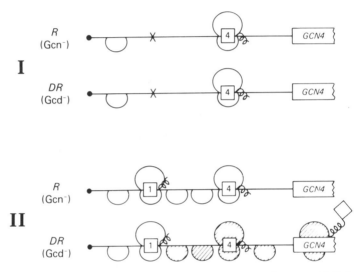

FIG. 10. Hypothetical molecular mechanism for the interactions between uORFs 1 and 4 in controlling translation initiation at the *GCN4* start site. The *GCN4* mRNA is shown schematically with only uORFs 1 and 4 present upstream from the GCN4 coding sequences. 40-S subunits and 80-S ribosomes are depicted bound to the mRNA. In the first two cases, uORF1 is missing due to a point mutation in its AUG codon. As a result, all 40-S subunits scan to uORF4 and initiate translation. Following translation termination at uORF4, no reinitiation occurs at the *GCN4* start site under either repressing (R, *gcn2*) or derepressing (DR, *gcd1*) conditions. When uORF1 is present upstream (third and fourth mRNAs), most ribosomes translate uORF1 and scanning can resume following termination at this site. Under repressing conditions, reinitiation occurs at uORF4 but no reinitiation follows termination at uORF4. In derepressing conditions, the behavior of 40-S subunits that engaged in prior translation of uORF1 is altered as the result of reduced GCD activity in the cell (hatched subunits). These altered initiation complexes are able to traverse uORF4 and reinitiate at the *GCN4* start site, either by skipping over the uORF4 AUG codon or by more efficient reinitiation following uORF4 translation. [The latter is favored by experiments in which the effect of uORF1 on translation of a uORF4–*lacZ* fusion was measured under repressing and derepressing conditions (87).] In a related model (83), scanning resumes following uORF1 translation only under derepressing conditions, and the reinitiation complexes generated under these conditions traverse uORF4 by either of the two mechanisms just described.

following termination. A modified version of this model was recently presented in which reinitiation following uORF1 translation is restricted to starvation conditions by its dependence on such positive regulators of *GCN4* expression as GCN2 (83). In this version, a reinitiating ribosome generated by translation of uORF1 needs no further alteration to advance through uORF4.

E. Initiation Rates at the 5'- and 3'-Proximal uORFs

The results summarized above suggest that both the 5'- and 3'-proximal uORFs are efficient translation initiation sites, at least when each is present as the first uORF in the mRNA leader. In fact, the nucleotides surrounding all five AUG start codons in *GCN4* mRNA closely resemble the consensus sequence for the initiation regions of highly expressed yeast genes (69, 86). Independent evidence that the uORFs are efficient start sites was provided by analyses of uORF–*lacZ* fusions. In one study, all sequences downstream from the second codon of uORF1 were deleted and replaced by *lacZ* sequences (83). A different construct was made by removing the stop codon of uORF1 and inserting *lacZ* sequences 27 nucleotides downstream from the uORF1 ATG codon (85). Similarly, *lacZ* sequences were fused to an elongated version of uORF4 at a site 39 nucleotides downstream from its ATG codon. All three uORF–*lacZ* fusions express high constitutive levels of fusion enzyme, comparable to that given by the *GCN4–lacZ* fusion in the absence of uORFs (83, 85).

These results are in accord with the aforementioned idea that the different regulatory functions of uORFs 1 and 4 are not determined by their efficiencies as translational start sites, but rather by the different probabilities that termination at the two sites will be followed by reinitiation events downstream. In addition, the fact that translation of the uORF1–*lacZ* fusions occurs at similar rates under repressing and derepressing conditions suggests that uORF1-positive function is not restricted to derepressing conditions by controlling its initiation rate. Rather, translation of uORF1 must be coupled with antagonism of GCD factors under starvation conditions to influence translational events at uORF4.

uORF3–*lacZ* and uORF4–*lacZ* fusions were examined in an attempt to identify the translational event that is regulated at these 3'-proximal uORFs by translation of uORFs 1 and 2. For example, uORF1 could reduce the translational block at uORFs 3 and 4 by suppressing initiation at these sites without equally reducing initiation at the *GCN4* start site. Such a differential effect on initiation rates could be related to the closer proximity of uORF1 to uORFs 3 and 4 versus the *GCN4* start codon (84). According to this model, translation of uORFs 3 and 4 would be reduced under derepressing conditions, when translation of the *GCN4* coding sequences increases. At odds with this expectation are the results of two different studies indicating that translation of uORF3–*lacZ* fusion is higher under derepressing than under repressing conditions when uORFs 1 and 2 are present upstream. Similar results were obtained for an uORF4–*lacZ* fusion (83, 87) In fact, there appears to be an equal probability of initiation at the uORF3, uORF4, or *GCN4* start site, when each is present as the next initiation codon downstream from uORF1 or uORFs 1 and 2 (Fig. 11).

Based on this result, it was proposed that an event associated with termination at the 3'-proximal uORFs is regulated to allow greater numbers of ribosomes to reinitiate at the *GCN4* start site in derepressing conditions following translation of these uORFs. For example, ribosomes might be more likely to remain attached to the mRNA and resume scanning following termination at uORFs 3 and 4 (87). A potential problem with these experiments is that insertion of *lacZ* sequences into uORFs 3 and 4 could have disrupted an important structure required to regulate initiation at these sites. One way to eliminate this possibility would be to measure translation from 3'-proximal uORFs that are competent translational control elements.

In summary, studies on the *cis*-acting regulatory elements in the *GCN4* mRNA leader have shown that at least two uORFs are required for translational control of *GCN4* expression. A combination of uORFs 1 and 4 gives a pattern of *GCN4* expression very similar to that of the wild-type gene. uORF4 is a strong negative element required to maintain repression of *GCN4* expression under nonstarvation conditions. By comparison, uORF1 is a weak negative element and is required upstream from uORF4 for derepressed *GCN4* expression under starvation conditions.

It is very probable that the uORFs are translated in the course of carrying

	Fractional Fusion Enzyme Expression					
	GCN4-lacZ		URF3-*lacZ*		URF4-*lacZ*	
Fusion	R	DR	R	DR	R	DR
●─X─X─────⊏⊃ ′*lacZ*	1.0	0.85	1.0	1.6	1.0	1.9
●─■─X─────⊏⊃ ′*lacZ*	0.34	0.55	0.39	0.92	0.39	0.45
●─■─■─────⊏⊃ ′*lacZ*	0.15	0.35	0.10	0.53	0.09	0.34

FIG. 11. uORFs 1 and 2 similarly affect translation of uORF3–*lacZ*, uORF4–*lacZ*, and *GCN4–lacZ* fusions. The presence or absence of uORFs 1 and 2 is indicated schematically on the left, and the relative expression of each of the three fusions is given for each combination of uORFs 1 and 2 under repressing (R, *gcn2* cells) and derepressing (DR, *gcd1* cells) conditions. The expression of each fusion in the absence of all uORFs (first line) has been normalized to a value of 1.0. uORF3 is absent in the uORF4–*lacZ* fusion and uORFs 3 and 4 are absent in the *GCN4–lacZ* fusion.

out their respective regulatory functions; however, it is unlikely that their peptide products participate in the control mechanism since the nucleotide sequences of the uORFs are not uniquely required for translational control. Both uORFs 1 and 4 appear to be efficient start sites, suggesting that their different efficiencies as translational barriers when present as solitary uORFs result from a greater probability of reinitiation following uORF1 translation compared to what occurs at uORF4.

The fact that uORF1 must be a leaky translational barrier to overcome the inhibitory effect of uORF4 on *GCN4* expression suggests that, in order to traverse uORF4 under starvation conditions, ribosomes must first translate uORF1 and resume scanning downstream. Perhaps prior translation of uORF1 changes the complement of factors associated with the ribosome from what is present in the conventional initiation complex, leading to an altered translational mechanism at uORF4 under starvation conditions. In this altered state, ribosomes may skip over the uORF4 start site or reinitiate at the *GCN4* AUG codon following uORF4 translation more frequently than occurs under normal conditions. The data favor the latter of these two mechanisms for traversing uORF4 sequences. An important objective of future research will be to determine the exact nucleotides surrounding uORFs 1 and 4 that modulate the efficiency of initiation/reinitiation events at these sites, and to identify the components of the translational apparatus that recognize and respond to these regulatory signals.

VI. *trans*-Acting Translational Regulators of GCN4

A. GCN2 Functions as a Protein Kinase in Stimulating GCN4 Expression

The *GCN2* and *GCN3* genes have been isolated and characterized, and deletions of each have no phenotype except to impair derepression of *GCN4* expression under starvation conditions (*13, 88*). The latter suggest that these factors are specifically involved in general amino-acid control. Interestingly, DNA sequence analysis revealed a strong similarity between a portion of the *GCN2* protein-coding sequences and the catalytic domain of eukaryotic protein kinases. Comparison of 65 different protein kinases reveals the existence of 11 different subdomains of sequence homology among these proteins, involving 15 nearly invariant amino acids and 18 conserved residues of similar chemical structure (*89*). All 33 of these highly conserved residues are present in the GCN2 protein sequence (*88, 90*).

One of the best characterized subdomains conserved in protein kinases includes the sequence Gly-X-Gly-X-X-Gly-X-Val followed 13–18 residues downstream by Ala-X-Lys. The lysine residue is believed to function in the phosphotransfer reaction, and amino-acid substitutions at this position invariably abolish kinase activity (89, 91). Substitution of the corresponding lysine residue in GCN2 (Lys-559) with arginine or valine abolished GCN2-positive regulatory function, whereas substitution of the adjacent nonconserved lysine residue with valine had no effect on GCN4 expression (90). In addition, wild-type GCN2 is required for expression of a roughly 100-kDa protein kinase activity present in greater amounts in amino-acid-starved cells than in cells grown under nonstarvation conditions (88). Since the molecular weight of GCN2 protein is now known to be about 180,000 (90), the 100-kDA species is probably a GCN2 degradation product or a distinct protein kinase that is activated by GCN2 under starvation conditions. These results strongly suggest that GCN2 stimulates GCN4 expression by acting as a protein kinase.

GCN2 mRNA is induced during starvation conditions, and this response requires the GCN4 gene product (92). In fact, a sequence present in the GCN2 5' noncoding DNA binds GCN4 protein in vitro. These results suggest that transcription of GCN2 increases under starvation conditions in a GCN4-dependent fashion. However, because introduction of the GCN2 gene into cells on a high copy-number plasmid is insufficient to completely derepress GCN4 expression, it was concluded that an increase in the specific activity of GCN2 protein kinase is required under starvation conditions for full derepression of genes subject to the general control, in addition to any increase in the amount of GCN2 protein that might occur in starved cells (88).

The deduced amino-acid sequence of the carboxyl terminus of GCN2 may provide an important clue about how its protein kinase activity is regulated by amino-acid availability. Roughly 530 residues in the carboxyl-terminal domain of GCN2 protein show a strong similarity to histidyl-tRNA synthetases (HisRS) from S. cerevisiae, humans, and E. coli. Several two-codon insertions and in-frame deletions in the HisRS-related coding sequences inactivate GCN2-positive regulatory function, suggesting that this region is required for protein kinase activity under starvation conditions (90). Given that aminoacyl-tRNA synthetases bind uncharged tRNA as a substrate and that accumulation of uncharged tRNA triggers derepression of the general control response (3), it was proposed that the GCN2 HisRS-related domain monitors the concentration of uncharged tRNA and activates the adjacent protein kinase moiety under starvation conditions, when uncharged tRNA accumulates. Because derepression of genes under the general control occurs in response to starvation for any of at least ten amino acids, it is not immediately obvious how a domain related to HisRS could monitor the charging levels of other tRNAs. One possibility is that GCN2 has diverged sufficiently from HisRS that it now lacks the ability to discriminate between different uncharged tRNA species (90).

No substrates for GCN2 kinase activity have been identified; however, the fact that *gcd* mutations suppress the nonderepressible phenotype of *gcn2* mutations makes these negative regulatory factors good candidates. Phosphorylation by GCN2 would be expected to inactivate GCD factors, thereby releasing translational repression of *GCN4* mRNA. Nearly all *gcd* mutations are pleiotropic and lead to conditional lethality at 36°C or unconditional slow growth, irrespective of amino-acid levels (*18, 21, 22*). The rates of incorporation of radioactive precursors into DNA, RNA, and protein are reduced and the cells arrest in the early G_1 phase of the cell cycle, when *gcd1* and *gcd2* mutants are shifted to the restrictive temperature (*18, 22, 93*). Moreover, deletions of *GCD1* and *GCD2* are unconditionally lethal (*13, 93, 94*). These results suggest that GCD1 and GCD2 contribute to an essential function required for entry into the cell cycle. Given that mutations in *GCD* genes impair *GCN4* translational control, this essential function may be involved with protein synthesis. In this view, GCN1, GCN2, and GCN3 would function to partially inactivate components of the translational machinery under starvation conditions and thereby alter the behavior of ribosomes during translation of the uORFs in *GCN4* mRNA. This hypothesis is appealing in view of the postulated protein kinase activity of GCN2, given that mammalian initiation factor eIF-2 is inhibited by phosphorylation of the α subunit under stress conditions that include amino-acid starvation (*95, 96*). An alternative explanation for the deleterious effects of *gcd* mutations on cell growth and division is that *GCD* factors play a more direct role in coordinating the yeast cell cycle with the availability of amino acids (*22*), in addition to their involvement in *GCN4* translational control.

B. Genetic Evidence for Direct Interactions between the Positive Factor GCN3 and Negative-Acting GCD Gene Products

The idea that *GCD* factors function in general protein synthesis is consistent with the relatively large number of *GCD* genes identified thus far: Many components of the translational machinery may be required for repression of *GCN4* expression under nonstarvation conditions. However, all such factors identified genetically need not be subject to regulation in wild-type cells in response to amino-acid starvation. For this reason, genetic interactions detected between the specific positive regulators *GCN1, GCN2,* and *GCN3* and particular *GCD* genes are useful in identifying GCD factors that participate directly in *GCN4* translational control. Such interactions have been reported for *GCN3* with *GCD1* and *GCD2*.

Certain *gcd1* mutations and alleles of *GCD2* originally designated as *gcd12* mutations have been isolated as suppressors of the *gcn3-101* mutation. Interestingly, wild-type *GCN3* partially overcomes the derepressed *GCN4* expression and temperature sensitivity for growth associated with these *gcd1* mutations, and completely overcomes the same defects in *gcd12* mutants. Replacement of *gcn3-101* with *gcn3::LEU2* (a *gcn3* deletion containing a

LEU2 insertion) had little effect on the Gcd⁻ phenotype in these *gcd1* and *gcd12* strains, indicating that loss of *GCN3* function is required for expression of the Gcd⁻ phenotype (97). Thus, the *GCN3* product can promote or substitute for the functions of GCD1 and GCD2 under nonstarvation conditions, even though it acts to antagonize these negative factors when cells are starved for amino acids.

One hypothesis to explain the ability of *GCN3* to overcome mutant phenotypes associated with *gcd1* and *gcd12* mutations is that GCN3 exists in a complex with these GCD factors and can stabilize thermolabile proteins encoded by mutant alleles of these genes. In a *gcn3* deletion strain, GCN3 would be absent from the complex and the thermolability of the *gcd* products would be exacerbated. An alternative explanation is that GCN3 can partially substitute for the functions of GCD1 and GCD2 under nonstarvation conditions (97).

The latter explanation is favored by recent results from DNA sequence analysis of *GCN3* and *GCD2*: The deduced sequence of the GCN3 protein shows significant similarity with the carboxyl-terminal segment of GCD2. This finding suggests that GCN3 is functionally related to a domain of GCD2, and that the effects of *gcd12* mutations are overcome by wild-type *GCN3* because these mutations specifically disrupt the GCN3-like domain of GCD2. Wild-type *GCN3* does not overcome the lethal effect of a *gcd2* deletion or the constitutive derepression of *GCN4* expression associated with a *gcd2-1* mutation (21). Presumably, the latter mutations affect a domain of GCD2 for which GCN3 cannot substitute. To account for the fact that GCN3 opposes GCD2 activity under starvation conditions, it was suggested that GCN3 is inactivated under these conditions, but continues to compete with GCD2 for binding sites or substrates (98). Because *GCN3* appears to be equally expressed under repressing or derepressing conditions (13), its ability to antagonize GCD factors under starvation conditions is thought to require a covalent modification (phosphorylation by GCN2?), or an altered interaction with some other molecule whose expression or activity is regulated by amino-acid levels.

Unfortunately, the deduced amino-acid sequences of the GCN3, GCD2, and GCD1 proteins provide no clues about their exact functions (13, 14, 98); consequently, biochemical studies will be needed to gain further insight into the precise roles these factors play in general protein synthesis and in modulating ribosomal recognition of the *GCN4* upstream AUG codons.

VII. Transcriptional Control of GCN4 Expression

GCN4 expression is subject to transcriptional regulation in addition to translational control. The steady-state level of *GCN4* mRNA increases about

2-fold in response to starvation in wild-type cells, and even greater increases are seen in *gcn2* and *gcn3* mutants (*26, 68*). The latter indicates that GCN2 and GCN3 are not required for the increased amounts of *GCN4* mRNA seen under starvation conditions. The fact that the magnitude of the increase is actually greater in these mutants than in wild-type cells probably reflects the fact that starvation is more severe in *gcn2* and *gcn3* cells because of their failure to stimulate translation of *GCN4* mRNA. By contrast, mutations in *GCN6* and *GCN7* lead to reduced levels of *GCN4* mRNA, suggesting that the products of these genes do stimulate *GCN4* expression at the transcriptional level (*16*).

Mutations in *GCD* genes lead to constitutive derepression of *GCN4* mRNA as well as increased synthesis of GCN4 protein (*26, 68*). However, an even greater increase in the amount of *GCN4* mRNA than what occurs in *gcd* mutants is insufficient in wild-type cells to derepress amino-acid biosynthetic genes to the extent seen in *gcd* mutants (*68*). In addition, measurement of *GCN4–lacZ* mRNA levels and fusion enzyme activities in *GCD* versus *gcd* mutant strains suggest that *gcd* mutations increase the abundance of fusion protein much more than fusion mRNA (*26, 68*). For these and other reasons discussed in previous sections, the *gcd* mutations are thought to affect *GCN4* expression primarily at the translational level. Nevertheless, increased *GCN4* mRNA abundance could make an important quantitative contribution to the extent of *GCN4* derepression seen in *gcd* mutants. It is not known whether GCD factors influence *GCN4* mRNA synthesis or turnover.

VIII. Conclusions

The transcriptional and translational regulatory events involved in the general amino-acid control of *S. cerevisiae* are summarized schematically in Fig. 12. Coordinate transcriptional regulation of amino-acid biosynthetic genes under the general control has been explained by the identification of binding sites at each co-regulated gene for the transcriptional activator protein GCN4. The GCN4 binding site fits the consensus sequence RRTGACTCATTT, with the core nucleotides TGACTC being the most important for a strong interaction with DNA. GCN4 contains separate domains for DNA binding and transcriptional activation. The former is homologous to DNA-binding domains in other eukaryotic transcriptional activators (AP-1-jun, fos, CPC1) and thus appears to have been highly conserved during evolution. It also contains a structural motif involving periodic leucine residues that may promote dimerization of GCN4, a function thought to be important for efficient DNA binding. The transcriptional activation domain of GCN4 contains acidic amino acids that appear to be arranged in a repeating

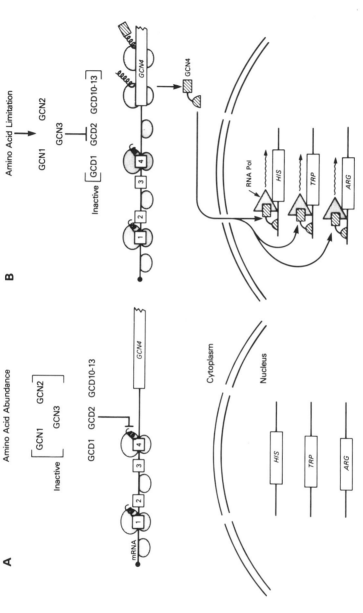

FIG. 12. Hypothetical model for the regulatory events involved in general amino-acid control. Synthesis of GCN4 protein and transcription of amino-acid biosynthetic genes under GCN4 control are depicted as being completely repressed under conditions of amino-acid abundance (A). (In fact, low-level *GCN4* expression and transcriptional activation are expected under these conditions.) Ribosomes can traverse the uORFs in *GCN4* mRNA and reach the *GCN4* start codon under starvation conditions (B) as the result of inactivation of GCD factors by GCN1, GCN2, and GCN3. The latter are activated when the level of aminoacyl-tRNA is low. GCN4 protein is shown as a two-domain molecule, one involved in DNA binding, the other domain making contact with a component of the transcriptional machinery, such as RNA polymerase (RNA Pol).

structure. It is not yet understood how this acidic domain stimulates transcription, but there are reasons to suspect an interaction with TATA-binding factor(s). It is also unclear how binding and transcriptional activation by GCN4 are integrated with the functions of other transcriptional factors involved in basal expression or amino-acid-specific repression of genes under general amino-acid control.

Transcriptional activation by GCN4 increases under conditions of amino-acid starvation because synthesis of GCN4 protein is stimulated in response to starvation. This derepression of *GCN4* expression occurs at the translational level and requires additional *trans*-acting factors, both positive (GCN) and negative (GCD). These factors interact to modulate the degree of translational inhibition exerted by four uORFs present in the leader of *GCN4* mRNA. The four uORFs constitute a complex transitional control element that regulates the progression of scanning ribosomes through the mRNA leader to the *GCN4* start codon. The 5'-proximal uORFs are required, in addition to GCN1, GCN2, and GCN3, for increased *GCN4* expression under starvation conditions. A working hypothesis to explain the positive regulatory function of the 5'-proximal uORFs suggests that ribosomes can resume scanning following translation of uORFs 1 and 2 and emerge from this event altered in a way that allows them to overcome the strong translational barrier at the 3'-proximal uORFs under starvation conditions.

GCN2 is thought to function as a protein kinase in stimulating *GCN4* expression in response to starvation. In addition, its homology with His-tRNA synthetases suggests that GCN2 is the immediate sensor of amino-acid starvation. In this view, accumulation of uncharged tRNA activates GCN2 protein kinase, leading to phosphorylation of one or more additional factors in the general control pathway. The sequence homology between GCN3 and GCD2 suggests that GCN3 acts directly to antagonize GCD2 function under starvation conditions by competition for a binding site or substrate of the latter. Perhaps phosphorylation by GCN2 triggers this antagonist function of GCN3. Because GCD1 and GCD12 are essential gene products, these proteins may be general translational factors whose functions are modified or attenuated under starvation conditions to allow increased translation initiation at the *GCN4* start codon. Pursuing this interesting possibility at the molecular level should yield new insights into the mechanism of translation initiation as well as a better understanding of how yeast cells maintain a constant supply of aminoacyl-tRNA for protein synthesis in the face of a changing environment.

REFERENCES

1. A. G. Hinnebusch, *CRC Crit. Rev. Biochem.* **21**, 277 (1986).
2. P. Niederberger, G. Miozzari and R. Huetter, *MCBiol* **1**, 584 (1981).

3. F. Messenguy and J. Delforge, *EJB* **67**, 335 (1976).
4. J. Delforge, F. Messenguy and J. Wiame, *EJB* **57**, 231 (1975).
5. A. Pierard, F. Messenguy, A. Feller and F. Hilger, *MGG* **174**, 163 (1979).
6. F. Ramos and J. Wiame, *MGG* **200**, 291 (1985).
7. A. G. Hinnebusch, *Microbiol. Rev.* **52**, 248 (1988).
8. S. Holmberg and F. G. L. Petersen, *Curr. Genet.* **13**, 207 (1988).
9. A. P. Mitchell and B. Magasanik, *MCBiol* **4**, 2767 (1984).
10. K. T. Arndt, C. Styles and G. R. Fink, *Science* **237**, 874 (1987).
11. F. Messenguy, *MGG* **169**, 85 (1979).
12. F. Messenguy, D. Colin and J. Ten Have, *EJB* **108**, 439 (1980).
13. E. M. Hannig and A. G. Hinnebusch, *MCBiol* **8**, 4808 (1988).
14. D. E. Hill and K. Struhl, *NARes* **14**, 10045 (1986).
15. P. Niederberger, M. Aebi and R. Huetter, *J. Gen. Microbiol.* **129**, 2571 (1983).
16. M. L. Greenberg, P. L. Myers, R. C. Skvirsky and H. Greer, *MCBiol* **6**, 1820 (1986).
17. R. C. Skvirsky, M. L. Greenberg, P. L. Myers and H. Greer, *Curr. Genet.* **10**, 495 (1986).
18. S. Harashima and A. G. Hinnebusch, *MCBiol* **6**, 3990 (1986).
19. A. G. Hinnebusch and G. R. Fink, *PNAS* **80**, 5374 (1983).
20. P. L. Myers, R. C. Skvirsky, M. L. Greenberg and H. Greer, *MCBiol* **6**, 3150 (1986).
21. P. Niederberger, M. Aebi and R. Huetter, *Curr. Genet.* **10**, 657 (1986).
22. M. Wolfner, D. Yep, F. Messenguy and G. R. Fink, *JMB* **96**, 273 (1975).
23. G. Lucchini, A. G. Hinnebusch, C. Chen and G. R. Fink, *MCBiol* **4**, 1326 (1984).
24. A. G. Hinnebusch, *PNAS* **81**, 6442 (1984).
25. G. Thireos, M. Driscoll-Penn and H. Greer *PNAS* **81**, 5096 (1984).
26. A. G. Hinnebusch, *MCBiol* **5**, 2349 (1985).
27. I. A. Hope and K. Struhl, *Cell* **43**, 177 (1985).
28. K. Arndt and G. R. Fink, *PNAS* **83**, 8516 (1986).
29. K. Struhl and D. E. Hill, *MCBiol* **7**, 104 (1987).
30. M. Driscoll-Penn, B. Galgoci and H. Greer, *PNAS* **80**, 2704 (1983).
31. M. Crabeel, R. Huygen, K. Verschueren, F. Messenguy, K. Tinel, R. Cunin and N. Glansdorff, *MCBiol* **5**, 3139 (1985).
32. G. Paravicini, H.-U. Mosch, T. Schmidheini and G. Braus, *MCBiol* **9**, 144 (1989).
33. R. Furter, G. Braus, G. Paravicini, H.-U. Mosch, P. Niederberger and F. Huetter, *MGG* **211**, 168 (1988).
34. H. Zalkin and C. Yanofsky, *JBC* **257**, 1491 (1982).
35. T. F. Donahue, R. S. Daves, G. Lucchini and G. R. Fink, *Cell* **32**, 89 (1983).
36. F. Nagawa and G. R. Fink, *PNAS* **82**, 8557 (1985).
37. A. G. Hinnebusch, G. Lucchini, and G. R. Fink, *PNAS* **82**, 498 (1985).
38. K. Struhl, *Nature* **300**, 284 (1982).
39. D. E. Hill, I. A. Hope, J. P. Macke, and K. Struhl, *Science* **234**, 451 (1986).
40. K. Struhl, *PNAS* **82**, 8419 (1985).
41. D. W. Russell, M. Smith, D. Cox, V. M. Williamson and E. T. Young, *Nature* **304**, 652 (1983).
42. M. O. Rotenberg and J. L. Woolford, *MCBiol* **6**, 674 (1986).
43. W. Chen, S. Tabor and K. Struhl, *Cell* **50**, 1047 (1987).
44. W. S. Moye and H. Zalkin, *JBC* **260**, 4718 (1985).
45. W. S. Moye and H. Zalkin, *JBC* **262**, 3609 (1987).
46. K. Nishiwaki, N. Hayashi, S. Irie, D. Chung, S. Harashima and Y. Oshima, *MGG* **208**, 159 (1987).
47. K. Struhl, W. Chen, D. E. Hill, I. A. Hope and M. A. Oettinger, *CSHSQB* **50**, 489 (1985).
48. K. Struhl, *MCBiol* **6**, 3847 (1986).

49. K. Struhl, *PNAS* **81**, 7865 (1984).
50. W. Chen and K. Struhl, *PNAS* **85**, 2691 (1988).
51. S. Hahn, E. T. Hoar and L. Guarente, *PNAS* **82**, 8562 (1985).
52. S. J. Silverman and G. R. Fink, *MCBiol* **4**, 1246 (1984).
53. I. A. Hope and K. Struhl, *Cell* **46**, 885 (1986).
54. I. A. Hope and K. Struhl, *EMBO J.* **6**, 2781 (1987).
55. P. K. Vogt, T. J. Bos and R. F. Doolittle, *PNAS* **84**, 3316 (1987).
56. K. Struhl, *Cell* **50**, 841 (1987).
57. D. Bohmann, T. J. Bos, A. Admon, T. Nishimura, P. K. Vogt and R. Tjian, *Science* **238**, 1386 (1988).
58. T. Curran and B. R. Franza, Jr., *Cell* **55**, 395 (1988).
59. I. B. Barthelmess, *Genet. Res* **39**, 169 (1982).
60. J. L. Paluh, M. J. Orbach, T. L. Legerton and C. Yanofsky, *PNAS* **85**, 3728 (1988).
61. K. D. Harshman, W. S. Moye-Rowley and C. S. Parker, *Cell* **53**, 321 (1988).
62. R. H. Jones, S. Moreno, P. Nurse and N. C. Jones, *Cell* **53**, 659 (1988).
63. W. S. Moye-Rowley, K. D. Harshman and C. S. Parker, *Gene Dev.*, **3**, 283 (1989).
64. W. H. Landschulz, P. F. Johnson and S. L. McKnight, *Science* **240**, 1759 (1988).
65. T. Kouzarides and E. Ziff, *Nature* **336**, 646 (1988).
66. I. A. Hope, S. Mahadevan and K. Struhl, *Nature* **333**, 635 (1988).
67. J. Ma and M. Ptashne, *Cell* **48**, 847 (1987).
68. P. P. Mueller, S. Harashima and A. G. Hinnebusch, *PNAS* **84**, 2863 (1987).
69. A. M. Cigan and T. F. Donahue, *Gene* **59**, 1 (1987).
70. M. Kozak, *NARes* **15**, 8125 (1987).
71. F. Sherman and J. W. Stewart, in "The Molecular Biology of the Yeast Saccharomyces: Metabolism and Gene Expression" (J. N. Strathern, E. W. Jones, and J. R. Broach, eds.), 301 pp. CSHLab, Cold Spring Harbor, New York, 1982.
72. P. T. Lomedico and S. J. McAndrew, *Nature* **299**, 221 (1982).
73. M. Kozak, *Cell* **34**, 971 (1983).
74. R. S. Zitomer, D. A. Walthall, B. C. Rymond and C. P. Hollenberg, *MCBiol* **4**, 1191 (1984).
75. H. Johansen, D. Schumperli and M. Rosenberg, *PNAS* **81**, 7698 (1984).
76. M. Kozak, *NARes* **12**, 3873 (1984).
77. C. Liu, C. C. Simonsen and A. D. Levinson, *Nature* **309**, 82 (1984).
78. T. F. Donahue and A. M. Cigan, *MCBiol* **8**, 2955 (1988).
79. M. Kozak, *Microbiol. Rev.* **47**, 1 (1983).
80. P. P. Mueller and A. G. Hinnebusch, *Cell* **45**, 201 (1986).
81. N. P. Williams, P. P. Mueller and A. G. Hinnebusch, *MCBiol* **8**, 3827 (1988).
82. D. Tzamarias, D. Alexandraki and G. Thireos, *PNAS* **83**, 4849 (1986).
83. D. Tzamarias and G. Thireos, *EMBO J.* **7**, 3547 (1988).
84. M. Kozak, *MCBiol* **7**, 3438 (1987).
85. P. P. Mueller, B. M. Jackson, P. F. Miller and A. G. Hinnebusch, *MCBiol* **8**, 5439 (1988).
86. R. Hamilton, C. K. Watanabe and H. A. DeBoer, *NARes* **15**, 3581 (1987).
87. A. G. Hinnebusch, B. M. Jackson and P. P. Mueller, *PNAS* **85**, 7279 (1988).
88. I. Roussou, G. Thireos and B. M. Hauge, *MCBiol* **8**, 2132 (1988).
89. S. K. Hanks, A. M. Quinn and T. Hunter, *Science* **241**, 41 (1988).
90. R. C. Wek, B. M. Jackson and A. G. Hinnebusch, *PNAS* **86**, 4579 (1989).
91. A. M. Edelman, D. K. Blumenthal and E. G. Krebs, *ARB* **56**, 567 (1987).
92. M. Driscoll-Penn, G. Thireos and H. Greer, *MCBiol* **4**, 520 (1984).
93. D. E. Hill and K. Struhl, *NARes* **16**, 9253 (1988).
94. C. J. Paddon and A. G. Hinnebusch, *Genetics*, **122**, 543 (1989).

95. J. W. B. Hershey, R. Duncan and M. B. Mathews, in "Current Communications in Molecular Biology: Translational Control" (M. B. Mathews, ed.), p. 1. *CSHLab*, Cold Spring Harbor, New York, 1986.
96. M. J. Clemens, A. Galpine, S. A. Austin, R. Panniers, E. C. Henshaw, R. Duncan, J. W. Hershey and J. W. Pollard, *JBC* 262, 767 (1987).
97. S. Harashima, E. M. Hannig and A. G. Hinnebusch, *Genetics* 117, 409 (1987).
98. C. J. Paddon, E. M. Hannig and A. G. Hinnebusch, *Genetics*, 122, 551 (1989).
99. T. F. Donahue, P. J. Farabaugh and G. R. Fink, *Gene* 18, 47 (1982).
100. K. Struhl, *PNAS* 79, 7385 (1982).
101. H. Zalkin, J. L. Paluh, M. Van Cleemput, W. S. Moye and C. Yanofsky, *JBC* 259, 3985 (1984).
102. M. Aebi, R. Furter, F. Prantl, P. Niederberger and R. Huetter, *Curr. Genet.* 8, 165 (1984).
103. R. Furter, G. Paravicini, M. Aebi, G. Braus, F. Prantl, P. Niederberger and R. Huetter, NARes 14, 6357 (1986).
104. I. R. Beacham, B. W. Schweitzer, H. M. Warrick and J. Carbon, *Gene* 29, 271 (1984).
105. H. Nyunoya and C. J. Lusty, *JBC* 259, 9790 (1984).
106. M. Werner, A. Feller and A. Pierard, *EJB* 146, 371 (1985).
107. M. Crabeel, S. Seneca, K. Devos and N. Glansdorff, *Curr. Genet.* 13, 113 (1988).
108. M. Mirande and J.-P. Waller, *JBC* 263, 18443 (1988).
109. M. C. Kielland-Brandt, S. Holmberg, J. G. L. Petersen and T. Nilsson-Tillgren, *Carlsberg Res. Commun.* 49, 567 (1984).
110. S. C. Falco, K. S. Dumas and K. J. Livak, *NARes* 13, 4011 (1985).
111. P. Friden and P. Schimmel, *MCBiol* 8, 2690 (1988).
112. J. G. L. Petersen and S. Holmberg, *NARes* 14, 9631 (1986).
113. J. P. Beltzer, L. L. Chang, A. E. Hinkkanen and G. B. Kohlhaw, *JBC* 261, 5160 (1986).
114. Y.-P. Hsu and P. Schimmel, *JBC* 259, 3714 (1984).
115. A. Andreadis, Y.-P. Hsu, G. B. Kohlhaw and P. Schimmel, *Cell* 31, 319 (1982).
116. A. Andreadis, Y.-P. Hsu, M. Hermodson, G. Kohlhaw and P. Schimmel, *JBC* 259, 8059 (1984).
117. A. Martinez-Arias, H. J. Yost and M. J. Casadaban, *Nature* 307, 740 (1984).
118. G. Miozzari, P. Niederberger and R. Huetter, *J. Bact.* 134, 48 (1978).
119. A. Schurch, J. Miozzari and R. Huetter, *J. Bact.* 117, 1131 (1974).
120. S. Teshiba, R. Furter, P. Niederberger, G. Braus, G. Paravicini and R. Huetter, *MGG* 205, 353 (1986).
121. B. Wipf and T. Leisinger, *J. Bact.* 140, 874 (1979).
122. P. Jacobs, J. Jauniaux and M. Grenson, *JMB* 139, 691 (1980).
123. F. Messenguy and E. Dubois, *MGG* 189, 148 (1983).
124. F. Messenguy, A. Feller, M. Crabeel and A. Pierard, *EMBO J.* 2, 1249 (1983).
125. S. J. Silverman, M. Rose, D. Botstein and G. R. Fink, *MCBiol* 2, 1212 (1982).
126. L. A. Urrestarazu, C. W. Borell and J. K. Bhattacharjee, *Curr. Genet.* 9, 341 (1985).
127. F. Meussdoerffer and G. R. Fink, *JBC* 258, 6293 (1983).
128. Y.-P. Hsu, G. B. Kohlhaw and P. Niederberger, *J. Bact.* 150, 969 (1982).
129. K. Zhou, P. R. G. Brisco, A. E. Hinkkanen and G. B. Kohlhaw, *NARes* 15, 5261 (1987).
130. J. A. Rafalski and S. C. Falco, *JBC* 263, 2146 (1988).
131. P. F. Miller and A. G. Hinnebusch, *Gene Dev.* 3, 1217 (1989).

Mechanisms Regulating Transient Expression of Mammalian Cytokine Genes and Cellular Oncogenes

RAYMOND REEVES*† AND
NANCY S. MAGNUSON‡

*Program in Biochemistry and
Biophysics
†Genetics and Cell Biology Program
‡Department of Microbiology
Washington State University
Pullman, Washington 99164

Abbreviations

AP-1, activator protein-1

ARRE, antigen regulatory response element (e.g., ARRE-1)

b, bovine (e.g., bIL-2)

c-*fos*, nuclear oncogene identified as the cellular cognate of the oncogene v-*fos*, the resident transforming gene of FBJ-murine osteosarcoma virus (FBJ-MSV)

c-*jun*, nuclear oncogene identified as the cellular homologue of the oncogene v-*jun*, the resident transforming gene of avian sarcoma virus 17 (ASV17)

c-*myb*, nuclear oncogene identified as the cellular cognate of the oncogene v-*myb*, the resident transforming gene of avian myeloblastosis virus

Progress in Nucleic Acid Research
and Molecular Biology, Vol. 38

c-*myc*, nuclear oncogene identified as the cellular cognate of the oncogene v-*myc* found in the avian defective retrovirus MC29

CsA, cyclosporine A

CSF, colony-stimulating factor

CTF, CCAAT-binding transcription factor (indistinguishable from NF-1)

DSE, dyad symmetry element

Fos, nuclear transcription factor; protein product of c-*fos*

GAL4, positive transcriptional activator protein of yeast

GCN4, positive transcriptional activator protein of yeast

G-CSF, granulocyte—colony-stimulating factor

GM-CSF, granulocyte/macrophage—colony-stimulating factor

h, human (e.g., hTNF)

IFN, interferon (e.g., α-IFN)

IκB, inhibitory factor κB

IL, interleukin (e.g., IL-2; see also R below)

IRE, interferon regulatory element (in DNA)

IRF, interferon regulatory factor (protein)

Jun, nuclear transcription factor (similar to AP-1); protein product of c-*jun*

kb, kilobase

kDa, kilodalton

L cells, strain of C3H mouse connective tissue cells derived from the permanently growing line NCTC clone 929

L-*myc*, structural homologue of c-*myc* and N-*myc*, first isolated from a human small-cell lung cancer cell line, where it was detected by the presence of gene amplification

m, murine (e.g., mIL-4)

M-CSF, macrophage—colony-stimulating factor

MLA-144, gibbon leukemia cell line

NF-1, nuclear factor-1 (indistinguishable from CTF)

NFAT-1, nuclear factor of activated T cells-1

NFIL-2A, nuclear factor IL-2A

NF-κB, nuclear factor κB

N-*myc*, structural homologue of c-*myc*, first identified on the basis of its amplification in a human neuroblastoma cell line

pim-1, putative oncogene implicated in T cell lymphomogenesis by its frequent activation by proviral insertion in murine leukemia virus (MuLV)-induced T-cell lymphomas

P, promoter (e.g., P_1)

PBL, peripheral blood lymphocyte

PBMC, peripheral blood mononuclear cell

PDGF, platelet-derived growth factor

Pol-II, RNA polymerase II

r, rat (e.g., rIL-3)

R, receptor (e.g., IL-2R)

Sp-1, nuclear transcription factor that specifically recognizes the promoter sequence GGGCGG

SRE, serum response element (in DNA)

SRF, serum response factor (protein)

T cell, thymus-derived lymphocytes

T-cell leukemia, neoplastic lymphocytes of T-cell origin

TE, transcription element (in DNA) (e.g., TE1)

TF, transcription factor (protein) (e.g., TFIID)

TNF, tumor necrosis factor

UTR, untranslated "tail" (3') region

VRE, virus response element (DNA)

> ". . . he who, seeing fossil shells on a mountain, conceived the theory of the deluge."
>
> Samuel Butler

Activation of resting mammalian cells to undergo division is normally initiated by extracellular signals and stimuli coupled to integrated intracellular effector pathways (signal transduction events) that lead to specific changes in genomic transcription and protein synthesis patterns. Of necessity, most of the cellular steps and molecules involved in such processes must be precisely controlled as well as temporally and spatially regulated. Abnormal functioning of any of the components of such a complex cascading pathway could lead to death, uncontrolled proliferation, or other cellular pathologies. Indeed, many viral and cellular oncogenes are now known to be aberrant or abnormally regulated genes coding for normal cellular growth factors or growth factor receptors, or factors involved in the initiation and regulation of gene expression. Likewise, abnormal expression of cytokines[1] has often been implicated in the development of leukemias, lymphomas, and other neoplastic events in the mammalian immune system.

A hallmark of the expression of an important subset of cytokine genes and cellular oncogenes is the transient nature of the appearance and disappearance of their mRNAs and proteins after stimulation of cells with appropriate excitatory molecules. Such transient gene expression is the result of coordinate biochemical regulatory mechanisms operating at many levels within the cell. These include precise regulation of gene transcription initiation, elongation and termination, control of posttranscriptional mRNA processing and selective mRNA degradation, as well as numerous other translational and posttranslational control processes.

---

[1] Cytokines are hormone-like gene products that mediate interactions between cells.

Owing to the interrelated and highly coordinated manner in which these various mechanisms operate within a cell, it is often difficult to evaluate accurately the relative contribution of any one mechanism to the overall control or regulation of transient gene expression. Nevertheless, within the past several years, significant advances have been made that are beginning to elucidate many of the individual molecular events involved in each of these different levels of control. The focus of this article is on recent findings pertaining to these various mechanisms and the way they interact to regulate the transient expression of many of the known cytokine genes and cellular oncogenes.

I. Stimulation of Transient Gene Expression

Mitogenic stimulation of resting nonneoplastic mammalian cells with growth factors, hormones, serum, or other stimuli, or the activation of quiescent lymphocytes with appropriate combinations of lectins, antigens, phorbol esters, and chemical ionophores, induces a complex series of intracellular events (1, 2, 2a). Within seconds, and in the absence of any RNA or protein synthesis, activation of ion channels, phosphatidylinositol turnover, and protein kinases can be observed. Presumably, these immediate "signal transduction" events result from the intrinsic activity of the complexes formed between various stimulatory molecules and their surface receptors.

Activation of protein kinase C (PKC) and increased Ca^{2+} mobilization are used as signal transduction processes in many different cell types (3, 3a, 4). When T lymphocytes are exposed to antigens, the complex of T-cell antigen receptor with CD3 transduces the external signal across the plasma membrane, generating intracellular signals (1). These signals activate phosphoinositidyl turnover, leading to production of diacylglycerol, which activates the kinase, and inositol 1, 4, 5-trisphosphate (IP3), which results in increases in both Ca^{2+} mobilization and influx (5). Subsequent downstream signal transduction events, possibly involving a cascade of phosphorylations and dephosphorylations, trigger a series of biochemical reactions in the nucleus that result in the activation or transcription of a battery of growth-factor genes and cellular oncogenes whose transient expression, in turn, eventually culminates in cell division and proliferation.

With the advent of recombinant DNA technology, many of these inducible and transiently expressed cytokine genes have been isolated and their modes of regulation and expression studied. For example, early investigations (6) employing cloned cDNAs detected transcription of c-*fos** mRNA within 10 minutes of lymphocyte stimulation and demonstrated (7, 16) that c-*myc* mRNA accumulates to high levels inside cells within 2 hours of stimulation. The observed activation of these early or "rapid response" genes provided the first indications that the expression of some cellular oncogenes may be linked to cellular proliferation (8). These observations also strongly suggest that specialized molecular mechanisms exist to regulate the expression of this group of readily induced and transiently expressed genes.

Furthermore, the techniques of modern molecular biology not only enable researchers to investigate the precise mechanisms controlling the expression of individual genes, but also allow the beginnings of investigations into the complex processes involved in forming the "growth factor cascade," in which the action of any given growth factor, cytokine, or cellular oncogene invariably influences the activity of others. Such cascades are now known to be a salient feature in the programmed growth, differentiation, and normal function of all mammalian cells.

Table I lists the half-lives of the mRNAs of some of the transiently expressed genes whose inducible regulation has been analyzed in detail. From these limited data, it appears that such genes can be conveniently divided into two groups, one with very short mRNA half-lives of up to 30 minutes (β-IFN, γ-IFN, GM-CSF, G-CSF, c-*fos*, c-*myc*, and c-*pim*-1) and the other

TABLE I

ESTIMATED HALF-LIVES OF TRANSIENTLY EXPRESSED GROWTH FACTOR GENE, CYTOKINE GENE, AND CELLULAR ONCOGENE mRNAs IN STIMULATED CELLS

Factor	Source	Estimated mRNA half-life (min)	References
IL-1β	Human monocyte/macrophage cell lines	<90	*15*
IL-2	Human T lymphocytes	60–120	*17, 18*
IL-3	Mouse helper T-lymphocyte cell line	<120	*19*
IL-4	Mouse T-lymphocyte line	<120	*20, 21*
β-IFN	Human fibroblasts	<30	*22, 23*
γ-IFN	Human lymphocytes	<30	*24, 25*
GM-CSF	Human and mouse lymphocytes	15–30	*26–28*
G-CSF	Human fibroblasts	15	*28*
M-CSF	Human monocytes	<60	*29*
TNF	Mouse macrophages	<120	*30, 31*
c-*fos*	Human and mouse cell lines	20–30	*32–34*
c-*jun*	Human and mouse cell lines	<90	*35*
c-*myb*	Mouse erythroleukemia cells	60–110	*36*
c-*myc*	Human and mouse T lymphocytes	12–30	*37, 38*
L-*myc*	Human small-cell lung cancer cells	90–150	*39*
N-*myc*	Human small-cell lung cancer cells	60–75	*39*
c-*pim*-1	Mouse hematopoietic cell lines	35	*40*

group with slightly longer half-lives of 1 to 2 hours (IL-1β, IL-2, IL-3, IL-4, TNF, c-*jun*, c-*myb*, L-*myc*, and N-*myc*). In contrast, most other mammalian cell mRNAs appear to be reasonably stable (*10–14*).

The rates of mRNA turnover in mammalian cells vary widely, with half-lives normally ranging from several hours to days (*9*). For example, the bulk polysome-associated poly(A)$^+$-mRNA in mouse L cells has a half-life of around 10 hours (*12*), whereas that of globin mRNA in erythroleukemia cells is about 60 hours (*13*). Reliable measurements of the half-lives of nine randomly selected, presumably abundant, mRNAs synthesized in actively growing Chinese hamster ovary cells, obtained by monitoring the decay of prelabeled transcripts by hybridization to cloned DNA probes, indicated that, of the nine mRNA species examined, eight had half-lives between 8 and 10 hours and the ninth had one of 3.5 hours (*14*). It has also been observed that a given mRNA may have different turnover rates, depending on the circumstances. IFN-β mRNA has a longer half-life when induced by Newcastle disease virus than with poly(rI)·poly(rC) (*23*). Overall, the data indicate that most mammalian mRNAs have relatively long half-lives, thus making the short half-lives of the gene transcripts listed in Table I interesting exceptions.

II. Time Course and Kinetics of Sequential Gene Expression

Prior to activation, resting or quiescent mammalian cells and lymphocytes exhibit little, if any, activity from endogenous cytokine genes or cellular oncogenes. However, immediately following stimulation there is a temporal sequence of gene transcriptional activations that seems to follow a pattern of expression characteristic for a given cell type. Nuclear transcription analyses (*41*) have been used to study the temporal sequence of gene activation following stimulation of human lymphocytes with the lectin phytohemagglutinin and phorbol myristate acetate. Similar procedures have been used in the study of the expression of the cellular oncogene c-*fos* in human monocytes stimulated with the phorbol ester 12-*O*-tetradecanoylphorbol 13-acetate (TPA) (*33*). Figure 1 schematically presents the combined results of the above studies, showing the characteristic temporal sequence of induced gene transcription and mRNA accumulation in stimulated human peripheral blood mononuclear cells (PBMCs), as detected by such nuclear run-off assays.

As shown in Fig. 1, within 10 minutes of the activation of these cells, there was a rapid increase in full-length c-*fos* transcripts that reached a maximum within 30 minutes (a 28-fold increase over that in uninduced cells) which then declined by three hours to undetectable levels (*33*). Similarly, c-*myc* was rapidly activated but did not reach peak transcription rates until

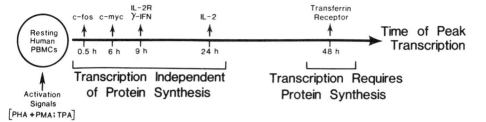

FIG. 1. Sequential gene expression in activated human peripheral blood mononuclear cells (PBMCs). Nuclear run-off assays were performed with isolated nuclei obtained from T cells (41) and mononuclear cells (42) for varying periods of time after lectin and phorbol ester treatment. Time [in hours (h)] of peak transcription from each of the assayed genes is shown schematically.

6–9 hours after activation (41). Expression of c-*myc* was followed sequentially by transcription of the genes encoding the IL-2 receptor (IL-2R) and γ-IFN that peaked at 9–15 hours after mitogen addition. This was followed by increases in IL-2 gene transcription that did not reach maximal levels, as determined by these *in vitro* nuclear assays, until about 24 hours after stimulation (see below) (41).

The temporally regulated transcription of each of the five inducible genes shown in Fig. 1 was not inhibited by addition of cycloheximide (ChX) to the cells in concentrations sufficient to block over 98% of protein synthesis (33, 41, 43). These observations indicate that the protein products of these genes are not required for the subsequent activation of mRNA transcription of the other genes; for example, the c-*fos* product is apparently not required for induction of c-*myc* transcription, nor is the c-*myc* protein, in turn, necessary for the later initiation of transcription from the IL-2R and IL-2 genes (43). In contrast to this family of rapidly induced genes (c-*fos*, c-*myc*, IL-2, IL-2R), which are transcribed in the absence of protein synthesis, the transferrin receptor gene was not expressed until 24 hours after stimulation and did not reach peak levels until 48 hours. Addition of ChX at the initiation of culture completely blocked transcription of the transferrin receptor gene, thus indicating an absolute dependence on prior protein synthesis for the activation of this gene (41).

The transient nature of the expression of rapidly inducible genes whose transcription is independent of continuing protein synthesis is readily apparent when the time course and kinetics of accumulation of individual mRNA species are examined. Typically in such experiments, resting PBMCs or quiescent cell lines are mitogenically stimulated and, at time points following activation, total cellular RNA is isolated from the cells and assayed for the relative levels of various individual mRNAs by standard RNA Northern blot analysis (44). The intensities of individual hybridizing mRNA bands observed on autoradiographs are then determined by densitometric scanning, and these relative values are plotted as a function of time after stimulation.

Figure 2 shows the results of studies of such kinetics of mRNA accumulation in stimulated PBMCs and lymphoid cells, compiled from a number of sources. From such time-course data it is apparent that each mRNA species is characterized by individual differences in its overall rates of accumulation and disappearance within stimulated cells. It would thus appear that not all transiently induced and expressed genes are regulated in precisely the same manner by different cells.

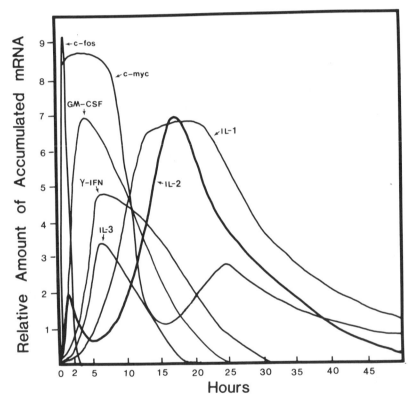

FIG. 2. Kinetics of accumulation of rapidly induced mRNAs in activated mammalian lymphoid cells. Data were derived from a number of different sources and are depicted on a single graph. Data for c-*fos* and c-*myc* were obtained from phytohemagglutinin (PHA)-stimulated human PMBCs (*44*). Data for IL-2 (*45*) and IL-1 (unpublished data) were obtained from bovine PBMCs stimulated by concanavalin A (ConA) plus PHA. Data for IL-3 and γ-IFN are from Con-A-stimulated murine T lymphocytes (*19*) and data for GM-CSF are from murine macrophages stimulated by fetal calf serum (*27*).

Indeed, as can be seen from the results shown in Fig. 3 (data derived from 17), even two very similar transcripts can have very different kinetics of accumulation in different types of lymphoid cells. This is illustrated by the fact that, after mitogen induction of the murine EL4.E1 lymphoma cell line, the intracellular level of IL-2 mRNA peaked at 10 hours and then declined to about half this amount by 24 hours, whereas after induction of the human Jurkat leukemia cell line, there was a rapid rise and fall in the intracellular level of IL-2 mRNA within about 5 hours (17). Even though such obvious variations exist, within a given cell the normal pattern of induction and transient expression of various genes is highly regulated and characteristic of that cell type.

Besides assaying for detectable mRNA transcripts, functional gene expression in activated mammalian cells is also commonly assessed by determining whether or not cells produce specific protein products as a consequence of induction. In general, the rate of synthesis of specific proteins in

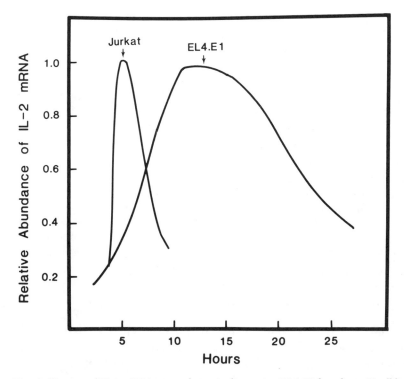

FIG. 3. Kinetics of IL-2 mRNA accumulation in the murine EL4.E1 lymphoma T-cell line and the human T-leukemia line Jurkat after stimulation with phorbol myristate acetate. Based on the data of Shaw et al. (17).

somatic cells is limited by, and closely parallels, the rates of synthesis and accumulation of their functional mRNAs (48, 49), and this also appears to be the case for intracellular proteins encoded by transiently expressed genes. In stimulated cells, the *in vivo* half-lives of the intracellular c-*myc* (50, 51), c-*Fos* (52), and c-*myb* (50s, 53) proteins are 30 minutes or less, closely approximating the estimated turnover rates of their respective mRNAs. Such results indicate that mammalian cells possess mechanisms for selectively degrading undamaged proteins whose intracellular concentrations must vary as a function of time (54–57).

Regarding cellular oncogene products, it is not known whether this rapid *in vivo* turnover is a function of protein degradation due to cotranslational processing at the polysome level (58) or is perhaps due to preferential recognition of specific features of these proteins by proteases. For example, it has been suggested that many short-lived cellular proteins, including numerous oncogene proteins, contain either specific internal amino-acid sequences (59) or particular amino-terminal amino-acid sequences (62, 63) that mark them for selective elimination by proteases. However, it is also possible that other features of protein structure, such as the degree of peptide flexibility (61), or perhaps secondary biochemical modifications such as multi-ubiquitination (54–57, 60) may play similar or complementary roles in the control of protein stability inside cells.

In contrast to the generally short half-lives of intracellular oncogene proteins, cytokines that are secreted from induced cells appear in some cases to be fairly stable. Figure 4 illustrates the time course of production of various secreted lymphokine proteins after alloantigen stimulation of a cultured murine T-lymphocyte cell line, L2 (64). In these experiments, standard bioassay procedures were used to determine the level of individual lymphokine proteins in the culture supernatants of the stimulated L2 cells. As the figure shows, over an 8-day period all of the secreted lymphokines (IL-3, IL-4, GM-CSF, γ-IFN) except the IL-2 protein appeared to be generally stable in the culture supernatant. Furthermore, the decline observed for the IL-2 protein after about 40 hours of culture was attributed not to lability of the IL-2 protein per se, but to the active proliferation of the L2 cells (which are dependent on the continued presence of the IL-2 lymphokine for growth), leading to the disappearance of IL-2 from the culture supernatant (64).

However, it is questionable whether the results of these and similar types of *in vitro* experiments can be considered indicative of the natural *in vivo* stability of secreted lymphokines inside the whole organism. Measurements of the stability of recombinant IL-2 administered to mice resulted in a serum half-life of the protein of about 2.5–3.5 minutes (65), and similar experiments in humans revealed a half-life of approximately 5–7 minutes with a second

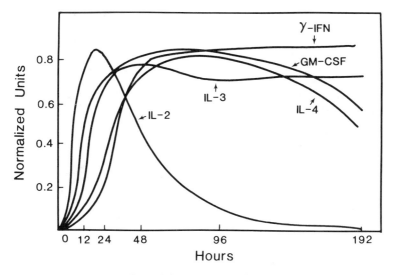

FIG. 4. Kinetics of secreted lymphokine protein production by the murine lymphocyte cell line L2 stimulated by alloantigen. Based on the data of Prystowsky *et al.* (*64*).

component of clearance of 30–120 minutes (*66, 67*). The kidney appeared to be the main site of clearance of IL-2 from the bloodstream in these *in vivo* experiments (*65*). Whether lymphokines and growth factors other than IL-2 are selectively and rapidly cleared from the blood and lymphatic system *in vivo* remains to be determined.

III. Lymphokines as a Distinctive Subset of Cytokines

Although the mode of regulation of most cytokine genes shares many characteristics with cellular oncogenes, it has been suggested (*17, 18, 46*) that the cytokines derived from T cells, collectively called lymphokines, form a specific subgroup of such factors because they possess a distinctive phenotype. For example, the induction and suppression of this class of genes have common features not shared by the rest of the genetic repertoire of cells. Among the features proposed to distinguish lymphokine genes are their selective inducibility by mitogens and phorbol esters, and the suppression of their transcriptional activity by the immunosuppressive drug cyclosporine A (CsA). Additionally, this group is characterized by superinduction of their mRNAs by inhibitors of protein synthesis such as ChX after transcription has been initiated (*18, 46*). Most lymphokine genes also share the unusual characteristic of having their expression repressed in cells treated with glucocorticoids, such as dexamethasone (*46a*).

In keeping with these suggestions, many of the known T-cell-derived factors and lymphokines (such as IL-2, IL-3, IL-4, G-CSF, M-CSF, GM-CSF, and γ-IFN) do exhibit these expected features. This constellation of easily identifiable biochemical phenotypes has led to the isolation of a number of cDNA clones with unusual lymphokine-like characteristics. About 60 such novel cDNA clones from normal stimulated human T cells have been isolated (47). The nucleotide sequences of two of these clones (pAT464 and pAT744) are similar to those of a newly discovered family of secreted factors including platelet factor 4, connective tissue activating factor III, macrophage inflammatory protein, a γ-IFN-induced factor, and a factor chemotactic for nucleophils (nucleophil-activating factor) (47). Collectively, these observations suggest that pAT464 and pAT744, as predicted, encode novel lymphokines and/or cytokines that may play significant roles in the regulation of the mammalian immune response (47).

IV. Mechanisms Regulating Transient Gene Expression

Cloned genes coding for an ever-increasing number of proteins involved in the cascade of biochemical events leading to cell division have made it feasible, within the last few years, to begin to elucidate many of the molecular requirements for regulating cell proliferation. Such clones have enabled the identification of functional *cis*-acting DNA elements that specifically respond to *trans*-acting regulatory factors involved in the control of transcriptional expression of these genes. Likewise, by being able to combine the capability of *in vitro* site-specific mutagenesis of isolated genes with the capacity to reintroduce these mutated genes back into living cells and organisms for study, it has recently been possible to investigate the *in vivo* function of specific genes and proteins in a manner not previously possible.

Employing such techniques, researchers have gathered considerable detailed information concerning mechanisms that regulate the *in vivo* activities of a number of genes coding for cytokines, growth factors and cellular oncogenes. Nevertheless, the principal generalization that can presently be drawn from all these investigations is that no one mechanism, or even a combination of currently known mechanisms, can adequately explain the observed complex patterns of transient gene expression as they occur in living cells. What is also abundantly clear is that at each possible level of cellular control, from the activation of gene transcription to postsynthetic modifications and degradative turnover of newly synthesized proteins, a plethora of biochemical control mechanisms seem to exist. The remainder of this review is confined to a discussion of selected examples of the molecular mechanisms thought to be operating at different levels of control within the cell to regulate transiently expressed genes.

V. Transcription of Genes by RNA Polymerase II

Considerable progress has been made during the last few years in elucidating the mechanisms that control the transcriptional expression of genes copied by RNA polymerase II (Pol II) (69–79). Much of this work has centered on identifying the specific DNA elements involved in the regulation and modulation of *in vitro* transcription, and on isolating and characterizing specific proteins or other factors that bind to these DNA sequences. However, the actual *in vivo* processes underlying gene transcription are much more complicated, involving not only specific DNA–protein interactions but also changes in chromatin structure, formation of stable initiation complexes, precise control of transcript initiation, elongation, and termination, as well as other components.

One of the most conceptually gratifying findings to emerge recently is that the protein products of certain previously identified cellular oncogenes are indeed involved in gene transcriptional regulation. Thus, the proteins coded for by the c-*fos* and c-*jun* oncogenes are transcription factors that bind to specific DNA regulatory elements (AP-1 sites) both *in vitro* and *in vivo* (80–88), and the protein product of the oncogene *erb*-A is the receptor for thyroid hormone (*114*).

On the other hand, one of the most unexpected findings arising from recent studies is the remarkably high degree of conservation of function between the protein transcription factors found in such distantly related organisms as yeast and mammals. For example, the yeast and human proteins that bind specifically to the regulatory CCAAT elements found near the 5′ end of most eukaryotic genes have functionally interchangeable subunits (89), and a yeast protein that binds the TATA box can functionally replace a similarly binding mammalian protein factor, TFIID, in *in vitro* transcription systems (90). Furthermore, a high degree of sequence similarity exists between the carboxyl-terminal domains of the Jun protein (the product of c-*jun*) of mammals and the yeast GCN4 protein transcription factor, and, in fact, these two domains are able to functionally replace each other in hybrid GNC4/Jun fusion proteins when tested both *in vitro* and *in vivo* (80, 115, 116). And finally, the yeast GAL4 activator protein can interact with the mammalian TFIID protein to stimulate Pol-II gene transcription *in vitro* (91, 92). These reports demonstrate that the mechanism by which RNA Pol-II transcription is promoted has been remarkably conserved during the evolution of eukaryotes.

A. Organization of the Promoter Region of a Protein-Coding Gene Transcribed by RNA Polymerase II

Although promoters for protein-coding genes vary somewhat in overall organization and sequence, they are generally arranged according to a common plan, as shown in Fig. 5. In such an arrangement, at least two types of promoter elements can be distinguished: those that select the start site of initiation of transcription, and those that modulate the rate of specific initiation (upstream elements and enhancers).

In terms of nucleotide base-pairs, the "selector region" (74) extends from approximately −45 to +30 (where +1 is the start site of RNA transcription), and contains two highly conserved sequences, the TATAAA (or TATA box) element at around −30, and CA at +1. General transcription factors bind to this region and direct RNA Pol II to the start site. The same general transcription factors are probably required for specific initiation and basal levels of transcription from most protein-coding genes (93–100). Near the 5' end of the selector region, usually within about 100 bp of the initiation site, are located one or more short (10–20 bp) sequences called "upstream elements," which serve as recognition sites for specific transcription factors (TFs). Two of the most common of these elements, the CCAAT box and the GGGCGG sequence, are, respectively, the specific binding sites for the CTF/NF-1 (101) and Sp-1 (69, 72, 102) TFs. However, it should be stressed that not all Pol-II genes necessarily have either (or both) of these upstream sequences (i.e., the CTF/NF-1 and Sp-1 elements), and that they are often replaced by

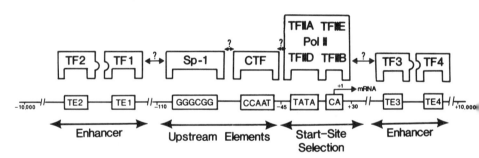

FIG. 5. Structure of a typical eukaryotic protein-coding gene promoter. The start-site selection region interacts with general transcription factors (TFIIA, TFIIB, TFIID, and TFIIE), which are common to most RNA polymerase II (Pol II) promoters. These general transcription factors (TFs), along with Pol II, form an initiation complex that can interact with other DNA–protein complexes formed by the binding of specific TFs to upstream or downstream transcription elements (TEs). It is common to find one or more TEs immediately upstream from the start-site selection region, such as the CCAAT and GGGCGG sequences shown in this diagram. These TEs, respectively, are the specific binding sites for the CTF and Sp-1 TFs. Efficient distal activation of transcription by enhancers appears to require the association of several TFs. The types of interactions that may exist to generate an active promoter complex with "looped-out" intervening DNA sequences are indicated by double-headed arrows with question marks, or by complementary shapes of symbols. TFs that do not bind DNA may be required for these interactions. Based on the data of Wasylyk (74) and Buratowski et al. (90, 90a).

other types of upstream elements that can act in either a positive or negative manner in modulating transcriptional activity.

These two promoter regions, the selection region and the upstream elements, can together be considered the basic organization for genes that are constitutively active or are expressed at the same level in all cells. However, more complex regulation of transcription, such as occurs for cytokine genes and cellular oncogenes, is achieved by additional transcription elements (TEs), which can be located and can function at distances up to 10,000 base-pairs upstream or downstream from the RNA start site (Fig. 5). Often two or more of these TEs can be located within special regions called enhancers. ["Enhancer" is a special term coined to describe any promoter sequence that can stimulate transcription in an orientation-independent fashion when located more than several hundred base-pairs upstream or downstream from a core promoter (103).] The TEs located either in enhancers or as individual elements flanking the 5' ends of genes are often the recognition and binding sites for cell- or tissue-specific TFs.

Purified TFs have been given a variety of different names (74, 93, 94, 104, 193) but most of them seem to be equivalent to the proteins designated TFIIA, TFIIB, TFIID, and TFIIE (95–97). These general TFs, along with Pol-II, are thought to assemble into stable "preinitiation" complexes (98–100, 193) in the promoter start-site selection region prior to actual initiation of RNA transcription. Figure 6 presents a hypothetical model, based on evidence from in vitro experiments (90, 90a, 95–100, 193), of the postulated sequential steps leading to the formation of a functional Pol-II initiation complex. It should be noted, however, that not all Pol-II transcribed genes contain a TATA-box promoter. Therefore, this model may only be applicable to a certain subset of protein-coding genes. Complex formation normally begins with the binding of factor TFIID to the TATA box followed by association of factor TFIIA to form a committed template. It is possible that commitment of a TATA-box-driven Pol-II-type gene requires only the binding of TFIID (97a, 193), and that TFIIA is a common, but perhaps not essential, component for this process.

Subsequently, although the sequential order of events is unclear, a stable preinitiation complex is established by the binding of TFIIB and Pol-II. At some later time, this preinitiation complex can be converted to a functional initiation complex that can begin RNA transcription by association with ATP, TFIIE, ribonucleotide triphosphates (NTPs), and possibly other factors (90, 90a). These common core promoter elements and protein complexes are thought to interact with the cell- and tissue-specific TE/TF complexes located in flanking enhancer regions in such a way as to modulate the rate of specific initiation of gene transcription (193). The most frequently suggested mechanism for accomplishing this functional interaction of such widely sepa-

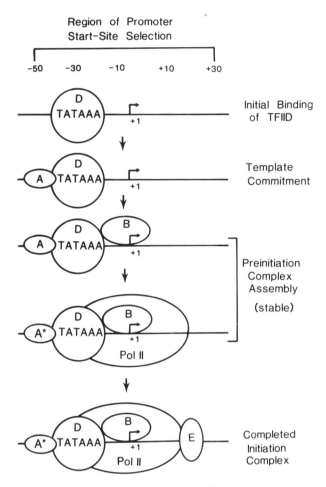

FIG. 6. Speculative scheme for the formation of stable transcription initiation complexes in the region of promoter start-site selection of protein-coding genes. The numbers at the top are nucleotide positions relative to the transcription initiation site at +1. A, B, D, and E are, respectively, the transcription factors TFIIA, TFIIB, TFIID, and TFIIE. The order of factor additions after the template commitment stage, involving the binding of TFIID to the TATA element, is uncertain. The asterisk on TFIIA in the preinitiation and complete initiation complexes is to signify that it is not known whether this factor is present at these stages. Based on the data of Buratowski *et al.* (*90, 90a*).

rated promoter elements is by the formation of protein–DNA complexes with "looping-out" of the intervening DNA sequences (*71, 77*).

At the onset of transcription, or shortly thereafter, many of the factors originally involved in complex formation (e.g., TFIIA, TFIIB, and TFIIE) dissociate from the TFIID promoter complex (*97a*) and are perhaps available for reuse elsewhere. From this simplified description, it is readily apparent that regulation of expression of protein-coding genes can be easily controlled at any one of the numerous intermediate steps along the complex pathway leading to transcription initiation (*90, 90a, 193*).

B. Regulation of Cellular Oncogene Expression at the Transcription Level

Two of the most thoroughly studied cellular oncogenes in terms of regulation of transient gene expression are c-*myc* and c-*fos*. The molecular mechanisms that control the expression of both genes are extremely complex and include regulation of changes in chromatin structure, gene amplification (in the case of c-*myc*), transcriptional activation, transcriptional attenuation, and differential control of mRNA and protein stability. It is, therefore, somewhat artificial to discuss any of these mechanisms in isolation from the others but, for pedagogic purposes, we will consider them separately.

1. TRANSCRIPTIONAL REGULATION OF c-*myc*

A variety of mechanisms regulate the transcription of all of the related members of the normal *myc* multi-gene family (c-*myc*, L-*myc*, and N-*myc*) (*16, 37, 39, 105–112*). At the most basic level, transcription of the *myc* genes seems to be correlated with changes in chromatin structure in the areas of DNA sequence involved with regulation or control (*105*). Alterations in chromatin structure are known to play important roles in the expression of genomic activity, particularly by controlling the binding accessibility of particular sequences of DNA (such as promoters, enhancers, and other transcriptional elements) by *trans*-acting regulatory factors (*106, 107*). For example, a number of DNase-I-hypersensitive sites can be detected in the chromatin structure located 5′ upstream of the murine c-*myc* genes that seem to be correlated with the potential of these genes to be actively transcribed. These and other observations strongly suggest that the accessibility of certain regulatory sequences of DNA necessary for the binding of transcriptional factors may be controlled by changes in chromatin structure in these areas (*106, 107*).

A considerable amount of work, essentially all of it based on *in vitro* nuclear "run-off" experiments, reveals that the normal mammalian c-*myc* locus is characterized by an intricate pattern of transcription (*39, 108–113*). Although variations can be found between such species as humans and mice, a generalized pattern of observed mammalian c-*myc* transcription is presented in Fig. 7. The salient features of this transcription can be summarized as follows:

(i) c-*myc* consists of three exons (E1–E3), but only two (E2 and E3) code for its protein. These two exons are also those found in the avian retrovirus MC29 containing the oncogenic v-*myc* counter part of the cellular c-*myc*

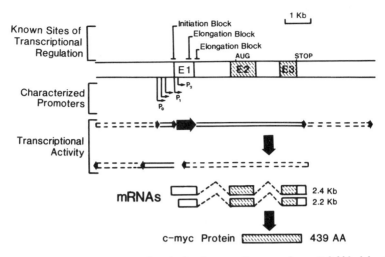

FIG. 7. Transcription patterns of an idealized mammalian c-*myc* locus. Solid black horizontal arrows indicate transcription units associated with known promoter elements, while open arrows indicate regions where transcription has been detected in nuclear run-on experiments without identification of the promoters. Dashed arrows indicate variable or minor species of transcripts that are not detected in most cell types.

oncogene (*108*). The two most abundant c-*myc* mRNAs found in mammalian cells, of 2.2 and 2.4 kilobase (kb) lengths, initiate at the P_1 and P_2 promoters and, therefore, bear unusually long 5′ noncoding regions of about 400 and 550 nucleotides, respectively. In some cases, minor quantities of transcripts of heterogeneous length can be detected in human cells that have initiated from the P_0 cryptic promoter region located about 0.6 kb upstream from the P_1 promoter.

(ii) Transcription of c-*myc* can be down-regulated, by inhibition of initiation, by a block to elongation, or by premature transcript termination (Fig. 7). For example, inhibition of initiation of transcription at P_1 and P_2 is responsible for the allelic exclusion in certain *myc*-transformed mouse plasmacytoma (*105*) and Burkitt's lymphoma (*111*) lines. Also, in unstimulated quiescent mammalian cells and in human HL-60 cells induced to undergo differentiation *in vitro*, major blocks to transcript elongation occur at locations near the end of exon 1 and in the exon-1/intron-1 border region (*110*). This blockage is the result of premature transcript termination in a fashion analogous to attenuation in prokaryotes, and occurs at two stretches of a thymine-rich sequence near the exon-1/intron-1 junction (*109*). When resting cells are induced to express c-*myc* by a variety of means, these blocks to elongation are obviated by an as-yet-undetermined mechanism, and full-length c-*myc* transcripts are synthesized efficiently (*108–111, 117–119*).

(iii) In some instances, minor amounts of "anti-sense" transcripts derived from the noncoding strand of c-*myc* have been detected (*105*), but whether these molecules play any functional role in the transcriptional or post-transcriptional regulation of c-*myc* expression is uncertain at the present time.

From these results, it is quite clear that the cell possesses quite complex and diverse mechanisms for regulating the transcriptional activity of c-*myc*. These capacities can easily explain the observed ability of the mammalian cell to respond readily to external stimuli by rapidly changing, either upward or downward, the rates of functional c-*myc* mRNA transcription (*37, 108, 112*).

2. TRANSCRIPTIONAL REGULATION OF c-*fos*

In certain respects, the modes of transcriptional regulation observed for c-*myc* can be considered paradigms for the way other rapidly induced cellular oncogenes are controlled. For example, similar premature transcription blocks have been identified near the 5' ends of both c-*myb* (*36, 118*) and c-*fos* (*120*), indicating that control of elongation by premature termination may be a widespread mechanism of gene regulation in eukaryotes, as it is in prokaryotes. In the case of c-*fos*, however, a number of novel transcriptional regulatory mechanisms have recently been described which, so far at least, have not been reported for other cellular oncogenes.

The c-*fos* gene is the cellular homolog of the v-*fos* oncogene carried by the FBJ murine osteosarcoma virus; however, the proteins coded for by these two genes have different carboxyl termini (*121*). In transfection experiments, c-*fos* can induce morphological transformation of mouse NIH-3T3 cells. However, for this to occur efficiently, the gene must be driven by a strong promoter sequence, such as a viral long terminal repeat, and certain (A+T)-rich sequences found in the 3'-untranslated tail region must be disrupted (*122*). Rapid induction of c-*fos* expression occurs (Fig. 2) when quiescent fibroblasts are stimulated to enter the cell cycle by exposure to whole serum or phorbol esters, or to polypeptide growth factors such as platelet-derived growth factors (PDGF) or epidermal growth factor (EGF) (*122*).

The induced protein product of c-*fos* (Fos) is found primarily in the nucleus and exhibits DNA-binding activity *in vitro* (*123*). For this and other reasons, the suggestion has been made that the Fos protein may act in signal transduction as a nuclear intermediary that couples short-term events elicited by receptor occupancy at the cell surface to longer-term events that are associated with changes in gene expression (*123*). Consistent with this suggestion are the finding that the viral v-Fos protein can *trans*-activate the expression of the mouse α-collagen gene (*130*) and the demonstration that c-*fos* expression greatly stimulates the transcriptional activity of the murine collagenase and other cellular genes in response to treatment of cells with phorbol esters (*124*).

Using *in vitro* mutagenesis and deletions, there has been identified a highly conserved enhancer-like element located between nucleotides −332 and −276 relative to the mRNA cap site that is essential for transcriptional activation of c-*fos* in response to serum (*125*). This so-called serum response element (SRE) is the specific binding site for an induced 67-kDa protein that has been purified and called either p67 (*126*) or serum response factor (SRF) (*127*). The p67/SRF protein acts as an essential positive transcription factor for serum-induced activation of c-*fos* by specifically binding to a 20-bp element of interrupted dyad symmetry (DSE) found within the SRE (*128*).

Recently, an additional protein with apparent size of 62 kDa was identified (*128*), which is an integral, but physically separable, part of a ternary complex formed with p67/SRF and the SRE. Alone, the p62 protein failed to bind the SRE but required DSE-bound p67/SRF and sequences both within and outside the SRE for its interaction with DNA. *In vivo*, the response of the c-*fos* promoter to stimulation by serum and phorbol esters was severely impaired by any mutations that abolished ternary complex formation between the SRE and the p62 and p67/SRF proteins *in vitro* (*128*).

These observations thus strongly suggest that the serum/phorbol ester inducibility of c-*fos* requires not only a stable initiation complex to form around the "core promoter" region [i.e., the site-selection region and the upstream elements (Figs. 5 and 6; also see above)], but requires in addition the formation of a ternary complex of positive transcription factors (p67/SRF and p62) on the 5′ upstream enhancer element (SRE). Whether these two spatially separated protein–DNA complexes interact physically with each other during the actual process of transcription initiation remains to be determined.

In addition to the positive regulation of c-*fos* offered by the SRE enhancer element and its bound p67/SRF+p62 transcription factors, serum-induced transcription of c-*fos* is also under a novel form of negative feedback regulation mediated by the Fos protein itself (*129*). As will be seen, however, this negative transcriptional autoregulation of c-*fos* by its own product is only part of a more complex regulatory picture in which the Fos protein exerts numerous pleiotropic effects, some positive and some negative, on the transcriptional expression of many different genes.

In the present example, the "*trans*-repression" of c-*fos* promoter activity by the Fos protein appears to result from the specific binding of the Fos protein (along with the protein AP-1/Jun, the product of the c-*jun*; *130–133*) to an AP-1 recognition site in the SRE enhancer region located 5′ upstream from c-*fos* itself (*129*). The association of Fos+AP-1/Jun with this enhancer region forms a complex that results in a down-regulation or shut-off of c-*fos* transcriptional activity induced by serum/phorbol ester. Thus, as depicted in Fig. 8, there appears to be an *in vivo* competition between the activating p67/SRF+p62 factors and the repressive Fos+AP-1/Jun factors for binding to the SRE enhancer region and, depending on which complex is formed over this region, the transcriptional activity of c-*fos* is either stimulated or shut off.

This negative autoregulatory role of the Fos protein in combination with the transcription factor AP-1/Jun on c-*fos* itself is, however, only one of many functions known for this unusual complex of nuclear oncogene protein products. Transcription factor AP-1 (activator protein-1) was described initially as

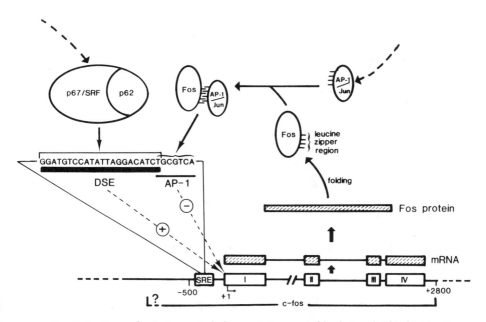

FIG. 8. Positive and negative control of transcription exerted by factors that bind to the 5' upstream serum response element (SRE) of the mammalian c-*fos* gene. Serum and phorbol ester stimulation of quiescent mammalian fibroblasts induces the positively acting protein factors p67/SRF and p62 to bind the dyad symmetry element (DSE) present in the SRE enhancer region 5' upstream from the c-*fos* coding exons (I–IV), thereby stimulating the initiation of mRNA transcription from the start site (+1) (*126–128*). The resulting Fos protein product can then act in a negative feedback or autoregulatory capacity to shut off transcription from c-*fos* by combining with AP-1/Jun protein transcription factor in forming a complex at an overlapping AP-1 recognition site also present in the SRE region adjacent to the DSE sequence (*129*). The Fos and AP-1/Jun proteins interact by means of the "leucine zipper" area to form a functional heterodimer that binds tightly to the highly conserved AP-1 recognition sequences found adjacent to most cellular genes induced by phorbol esters (*80–87*).

a DNA-binding activity in HeLa cells that specifically recognizes and stimulates the enhancer elements of SV40 virus and the human metallothionein IIA gene (134). AP-1 consensus binding sites are highly conserved and also occur in the control regions of viral and cellular genes induced by stimulation of cells by treatment with phorbol esters (131, 135).

Tandemly linked AP-1 binding sites mediate the elevated transcription of many heterologous "marker" genes after phorbol ester treatment of transfected cells (82–84). Purification of the factors that specifically bind to AP-1 sites both *in vitro* and *in vivo* revealed that they consist of a family of proteins closely related to the product of the cellular oncogene c-*jun*, one of the most abundant members being the Jun protein itself (131–133). Many subsequent studies (80–87) show that the AP-1/Jun family of proteins interacts specifically with members of the Fos family of proteins, both *in vivo* and *in vitro*, to stimulate the transcription of many genes responsive to AP-1 (84).

Structural and mutagenesis studies show that the Fos and AP-1/Jun heterodimer complexes are held together by means of the "leucine zipper" (85–87), identified in the structure of many regulatory proteins that function as dimers or larger oligomers. The regulatory roles played *in vivo* by the Fos and AP-1/Jun proteins are thus extremely complex and their effects on the transcriptional activity of a given gene cannot always be predicted with certainty in advance of experimentation.

C. Transcriptional Regulation of Cytokine Genes

A general rule that seems to apply to the 5′ promoter regulatory regions of most Pol-II genes, and one that is not readily apparent from the diagram in Fig. 5, is that often there are overlapping *cis*-acting TEs within this region, resulting in a situation in which a competition for specific binding by the cognate TFs may result in altered transcription from the adjacent gene. Such a situation is well illustrated by the promoter region of certain cytokine genes.

1. TRANSCRIPTIONAL REGULATION OF INTERFERON GENES

In humans there are three types of interferon genes: α-IFN, β-IFN, and γ-IFN. α-IFN is produced by activated monocytes, β-IFN by stimulated fibroblasts, and γ-IFN by stimulated T cells. Induction of the IFN genes comes about primarily by the activation of transcription. Both α- and β-IFNs are inducible as a result of viral infection, by exposure to double-stranded RNAs, or by other growth factors and cytokines such as PDGF, colony-stimulating factor-1 or interleukin-1 (136). On the other hand, as expected, γ-IFN is inducible by agents that activate lymphocytes (136).

Activation of mRNA transcription in all of the IFN genes is mediated by regulatory elements located in the 5′-flanking sequences of the genes. As in most other genes, changes in chromatin structure (monitored by the appearance of DNase-I-hypersensitive sites) occur in the 5′-flanking regions of the IFN genes prior to initiation of transcription (137, 138).

As shown in Fig. 9, the 5′ sequences of both the α-IFN and β-IFN of humans show some degree of homology with each other (139, 140). By deletion mapping and site-specific mutagenesis, followed by introduction of the mutant IFN genes into various host cells, a number of laboratories have identified the DNA sequences responsible for induction-specific transcription of the genes. For example, the sequences required for virus-mediated induction of transcription [the virus response element (VRE)] have been located between nucleotides −117 and −74 of the α-IFN gene (141) and between −109 to −64 of the β-IFN gene (142) with respect to the cap site. In the VRE of the β-IFN gene, there is a virus-inducible enhancer sequence consisting of the repeated hexanucleotide A-A-R-K-G-A that is repeated seven times between nucleotides −109 and −65 (144). In contrast, the VRE of the α-IFN gene contains only two such enhancer sequences (Fig. 9). Also shown in Fig. 9 are positive regulatory sequences found in both the α- and β-IFN genes that overlap the VRE region (residues −80 to −58), which function as weakly constitutive transcription elements under appropriate experimental conditions (143, 144). In addition, both the α- and β-IFN

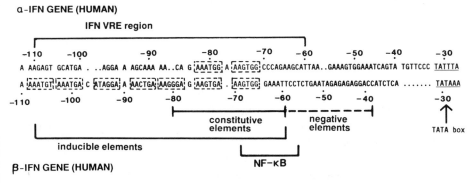

FIG. 9. The 5′ upstream regulatory elements within the human α-IFN and β-IFN genes (139, 140). The region required for virus-mediated induction of transcriptional activity [the virus response element (VRE)] is shown, as are overlapping sequences involved in constitutive basal level synthesis (constitutive element), the NF-κB factor binding site of β-IFN that is inducible by exposure of cells to dsRNA, and the negative regulation element that suppresses expression of the α-IFN and β-IFN genes in unstimulated cells. The repetitive hexameric sequences are framed. Gaps are introduced to maximize sequence homology between the two genes. Based on the data of Taniguchi (75) and Sen and Baltimore (185, 186).

genes contain a negative repressor element (located between nucleotides −58 and −38) that prevents the functioning of the virus-inducible and constitutive elements in uninduced cells (*144*).

A new positive regulatory element in the human β-IFN promoter that activates transcription in response to virus infection or exposure of fibroblast cells to dsRNA has recently been identified (*184*). This dsRNA-inducible element has considerable sequence similarity (GTGGGAAATTC) to a previously identified enhancer sequence for the human immunoglobulin κ light-chain, called NF-κB (*185, 186*). As shown in Fig. 9, the putative NF-κB enhancer overlaps portions of the virus-inducible, constitutive, and negative regulatory elements found within the β-IFN VRE region. Furthermore, following induction of β-IFN in fibroblasts, a protein factor can be isolated from the dsRNA-induced cells that specifically binds to this NF-κB-like sequence (*184*). This induced fibroblast protein factor appears to be indistinguishable from the protein TF NF-κB earlier identified in mature B cells (*185*).

The binding activity of authentic NF-κB protein, and stimulation of expression of promoters containing NF-κB binding sites, are activated by lipopolysaccharide (LPS) treatment of pre-B cells or by phorbol ester treatment of a variety of cell types (*187–190*). Recently, it has been shown (*191, 192*) that the NF-κB protein is constitutively present in the cytoplasm of uninduced cells in an inactive form as a complex with an inhibitory protein (IκB). The active form of the protein can be liberated from this inactive NF-κB–IκB complex by treatment of cytoplasmic extracts with detergents (*192*), prompting the suggestion that the natural activation of the NF-κB TF *in vivo* occurs by a posttranscriptional unmasking mechanism (*192*). Likewise, it has been suggested that the induction of human β-IFN in fibroblasts can occur by a similar posttranscriptional mechanism in which an NF-κB-like factor present in the cytoplasm is unmasked as a result of dsRNA treatment of cells. The newly freed protein then translocates to the nucleus where it binds to the putative NF-κB enhancer site in the promoter and stimulates transcription of the β-IFN gene (*184*).

Farther 5′ upstream from the VRE regions in both the α-IFN and β-IFN genes there are a number of additional putative TEs such as Sp-1 and AP-1 recognition sites (*145*). Efforts to isolate the protein TFs that specifically bind to these upstream interferon regulatory elements (IREs) are beginning to succeed. Multiple protein–DNA interactions within the IREs of the human β-IFN gene have been identified (*145*), and the cDNA encoding a mouse nuclear factor called interferon regulatory factor-1 (IRF-1) that specifically binds to the seven conserved 5′ upstream viral enhancer elements of the human and mouse β-IFN genes, has been cloned (*146*).

2. Transcriptional Regulation of the IL-2 Gene

The 5'-flanking promoter region of the human IL-2 gene undergoes significant chromatin structure changes when peripheral blood T-cells or Jurkat T-cells are activated. Normally, the 5' region of unstimulated T cells exhibits three areas of hypersensitivity to DNase I, but, when these cells are stimulated with mitogens, the promoter region of the IL-2 gene develops an additional hypersensitive site in the region of the upstream regulatory elements close to the transcriptional start site (147). These DNase-I-hypersensitive areas of chromatin are generally where *cis*-acting regulatory DNA sequences have been identified and characterized (147–150).

In both the human and mouse IL-2 genes there are well-conserved DNA sequences within the 5'-flanking regions (149) that are functional DNA elements required for IL-2 gene expression in activated T cells (148, 150). These functional areas were localized by excising possible DNA regulatory sequences from the IL-2 gene and fusing them to the marker or "reporter" gene coding for the bacterial chloramphenicol acetyltransferase (CAT) enzyme (148, 150). The resulting hybrid fusion genes were each introduced into either T lymphoid cell and non-T cell clones and the transient expression of the transfected CAT gene was assayed by standard procedures following stimulation of recipient cells by mitogens.

These experiments revealed that: (i) the 5' boundary of the sequences required for maximal induction lies between positions -319 and -264 with respect to the IL-2 mRNA cap site; (ii) the sequence of DNA between -319 and -52 functions in an orientation-independent manner as a transcriptional enhancer element, and can stimulate transcription from a heterologous β-IFN promoter sequence in induced T cells; (iii) sequences downstream from nucleotide -81 contain a silent "cryptic promoter" element that can be activated by a heterologous enhancer (i.e., the β-IFN inducible enhancer) in non-T cells, indicating that the promoter function per se is not restricted to T cells. Similar results have been obtained by others (151, 152).

Little is known about the nature of the nuclear proteins that may interact with the IL-2 regulatory elements described above. However, within the transcriptional enhancer region at -185 to -176 of the human IL-2 gene there is a sequence similar to the AP-1 site that is adjacent to most phorbol ester-induced genes. Since phorbol esters (as activators of protein kinase C) can replace accessory cells such as macrophages (or IL-1) during IL-2 induction in T lymphocytes (1), the intriguing possibility exists that the heterodimer protein transcription complex Fos+AP-1/Jun may be involved with IL-2 gene regulation. Furthermore, there are two additional sequences in the IL-2 enhancer region, (nucleotides -93 to -63 and -285 to -255) that will transcriptionally activate a linked heterologous promoter in response to stimulatory signals emanating from the surface antigen receptor of T cells (153, 154). These two TEs are called antigen receptor response elements (ARRE-1 and ARRE-2, respectively) (154).

The two ARREs are the specific binding sites for two different protein complexes. One factor, NFAT-1 (for nuclear factor of activated T cells), a protein found only in the nuclei of activated T lymphocytes, binds specifically to ARRE-2. The second factor, NFIL-2A (for nuclear factor IL-2A), binds specifically to ARRE-1 and is found in the nuclei of both resting and stimulated T cells. Interestingly, NFIL-2A may have a negative function in resting T cells (154), suggesting that this regulatory protein has a dual function in lymphocytes: to suppress expression of the IL-2 promoter in nonactivated T cells, and to activate it after cells are stimulated.

Normal resting T lymphocytes require both triggering of the antigen

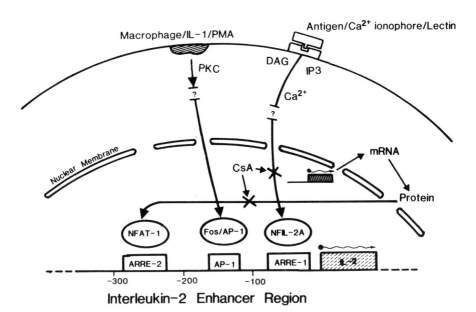

FIG. 10. A tentative model proposed by Crabtree (154) of the pathways involved in the activation of transcription of the IL-2 gene in the Jurkat human T-cell line. It is not known whether the gene activated to produce the NFAT-1 complex encodes the actual DNA-binding activity or only contributes to the formation of the protein–DNA complex. The sites of proposed inhibitory action of cyclosporine A (CsA) are indicated. DAG, Diacylglycerol; IP3, inositol 1,4,5-trisphosphate; PKC, protein kinase C; NFAT-1, nuclear factor of activated T cells; NFIL-2A, nuclear factor IL-2A; AARE-1 and -2, antigen regulatory response elements −1 and −2. Based on the data of Shaw et al. (153) and Crabtree (154).

receptor and activation of PKC for optimal production of IL-2 and proliferation (1). These complex physiological interactions of the T-cell receptor with its ligands can be mimicked in part by such simple stimuli as calcium ionophores, plant lectin, and antibodies to the antigen receptor, and by direct activation of PKC by treatment of cells with phorbol esters. Likewise, as noted above, the IL-2 transcriptional enhancer region also requires both types of signals for its function in transfected cell lines (151, 154).

A model based on this reasoning, depicted in Fig. 10, suggests that the control region of the IL-2 gene is a mosaic of regulatory elements that respond to signals originating from the stimulated antigen receptor, and to signals initiated with the activation of PKC. The model further proposes that signals emanating from two different membrane receptors may be integrated at the level of the enhancer elements to regulate the transcriptional response of the IL-2 gene.

VI. Posttranscriptional Regulation of Cytokine Genes and Cellular Oncogenes

Posttranscriptional control mechanisms play a significant role in regulating expression of many of the well-characterized cytokine genes and cellular oncogenes, including β-IFN (22, 23, 194, 195), γ-IFN (24), IL-2 (17, 18, 46, 196, 197), GM-CSF (26–28, 198), G-CSF (29, 199), M-CSF (199), c-myc (16, 36, 37, 108, 113, 119, 200–202), c-fos (33, 34, 42, 117, 120, 203, 204), and c-myb (36). Regulation of the rate of mRNA degradation is now recognized as a major control point in the expression of these and certain other transiently expressed genes (205–209). For example, there is evidence from many sources, some of which is discussed above, for effects of phorbol esters, inhibitors of transcription such as actinomycin D, and inhibitors of protein synthesis such as cycloheximide, on the modulation of specific mRNA degradation pathways (22, 23, 26, 27, 194–197).

Collectively, this work clearly demonstrates that synthesis and accumulation of specific mRNAs can be experimentally uncoupled: the rates of initiation and ongoing transcription do not always correlate with the rate of accumulation of mRNA transcripts. Thus, in addition to temporal induction of mRNA transcription, selective mRNA degradation by nucleases also plays a crucial role in controlling the level and duration of the expression of certain genes.

A. The Conserved Poly(UAUU) Sequence and mRNA Stability

We (164, 210) and others (26, 31) have identified and experimentally verified (26, 196) that a conserved (A+T)-rich sequence common to many transiently expressed genes confers instability on transcribed mRNAs. As shown in Table II, this highly conserved stretch of DNA frequently consists of tandem repeats of the tetranucleotide (TATT) sequence, i.e., (TATT)$_n$, which is transcribed as the cognate (UAUU)$_n$ sequence in the 3'-untranslated tail regions (3' UTRs) of the mRNAs of most of the known cytokine genes and proto-oncogenes (164, 210).

Significantly, in some cases these (A+T)-rich regions in the 3' UTRs are more highly conserved than the protein coding regions of homologous genes. For example, there is greater similarity between the 3' UTRs of the human, mouse, and bovine IL-2 genes (164, 210) than there is between the protein coding regions of these genes, and most of this homology is due to the conserved (A+T)-rich sequences (164, 210). Furthermore, as can be seen in Table II, the length, distribution, and degree of conservation of the (TATT)$_n$ sequences vary considerably between different cytokine genes and nuclear oncogenes. This suggests that even though a common destabilizing sequence may be present in these different genes, the secondary structure assumed by these (UAUU)$_n$ sequences in the 3' UTRs probably also plays a significant role in conferring structural individuality on the different mRNA species (196, 211).

Nevertheless, it seems likely that the conserved 3' UTR destabilizing signal may represent only one of several different sequences or structural features that may contribute to the observed differences in stability of individual mRNAs. In c-*fos* mRNA, for example, additional determinants of instability also reside in the 5'-untranslated regions of these molecules (203). Such multiple mechanisms may likewise be controlling the differential stability of c-*myc* mRNAs (201).

Two types of experiments test whether or not the conserved (A+T)-rich sequences found in the 3' UTRs of transiently expressed genes are involved in mRNA instability. In one case, a synthetic 51-bp DNA segment containing the (A+T)-rich sequences found in the 3' UTR of the human GM-CSF gene (cf. Table II) was inserted into the 3' UTR of the rabbit β-globin gene (26). This hybrid gene was introduced by transfection into NIH-3T3 cells and the stability of the transcribed mRNA was monitored. It was found that transcripts from the globin genes containing the inserted (A+T)-rich sequences, but not transcripts from control globin genes lacking these sequences, were very unstable, with half-lives of less than 30 minutes (26). The instability conferred by the (A+U)-sequence in the globin mRNA was also partially alleviated by treatment of the transfected cells with cycloheximide. It was therefore proposed that the (A+U)-sequences are the recognition signal for an mRNA-processing pathway that specifically degrades mRNAs containing such 3' UTR sequences (26).

TABLE II

EXAMPLES OF CONSERVED $(TATT)_n$-CONTAINING SEQUENCES LOCATED
IN THE 3'-UNTRANSLATED TAIL REGIONS OF TRANSIENTLY EXPRESSED GENES[a]

Gene	Sequence	References
INTERFERONS:		
a2-mIFN:	TATTTATTTATTTATTTATTTATTTATTTATTTAATgcTATTAATATAATTAA	155
aH2-hIFN:	TATTTATTTAAATATTTATTTATTTAAcTATTTTTATTATTTTAAATTATT	156
aF-hIFN:	TAATTATcTATcTATTgAAATATTTATTTATTTATTAgATTTAAATTATT	156
aG-hIFN:	TATTcTATcTATTTTATcTATc....TAATcTATTTAAATATTTATTTATTTA	156
b-hIFN:	TATTAAATTATgAgTTATTTTTATTTATTTAAATTTTATTTTggAAAA	157
b-mIFN:	TATTAATTTATAATTTAAATTATTTTcTAcTTTTTATT	158
c-hIFN:	TATTTATTAATATTTAAcATTATTTATAgggAATATATT	159
c-mIFN:	TATTTATTAATATTTAAAAcTATTTATATggAgAATcTATT	160
INTERLEUKINS:		
hIL-1a:	TATTTTTTAATTATTATTTATATATgTATTTATAAATATATTTAAgATAATATTAATAT	161
mIL-1a:	TATTTTATATATgTATTTATTAATATATTTATgATAATTATATTATTTAT	162
rIL-1:	TATTTATATgTATgTATTTATAAATgTATTTAAgTAATAATTATTATTATATTTATA	163
bIL-2:	TATTTATTTAAATATTTAAAATTTATATTTATTTT	164
hIL-2b:	TATTTATTTATTTATTTgTTTgTTTgTTTgTTTATTTcATTggTcTAATTTATT	165
hIL-2c:	TATTTATTTAAATATTTAAATTTTATATTTATTgT	166
mIL-2:	TATTTATTTAAATATTTAAcTATTAAT..TTATTTTTTT	167
mIL-3:	TATTTATTTATgTATTTATgTATTTATTTATTTATT	168
rIL-3:	TATTTTATTcTATTAAggcTATTTATgTATTTATgTATTTATTTATTTATTA	169
mIL-4:	AATTTTTAATggTTTTATTTTTAATTATTTATATATTTATAATT	170
mIL-5:	TATTTTAATTATTTTTAATTTATTAATATTTAAATAT(.)TTAATTTAT..TATATTT	171
COLONY STIMULATING FACTORS:		
hGM-CSF:	TAATATTTATATATTTATATTTTTAAAATATTTATTTATTTATTTATTT...TATTTATT	172
mGM-CSF:	TTTATTTATATATTTATATTTTTAAAATATTATTTATTTATTTATTTATTT	173
hG-CSF:	TATTTATcTcTATTTAATATTTATgTcTATTTAA....ATATTTAA	174
mTNF:	TATTTATTTATTTATTTATTATTTATTTATTTAcAgATgAATgTATTTATT	175
hTNF:	ATTATTTATTATTTATTTATTATTTATTTATTTA	176
hLT:	TATTATgAA...AAAAAAATTAATATTTATTTATTTAT	177
CELLULAR ONCOGENES:		
h-c-*fos*:	TATTgTgTTTTTAATTTATTTATTAAgATTcTcAgATATTTATATTTTTATTTTATT	178
m-c-*fos*:	TTTTTATT..TTTcAATTTATTTATTTAAgAT...ATATTTTATATTTTTATTTTATT	179
h-c-*myc*:	TATTAAgAATTgAATT..(.)..TATTTA...TATT.....TAAATATT...TATTA	180
h-c-*pim-1*:	TATTTT...TATTTA....TATTTATTTATTTATTTATTTT...TATTTATT...TATT	181
m-c-*pim-1*:	TATTT...TATTTTAT...TATT...TATTTATTTATTTATTTATTT....TATT	182
h-c-*myb*:	TATTTAT...(.)..TTATATTTTTATT...TAATTTAATTT..TATT..TATT.TATAT	183

[a] h, Human; m, murine; r, rat; b, bovine.

In a second experimental system, either the entire 3' UTR of the bovine
IL-2 gene or a synthetic $(TATT)_{13}$ oligonucleotide was ligated to the 3' end of
the "marker" bacterial gene coding for CAT (196). These hybrid fusion genes
were then introduced by transfection into a bovine lymphoid cell line, and
expression of the CAT gene inside the recipient cells was monitored and
shown to be inducible by cycloheximide. In the absence of this induction, the
transcribed CAT mRNA was extremely unstable and no expression of the CAT
protein could be detected in the transfected cells (196). Significantly different
results were obtained, however, if these same lymphoid cells were transfected
with a hybrid CAT fusion gene in which the synthetic $(TATT)_{13}$ oligonucleotide was inserted in an inverted 5'–3' orientation relative to the protein
coding strand of the CAT gene [so that instead of $(UAUU)_{13}$ in the 3' UTR of
the transcribed mRNA, there was $(AAUA)_{13}$]. In this case, the hybrid gene
transcribed stable CAT mRNA inside the recipient cells, and constitutive
synthesis of CAT enzyme protein was detected in the cells without ChX
treatment (196).

These findings demonstrated directly that the poly(UAUU) motif (but not
an (A + U)-rich sequence with a different order) confers instability on mRNAs
in vivo, and that treatment of recipient cells with the protein synthesis
inhibitor ChX results in marked stabilization of such mRNAs. The results
also suggest that bovine lymphoid cells contain a labile nuclease (or nucleases) that recognize $(UAUU)_n$ as a signal for preferential degradation of
mRNA, and that ChX treatment of recipient cells inhibits the production of
this short-lived nuclease.

Further biochemical experiments confirm the existence of such labile
nucleases in these cells and suggest that the enzymes utilize the secondary
structure formed by the poly(UAUU)-containing 3'-untranslated tail region
as a recognition signal for selective degradation of mRNAs (196). These
results appear to be consistent with the demonstrations (17, 18, 197) that,
following human lymphocyte activation, the accumulation of IL-2 mRNA is
promptly "shut off," and that this down-regulation requires the synthesis of a
short-lived protein repressor whose production can be prevented by treatment of stimulated cells with ChX or other inhibitors of protein synthesis.
However, the biochemical nature and mode of action of these lymphoid cell
nucleases are unknown, and the enzymes have proven difficult to isolate,
probably owing to their extreme lability within cells.

Figure 11 presents postulated mechanisms regulating the level of IL-2
mRNA in stimulated mammalian T lymphocytes, based on current information (17, 18, 148–155, 196, 197). The essential features of the proposed
model are: (i) transcription of the IL-2 gene requires continuous delivery of
induction signals emanating from the cell surface (via the NFAT-1, NFIL-2A,
and Fos + AP-1/Jun proteins); (ii) induction of a labile RNase system (acting at

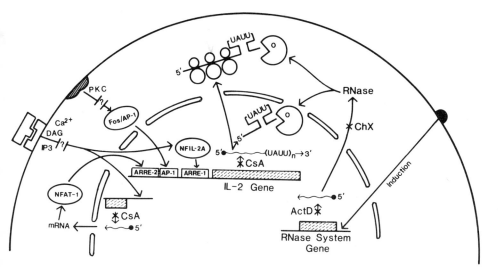

FIG. 11. Postulated mechanisms regulating the level of IL-2 mRNA in activated mammalian T lymphocytes. In this model, it is assumed that initiation and maintenance of IL-2 gene transcription depend on continuous delivery of induction signals from receptors on the cell surface mediated by the cytoplasmic and nuclear signal transduction pathways outlined in Fig. 10. In addition, the model proposes a labile RNase system that is selective for the degradation of poly(UAUU)-containing mRNAs (including the IL-2 mRNA) is induced and maintained by the same (or perhaps similar) signal transduction pathways, which also induce a set of other coordinately expressed lymphokines. As discussed in the text, it is proposed that the activity of the RNase degradative system (which in lymphocytes may be active in the cytoplasm and/or the nucleus) is sensitive to both cycloheximide (ChX) and actinomycin D (ActD) inhibition because of its extremely rapid turnover in lymphoid cells. Abbreviations are as in Fig. 10.

the level of the cytoplasm and/or the nucleus; *196, 205–209*) that specifically recognizes sequences or structural features [such as poly(UAUU)] of mRNAs destined for selective and rapid degradation; and (iii) sensitivity of the RNase system to inhibition by both cycloheximide and actinomycin D because of its rapid rate of turnover.

Although obviously simplified compared to the true *in vivo* modes of regulation of IL-2 expression, such a model explains many observations concerning the action of various inhibitors known to affect IL-2 expression in stimulated T cells. For example, the specific inhibitory action of cyclosporine A on IL-2 expression is in part explained by selective blockage by the drug of not only IL-2 gene transcription but also blockage of transcription of both the NFAT-1 and NFIL-2A genes. Likewise, the "superinduction" of IL-2 mRNA by inhibitors of both protein and mRNA synthesis probably results from the stabilization and accumulation of IL-2 mRNA due to the rapid disappearance from the cell of labile nucleases, which otherwise would preferentially destroy this mRNA.

B. Mechanisms of mRNA Stabilization

Other cytokine genes and cellular oncogenes also display similar post-transcriptional controls of mRNA accumulation, as described above for IL-2. Induction of the β-IFN gene results in activation of transcription, but stabilization of the mRNA after induction contributes to the maintenance of mRNA levels (22, 23, 195). Likewise, the importance of mRNA stabilization has been emphasized (194) by the fact that β-IFN mRNA transcription of the human gene introduced by transfection into mouse cells occurs at the same rate whether or not the cells are induced by treatment with cycloheximide or poly(rI)·poly(rC). Nevertheless, β-IFN mRNA accumulation occurs only in the induced cells and not in the uninduced cells (194). These results are best explained, as in the case of IL-2, by the stabilization of the mRNA in the induced cells as a result of the blockage of de novo synthesis of a short-lived nuclease(s).

However, in addition to this type of regulation, it seems likely that other mechanisms may also exist in induced cells to specifically stabilize transiently expressed mRNAs. For example, accumulation of GM-CSF mRNA in stimulated macrophages is not the result of induction or enhancement of gene transcription but the result of mRNA stabilization, and induction of mRNA depends on ongoing protein synthesis (27). These results imply that stimulation of the macrophages induces the synthesis of protein(s) that stabilize(s) the GM-CSF mRNA and prevents its degradation (27).

There is a somewhat novel suggestion (212) of a possible mechanism to stabilize intrinsically labile mRNA species containing the conserved poly(UAUU) sequence. This draws attention to the striking complementarity between these (A+U)-rich regions and a sequence found at the 3′ ends of a particular group of cytoplasmic molecules, called the B2 family of RNAs (213, 214). B2 RNAs are transcribed from highly repetitive (A+T)-rich sequences in the mouse genome by RNA Pol III; they accumulate particularly in the cytoplasm of quiescent mouse fibroblasts stimulated to proliferate by serum (212). B2 RNAs are also found in high concentrations in the nonpolysomal fraction of rapidly dividing embryonic cells or cells transformed by tumor viruses or chemical carcinogens. A highly conserved consensus sequence found in the 3′ end region of all of the members of the B2 family of RNAs, AU(AAUA)$_3$AAU (213, 214), contains three tandem complementary copies of the poly(UAUU) sequence (Table II) flanked by (A+U)-rich stretches of RNA.

The thermodynamic parameters involved in the potential base-pair interactions between this conserved B2 sequence and the complementary poly(UAUU) sequences found in the UTRs of a number of transiently expressed mRNAs (hIL-1, h-c-*fos*, α-hIFN, mGM-CSF, β-hIFN, β₂-mIFN, mTNF, mIL-3, h-c-myc, and mIL-4) have been described and calculated. As a consequence of these B2 complementary sequences, in some cases up to 17 uninterrupted base-pairs can be formed between the B2 RNAs and the UTRs of these cytokine genes and nuclear oncogenes. The calculated thermodynamic parameters for such duplex formations gave values similar in magnitude to those that describe the interaction of the Shine–Dalgarno sequence in 16-S rRNA with complementary sequences in certain prokaryotic mRNAs (*212*).

On the basis of these calculations, it was proposed (*212*) that the B2 RNAs (or equivalent RNAs containing related sequences in other species) might form stable complexes with labile mRNAs and, as a result of these interactions, increase their stability by protecting them against nucleases with specificity for single-stranded (A+U)-rich regions. If these ideas are correct, small differences in the conserved sequences between members of the family of B2 transcripts (*214*) would be expected to result in different affinities for various poly(UAUU)-containing mRNAs (Table II). Thus, changes in the composition of the B2 RNA population might differentially regulate the stability of individual cytokine and oncogene mRNAs by altering their susceptibility to nucleolytic degradation (*212*).

C. Pathologies of Dysregulation of mRNA Decay

From the foregoing discussion, it seems likely that dysregulation of the selective mRNA degradation system specific for labile mRNAs might contribute to the generation of various pathologies and cancers. Indeed, a number of intriguing examples of abnormalities possibly associated with a malfunctioning of the normal system for selectively "tagging" and destroying poly(UAUU)-containing mRNAs have been reported.

Certain deletions in the UTR of murine c-*fos* activate the transforming potential of this proto-oncogene gene in transfected cells (*122*). Deleting a 67-basepair sequence containing the highly conserved poly(TATT) destabilizing sequence from the UTR of c-*fos* converts it to a transforming oncogene (*215*). This limited UTR deletion in c-*fos* results in a significant increase in stability of the transcribed mRNA, which, likewise, correlates with the transforming potential of the altered c-*fos*. Both phenotypes could be reversed by reintroduction of the deleted DNA sequence back into the altered c-*fos* (*216–218*). Analogously, activation of the transforming potential of human c-*fos* requires mRNA stabilization that, in turn, results in increased amounts of modified Fos proteins being accumulated within transformed cells (*204*).

Oncogenic transformation by the nonacute transforming retroviruses depends on the activation of cellular genes by integrated proviruses. Usually, such cellular gene induction occurs either as a result of activation of transcription from an integrated viral promoter or by virtue of the enhancer activity of the integrated proviral LTR. However, in the case of proviral activation of mouse *pim*-1, oncogenic transformation in most cases appears to result from a different mechanism.

The *pim*-1 oncogene was first discovered in mice and is activated by insertion of retroviruses in murine leukemia virus (MuLV)-induced T-cell lymphomas (219). In a high proportion (approximately 70%) of these MuLV-induced lymphomas, the sites of proviral integration are clustered in the 3' exon of *pim*-1, which contains the terminal portion of the protein-coding sequence and the 3' UTR of the mRNA with its conserved poly(TATT) sequences (220; Table II). All transforming proviruses integrated in this 3' exon lie between the termination codon of the *pim*-1 protein-coding sequence and the downstream (A+T)-rich sequences. Furthermore, proviruses integrate in the UTR in such a way that the viral LTR sequence causes a truncated or shortened mRNA transcript to be produced (220).

Tumors in which MuLV proviruses are integrated in the 3' exon also show the highest *pim*-1 mRNA levels, and it has been hypothesized that the observed increased levels of shortened mRNA transcripts provide the driving force for selective outgrowth of these tumors *in vivo* (220). Consistent with this suggestion, recent experiments provide direct evidence for the oncogenic transforming potential of *pim*-1 in transgenic mice (221). It is possible that human *pim*-1 may likewise be involved with certain forms of cancer. The cDNA for human *pim*-1 has been cloned (222) and used to localize this gene to a region (p21) on chromosome-6 known to be involved in translocations in some acute leukemias (223). Additionally, the human *pim*-1 protein has tyrosine phosphorylating activity, suggesting that it is a new member of the subgroup of oncogenes coding for tyrosine kinase enzymes (224).

A number of additional examples of pathologies possibly associated with dysregulation of cytokine gene expression resulting from altered levels of transiently expressed mRNAs have recently been summarized (75). Among these is the apparent involvement of an aberrantly operating IL-2 autocrine loop in the development and/or maintenance of human adult T-cell leukemias as a result of infection by the lymphotrophic retrovirus HTLV-1. An anomalously operating IL-2 autocrine loop mechanism has also been reported in non-Hodgkin's T-cell lymphoma (225) and gibbon T-cell leukemia (226). The latter example is of special interest because the gibbon MLA-144 leukemia cell line differs from every other known T-cell line in that it constitutively makes IL-2 without stimulation by antigen, lectin, or phorbol esters. The MLA-144 line has a single copy of the gibbon leukemia virus inserted into the 3' UTR of the IL-2 gene, suggesting that constitutive production of IL-2 in this line may be related to this proviral integration site (226). The importance of constitutive IL-2 production in the proliferation of the MLA-144 cell line was suggested by glucocorticoid inhibition of IL-2 production, which demonstrated that the MLA-144 cell line proliferates via an aberrantly active autocrine mechanism involving IL-2 (227). Thus, Chen *et al.* speculate that the integration of the gibbon leukemia virus in the 3' UTR of the IL-2 gene may be critical in regulating the autonomous growth of the malignant MLA-144 cell line (226).

VII. Concluding Remarks

In this review, we have briefly examined the molecular mechanisms currently thought to be operating to control the level of accumulation of transiently expressed growth factor gene and cellular oncogene products synthesized by mammalian cells stimulated to undergo proliferation. Such transient gene expression is the result of complex but coordinated biochemical regulatory pathways operating at many levels within the cell. These include precise regulation of transcription initiation, elongation, termination, control of posttranscriptional mRNA processing, and selective mRNA degradation, as well as numerous other translational and posttranslational control mechanisms.

Prior to mitogenic activation, normal resting or quiescent mammalian cells and lymphocytes exhibit little, if any, transcriptional activity from endogenous growth factor genes. Immediately following stimulation, however, there is a characteristic temporal sequence of transient gene transcriptional activations and induced accumulations of specific mRNAs and proteins. In many cases, the half-lives of these transiently expressed mRNAs and proteins are extremely short compared to most cellular macromolecules. For example, the half-lives of many of the rapidly induced cellular oncogene products are considerably less than one hour, and the half-lives of many cytokine gene products are in the range of one to two hours. A number of different mechanisms contribute to these fast turnovers, but for cytokine genes and oncogenes, the primary levels of control seem to lie with regulation of transcription initiation and termination, and with preferential posttranscriptional degradation of specific mRNAs and proteins.

The availability within the past few years of an ever-increasing number of cloned genes coding for cytokines and oncogene products has allowed for detailed studies of the DNA sequences and protein factors involved in both transcriptional and posttranscriptional controls of transient gene expression. These studies have resulted in the identification of numerous *cis*-acting

DNA regulatory elements flanking the protein-coding regions of genes transcribed by RNA Pol II, and the isolation of specific *trans*-acting regulatory proteins that bind to these elements.

In certain cases it has been experimentally demonstrated, both *in vitro* and *in vivo,* that the association of specific protein factors with their cognate binding sites in the promoter and enhancer regions of genes determines whether the gene will be transcriptionally active. In this regard, one of the conceptually most gratifying discoveries to emerge recently has been the demonstration that the protein products of certain previously identified nuclear oncogenes are themselves *trans*-activating transcriptional regulatory molecules. For example, the protein product of the transiently expressed c-*jun* oncogene, Jun, has been identified as a member of the AP-1 family of *trans*-activating proteins that bind specifically to the AP-1 promoter elements found adjacent to most phorbol-ester-induced genes. Additionally, the protein product (Fos) of the rapidly induced oncogene c-*fos* associates with the AP-1/Jun protein to form a functional complex that regulates the efficiency of transcriptional activation from AP-1 promoter elements. Thus, as discussed in this review, there are now several well-documented examples in which the transitory expression of cytokine gene and oncogene transcription is directly regulated by other transiently expressed gene products.

Posttranscriptional control mechanism also play a significant role in the regulation of transient gene expression. In particular, there are many examples in which the rate of synthesis of a particular cytokine or proto-oncogene mRNA species does not directly correlate with its rate of accumulation within the cell. In these instances, selective posttranscriptional mRNA degradation plays a dominant role in the regulation of gene expression. Recently, a conserved (A+T)-rich sequence has been identified in the 3' UTR of most transiently expressed growth factor and cytokine genes as well as in many oncogenes; this sequence confers selective instability on the mRNAs transcribed from these genes. The highly conserved DNA sequence, poly(TATT), is transcribed as the cognate poly(UAUU) in the untranslated 3' regions of the mRNAs of these genes, where it acts as a structural signal for selective elimination by one or more labile cellular nucleases.

During normal induction of transient gene expression, both the rates of synthesis and of degradation of growth factor gene and oncogene products are under precise but delicate regulation. A number of intriguing examples have been reported that suggest that aberrant changes affecting the rates of transcription, degradation, or accumulation of the products of such genes may result in abnormal cell growth or possibly neoplasia. It seems reasonable to expect that future work will reveal additional examples of diseases induced by alterations in the complex pathways regulating transient gene expression.

REFERENCES

1. H. Clevers, B. Alarcon, T. Wileman and C. Terhorst, *Annu. Rev. Immunol.* **6**, 629 (1988).
2. G. Guroff (ed.), "Oncogenes, Genes and Growth Factors." Wiley, New York, 1987.
2a. J. M. Almendral, D. Sommer, H. MacDonald-Bravo, J. Burckhardt, J. Perera and R. Bravo, *MCBiol* **8**, 2140 (1988).
3. E. Rosengurt and J. Sinnet-Smith, *This Series* **35**, 261 (1986).
3a. Y. Nishizuka, *Nature* **308**, 693 (1984).
4. M. J. Berridge and R. F. Irvine, *Nature* **312**, 315 (1984).
5. A. Weise, J. Imboden, K. Hardy, B. Manter, C. Terhorst and J. Stobo, *Annu. Rev. Immunol.* **4**, 593 (1986).
6. M. E. Greenberg and E. B. Ziff, *Nature* **311**, 433 (1984).
7. K. Kelly, B. H. Cochran, C. D. Stiles and P. Leder, *Cell* **35**, 603 (1983).
8. W. Tanner and D. Gallwitz (eds.), "Cell Cycle and Oncogenes." Springer-Verlag, Berlin and New York, 1986.
9. R. Raghow, *Trends Biochem. Sci. (Pers. Ed.)* **12**, 358 (1987).
10. R. H. Singer and S. Penman, *JMB* **78**, 321 (1973).
11. L. S. Berger and H. L. Cooper, *PNAS* **72**, 3873 (1975).
12. J. R. Greenberg, *Nature* **240**, 102 (1972).
13. V. Volloch and D. Housman, *Cell* **23**, 509 (1981).
14. M. M. Harpold, M. C. Wilson and J. E. Darnell, *MCBiol* **1**, 188 (1981).
15. P. E. Auron and A. C. Webb, *Lymphokines* **14**, 33 (1987).
16. K. Kelly and U. Siebenlist, *Annu. Rev. Immunol.* **4**, 317 (1986).
17. J. Shaw, K. Meerovitch, R. C. Bleackley and V. Paetkau, *J. Immunol.* **140**, 2243 (1988).
18. V. Paetkau, J. Shaw, J. F. Elliot, C. Havele, B. Pohajdak and R. C. Bleackley, *Lymphokines* **13**, 73 (1987).
19. T. Yakota, S. Miyatake, H. Hagiwara, T. Mosmann, J. Conaway, R. Conaway, A. Miyajima, Y. Takebe, N. Arai, F. Lee and K. Arai, *Lymphokines* **15**, 393 (1988).
20. M. A. Brown, C. Watson, J. Ohara and W. Paul, *Cell. Immunol.* **98**, 538 (1986).
21. W. E. Paul and J. Ohara, *Annu. Rev. Immunol.* **5**, 429 (1987).
22. N. B. K. Rai and P. M. Pitha, *PNAS* **78**, 7426 (1981).
23. N. B. K. Rai and P. M. Pitha, *PNAS* **80**, 3923 (1983).
24. H. A. Young, L. Varesio, and P. Hwu, *MCBiol* **6**, 2253 (1986).
25. P. W. Gray and D. V. Goeddel, *Lymphokines* **13**, 151 (1987).
26. G. Shaw and R. Kamen, *Cell* **46**, 659 (1986).
27. B. Thorens, J.-J. Mermod and P. Vassalli, *Cell* **48**, 671 (1987).
28. H. P. Koeffler, J. Gasson and A. Tobler, *McBiol* **8**, 3432 (1988).
29. J. Horiguchi, E. Sariban and D. Kufe, *McBiol* **8**, 3951 (1988).
30. B. Beutler and A. Cerami, *Lymphokines* **14**, 203 (1987).
31. B. Buetler, N. Krochiin, I. Milsark, C. Luedke and A. Cerami, *Science* **232**, 977 (1986).
32. R. L. Mitchell, L. Zokas, R. Schreiber and I. M. Verma, *Cell* **40**, 209 (1985).
33. E. Sariban, R. Luebbers and D. Kufe, *MBCiol* **8**, 340 (1988).
34. T. Wilson and R. Treisman, *Nature* **336**, 396 (1988).
35. P. Angel, K. Hattori, T. Smeal and M. Karin, *Cell* **55**, 875 (1988).
36. R. J. Watson, *MCBiol* **8**, 3938 (1988).
37. T. Lindsten, C. H. June and C. B. Thomson, *EMBO J.* **7**, 2787 (1988).
38. S. G. Swartwout and A. J. Kinniburgh, *MCBiol* **9**, 288 (1989).
39. G. Krystal, M. Birrer, J. Way, M. Nau, E. Sausville, C. Thompson, J. Minna and J. Battey, *MCBiol* **8**, 3373 (1988).
40. F. Dautry, D. Weil, J. Yu and A. Dautry-Varsat, *JBC* **263**, 17615 (1988).

41. M. Kronke, W. J. Leonard, J. M. Depper and W. C. Greene, *J. Exp. Med.* **161**, 1593 (1985).
42. H. J. Rahmsdorf, A. Schonthal, P. Angel, M. Litfin, U. Ruther and P. Herrlich, *NARes* **25**, 1643 (1987).
43. W. C. Greene and W. J. Leonard, *Annu. Rev. Immunol.* **4**, 69 (1986).
44. J. C. Reed, J. D. Alpers, P. C. Nowell and R. G. Hoover, *PNAS* **83**, 3982 (1986).
45. A. Weinberg, N. Magnuson, R. Reeves, C. Wyatt and J. Magnuson, *J. Immunol.* **141**, 1174 (1988).
46. J. Shaw, K. Meerovitch, J. F. Elliott, R. C. Bleackley and V. Paetkau, *Mol. Immunol.* **24**, 409 (1987).
46a. J. Culpepper and F. Lee, *Lymphokines* **13**, 275 (1987).
47. P. F. Zipfel, J. Balke, S. G. Irving, K. Kelly and U. Siebenlist, *J. Immunol.* **142**, 1582 (1989).
48. K. Moldave, *ARB* **54**, 1109 (1985).
49. J. R. Nevins, *ARB* **52**, 441 (1983).
50. B. Luscher and R. N. Eisenman, *MCBiol* **8**, 2504 (1988).
50a. G. Ramsey, G. I. Evan and J. M. Bishop, *PNAS* **81**, 7742 (1984).
51. R. N. Eisman, C. Y. Tachibana, H. D. Abrams and S. K. Han, *MCBiol* **5**, 114 (1985).
52. T. Curran, A. D. Miller, L. Zokas and I. M. Verma, *Cell* **36**,259 (1984).
53. W. J. Boyle, M. A. Lambert, A. C. Li and M. Baluda, *MCBiol* **5**, 3017 (1985).
54. D. Finley and A. Varshavsky, *Trends Biochem. Sci. (Pers. Ed.)* **10**, 343 (1985).
55. A. Hershko and A. Ciechanover, *This Series* **33**, 19 (1986).
56. J. S. Bond and P. E. Butler, *ARB* **56**, 333 (1987).
57. A. Hershko, *JBC* **263**, 15237 (1988).
58. S. M. Arfin and R. A. Bradshaw, *Bchem* **27**, 7979 (1988).
59. S. Rogers, R. Wells and M. Rechsteiner, *Science* **234**, 364 (1986).
60. M. Rechsteiner (ed.), "Ubiquitin." Plenum, New York, 1988.
61. K. V. Rote and M. Rechsteiner, *JBC* **261**, 15430 (1986).
62. A. Bachmair, D. Finley and A. Varshavsky, *Science* **234**, 179 (1986).
63. A. Bachmair and A. Varshavsky, *Cell* **56**, 1019 (1989).
64. M. B. Prystowsky, G. Gotten, S. K. Pierce, J. Shay, J. Olshan and F. W. Fitch, *Lymphokines* **12**, 13 (1985).
65. J. Donohue and S. A. Rosenberg, *J. Immunol.* **130**, 2203 (1983).
66. M. T. Lotze, L. W. Frana, S. O. Sharrow, R. J. Rob and S. A. Rosenberg, *J. Immunol.* **134**, 167 (1985).
67. M. T. Lotze, Y. L. Matory, S. E. Ettinghausen, A. A. Rayner, S. O. Sharrow, C. A. Y. Seipp, M. C. Custer and S. A. Rosenberg, *J. Immunol.* **135**, 2865 (1985).
68. Reference deleted in revision.
69. W. Dynan and R. Tjian, *Nature* **316**, 774 (1985).
70. S. McKnight and R. Tjian, *Cell* **46**, 795 (1986).
71. M. Ptashne, *Nature*, **322**, 697 (1986).
72. J. T. Kadonaga, K. A. Jones and R. Tjian, *Trends Biochem. Sci. (Pers. Ed.)* **11**, 20 (1986).
73. T. Maniatis, S. Goodbourn and J. A. Fischer, *Science* **236**, 1237 (1987).
74. B. Wasylyk, *CRC Crit. Rev. Biochem.* **23**, 77 (1988).
75. T. Taniguchi, *Annu. Rev. Immunol.* **6**, 439 (1988).
76. W. Schaffner, *Nature* **336**, 427 (1988).
77. M. Ptashne, *Nature* **335**, 683 (1988).
78. J.-P. Shaw, P. J. Utz, D. B. Durand, J. J. Toole, E. A. Emmel and G. R. Crabtree, *Science* **241**, 202 (1988).
79. G. R. Crabtree, *Science* **243**, 355 (1989).
80. T. Curran and B. R. Franza, *Cell* **55**, 395 (1988).
81. J. L. Marx, *Science* **242**, 1377 (1988).

82. F. J. Rauscher, L. C. Sambucetti, T. Curran, R. J. Distel and B. M. Spiegelman, *Cell* **52**, 471 (1988).
83. R. Chiu, W. J. Boyle, J. Meek, T. Smeal, T. Hunter and M. Karin, *Cell* **54**, 541 (1988).
84. T. J. Bos, D. Bohmann, H. Ysuchie, R. Tjian and P. Vogt, *Cell* **52**, 705 (1988).
85. T. Kousarides and E. Ziff, *Nature* **336**, 646 (1988).
86. M. Schuermann, M. Neuberg, J. B. Hunter, T. Jenuwein, R.-p, Ryseck, R. Bravo and R. Muller, *Cell* **56**, 507 (1989).
87. R. Turner and R. Tjian, *Science* **243**, 1689 (1989).
88. R. Gentz, G. J. Rauscher, C. Avate and T. Curran, *Science* **243**, 1695 (1989).
89. L. A. Chodosh, J. Olesen, S. Hahn, A. S. Baldwin, L. Guarente and P. A. Sharp, *Cell* **53**, 25 (1988).
90. S. Buratowski, S. Hahn, P. A. Sharp and L. Guarente, *Nature* **334**, 37 (1988).
90a. S. Buratowski, S. Hahn, L. Guarente and P. A. Sharp, *Cell* **56**, 549 (1989).
91. M. Horikoshi, M. F. Carey, H. Kakidani and R. G. Roeder, *Cell* **54**, 665 (1988).
92. Y.-S. Lin, M. F. Carey, M. Ptashne and M. R. Green, *Cell* **54**, 659 (1988).
93. M. Samuels, A. Fire and P. A. Sharp, *JBC* **257**, 14419 (1982).
94. V. Moncollin, N. G. Miyamoto, X. M. Zehng and J. M. Egly, *EMBO J.* **5**, 2577 (1982).
95. D. Reinberg and R. G. Roeder, *JBC* **262**, 3310 (1987).
96. D. Reinberg, M. Horikoshi and R. G. Roeder, *JBC* **262**, 3322 (1987).
97. M. Horikoshi, T. Hai, Y.-S. Lin, M. R. Green and R. G. Roeder, *Cell* **54**, 1003 (1988).
97a. M. W. Van Dyke, M. Sawadogo and R. G. Roeder, *MCBiol* **9**, 342 (1989).
98. B. L. Davison, J. M. Egly, E. R. Mulvihill and P. Chambon, *Nature* **301**, 680 (1983).
99. D. D. Brown, *Cell* **37**, 359 (1984).
100. D. K. Hawley and R. G. Roeder, *JBC* **262**, 3452 (1987).
101. K. A. Jones, J. T. Kadonaga, P. J. Rosenfeld, T. J. Kelly and R. Tjian, *Cell* **48**, 79 (1987).
102. M. Briggs, J. T. Kadonaga, S. P. Bell and R. Tjian, *Science* **234**, 47 (1986).
103. E. Serfling, M. Jasin and W. Schaffner, *Trends Genet.* **1**, 224 (1985).
104. R. Reeves and T. S. Elton, *J. Chromatogr. Biomed. Appl.* **418**, 73 (1988).
105. P. D. Fahrlander, M. Piechaczyk and K. B. Marcu, *EMBO J.* **4**, 3195 (1985).
106. R. Reeves, *BBA* **782**, 343 (1984).
107. R. Reeves, *in* "Chromosome and Chromatin Structure" (K. Adolph, ed.), Vol. 1, p. 109. CRC Press, Boca Raton, Florida, 1988.
108. M. Piechaczyk, J.-M. Blanchard and P. Jeanteur, *Trends Genet.* **3**, 47 (1987).
109. D. Bentley and M. Groudine, *Cell* **53**, 245 (1986).
110. D. Bentley and M. Groudine, *Nature* **321**, 702 (1986).
111. D. Bentley and M. Groudine, *MCBiol* **6**, 3481 (1986).
112. F. Kaye, J. Battey, M. Nau, B. Brooks, E. Seifter, J. De Greve, M. Birrer, E. Sausville and J. Minna, *MCBiol* **8**, 186 (1988).
113. J. C. Reed, P. C. Nowell and R. G. Hoover, *PNAS* **82**, 4221 (1985).
114. C. Weinberg, C. C. Thompson, E. S. Ong, R. Lebo, D. Gruol and R. M. Evans, *Nature* **234**, 641 (1986).
115. N. J. Short, *Nature* **331**, 393 (1988).
116. K. Struhl, *Nature* **332**, 649 (1988).
117. R. Bravo, M. Neuberg, J. Burckhardt, J. Almendral, R. Wallich and R. Muller, *Cell* **48**, 251 (1987).
118. T. Bender, C. Thompson and W. Kuehl, *Science* **237**, 1473 (1987).
119. J.-M. Blanchard, M. Piechaczyk, C. Dani, J.-C. Chambard, A. Franchi, J. Pouyssegur and P. Jeanteur, *Nature* **317**, 443 (1985).
120. P. Fort, J. Rech, A. Vie, M. Piechaczyk, A. Bonnieu, P. Jeanteur and J.-M. Blanchard, *NARes* **15**, 5657 (1987).
121. T. Curran, W. P. MacConnell, F. van Straaten and I. M. Verma, *MCBiol* **3**, 914 (1983).

122. A. D. Miller, T. Curran and I. M. Verma, *Cell* **36**, 51 (1984).
123. L. C. Sambucetti and T. Curran, *Science* **234**, 1417 (1986).
124. A. Schonthal, D. Herrlich, H. J. Rahmsdorf and H. Ponta, *Cell* **54**, 325 (1988).
125. R. Treisman, *Cell* **42**, 889 (1985).
126. H. Schroter, P. E. Shaw and A. Nordheim, *NARes* **15**, 10145 (1987).
127. R. Treisman, *EMBO J.* **6**, 2711 (1987).
128. P. E. Shaw, H. Schroter and A. Nordheim, *Cell* **56**, 563 (1989).
129. P. Sassone-Corsi, J. C. Sisson and I. M. Verma, *Nature* **334**, 314 (1988).
130. C. Setoyama, R. Frunzio, G. Lian, M. Mudryi and B. DeCrombrugghe, *PNAS* **83**, 3213 (1986).
131. P. Angel, M. Imagawa, R. Chiu, B. Stein, R. J. Imbra, H. J. Rahmsdorf, C. Jonat, P. Herrich and M. Karin, *Cell* **49**, 729 (1987).
132. D. Bohmann, T. J. Bos, T. Nishimura, P. K. Vogt and R. Tjian, *Science* **238**, 1386 (1987).
133. T. J. Bos, D. Bohmann, H. Tsuchie, R. Tjian and P. K. Vogt, *Cell* **52**, 705 (1988).
134. W. Lee, A. Haslinger, M. Karin and R. Tjian, *Nature* **235**, 368 (1987).
135. W. Lee, P. Mitchell and R. Tjian, *Cell* **49**, 741 (1987).
136. C. Weissman and H. Weber, *This Series* **33**, 251 (1986).
137. K. J. Hardy, B. M. Peterlin, R. E. Atchison, and J. D. Stobo, *PNAS* **61**, 542 (1985).
138. K. J. Hardy, B. Manger, M. Newton and J. D. Stobo, *J. Immunol.* **7**, 2353 (1987).
139. U. Weidle and C. Weissman, *Nature* **303**, 442 (1983).
140. S. Ohno and T. Taniguchi, *NARes* **11**, 5403 (1983).
141. H. Ragg and C. Weissmann, *Nature* **303**, 439 (1983).
142. J. Ryals, P. Dierks, H. Ragg and C. Weissman, *Cell* **41**, 497 (1985).
143. T. Fujita, S. Ohno, H. Yasumitsu and T. Taniguchi, *Cell* **42**, 489 (1985).
144. S. Goodbourn, K. Zinn and T. Maniatis, *Cell* **41**, 509 (1985).
145. S. Xanthoudakis, L. Cohen and J. Hiscott, *JBC* **265**, 1139 (1989).
146. T. Fujita, Y. Kimura, M. Miyamoto, E. L. Barsoumian and T. Taniguchi, *Nature* **337**, 270 (1989).
147. M. Miyamoto, T. Fujita, Y. Kimura, M. Maruyama, H. Harada, Y. Sudo, T. Miyata and T. Taniguchi, *Cell* **54**, 903 (1989).
148. U. Siebenlist, D. B. Durand, P. Bressler, N. J. Holbrook, C. A. Norris, M. Kamoun, J. A. Kant and G. R. Crabtree, *MCBiol* **6**, 3042 (1986).
149. A. Fuse, T. Fujita, H. Yasumitsu, N. Kashima, K. Hasegawa and T. Taniguchi, *NARes* **12**, 9323 (1984).
150. T. Fujita, H. Shibuya, T. Ohashi, K. Yamanishi and T. Taniguchi, *Cell* **46**, 401 (1986).
151. D. B. Durand, M. R. Bush, J. G. Morgan, A. Weiss and G. R. Crabtree, *J. Exp. Med.* **165**, 395 (1987).
152. T. Taniguchi, T. Fujita, M. Hatakeyama, H. Mori, H. Matsui, T. Sato, J. Hamuro, S. Minamoto, G. Yamada and H. Shibuya, *CSHSQB* **51**, 577 (1987).
153. J.-P. Shaw, P. J. Utz, D. B. Durand, J. J. Toole, E. A. Emmel and G. R. Crabtree, *Science* **241**, 202 (1988).
154. G. R. Crabtree, *Science* **243**, 335 (1989).
155. G. D. Shaw, W. Boll, H. Taira, N. Mantei, P. Lengyel and C. Weissmann, *NARes* **11**, 555 (1983).
156. D. V. Goeddel, D. W. Leung, T. J. Dull, M. Gross, R. M. Lawn, R. McCandliss, P. H. Seeburg, A. Ullrich, E. Yelverton and P. W. Gray, *Nature* **290**, 20 (1981).
157. S. Ohno and T. Taniguchi, *PNAS* **78**, 5305 (1981).
158. Y. Higashi, Y. Sokawa, Y. Watanabe, Y. Kawade, S. Ohno, C. Takaoka and T. Taniguchi, *JBC* **258**, 15 (1983).
159. P. W. Gray, D. W. Leung, D. Pennica, E. Yelverton, R. Najarian, C. C. Simonsen, R.

Derynck, P. J. Sherwood, D. M. Wallace, S. L. Berger, A. D. Levinson and D. V. Goeddel, *Nature* **295**, 503 (1982).

160. P. W. Gray and D. V. Goeddel, *PNAS* **80**, 5842 (1983).

161. C. J. March, B. Mosley, A. Larsen, D. P. Cerretti, G. Braedt, V. Price, S. Gillis, C. S. Henney, S. R. Kronheim, K. Grabstein, P. J. Conlon, T. P. Hopp and D. Cosman, *Nature* **315**, 641 (1985).

162. P. T. Lomedico, U. Gubler, C. Hellman, M. Dukovilch, J. G. Giril, Y. E. Pan, K. Collier, R. Seminonow, A. O. Chua and S. B. Mizel, *Nature* **312**, 458 (1984).

163. Y. Furutani, M. Notake, M. Yamayoshi, J. Yamagishi, H. Nomura, M. Ohue, R. Furuta, T. Fukui, M. Yamada and S. Nakamura, *NARes* **13**, 5869 (1985).

164. R. Reeves, G. Spies, M. Nissen, C. Buck, A. Weinberg, P. Barr, N. Magnuson and J. Magnuson, *PNAS* **83**, 3228 (1986).

165. P. E. Auron, A. C. Webb, L. J. Rosenwaser, S. F. Mucci, A. Rich, S. M. Wolff and C. A. Dinarello, *PNAS* **81**, 7907 (1984).

166. T. Taniguchi, H. Matsui, T. Fujita, C. Takaoka, N. Kashima, R. Yoshimoto and J. Hamuro, *Nature* **302**, 305 (1983).

167. R. Kashima and C. Nishi-Takaoka, T. Fujita, S. Taki, G. Yamada, J. Hamuro and T. Taniguchi, *Nature* **313**, 402 (1985).

168. H. D. Campbell, S. Ymer, M. Fung and I. G. Young, *EJB* **150**, 297 (1985).

169. D. R. Cohen, A. J. Hapel and I. G. Young, *NARes* **14**, 3641 (1986).

170. Y. Noma, P. Sideras, T. Naito, S. Bergstedt-Lindquist, C. Azuma, E. Severinson, T. Tanabe, T. Kinaishi, F. Matsuda, Y. Yaoita and T. Honjo, *Nature* **319**, 640 (1986).

171. T. Hirano, K. Yasukawa, H. Harada, T. Taga, Y. Wantanabe, T. Matsuda, S. Kashiwamura, K. Makajima, K. Koyama, A. Iwanatsu, S. Tsunasawa, L. Sakiyama, H. Matsui, Y. Takahara, T. Taniguchi and T. Kishimoto, *Nature* **324**, 73 (1986).

172. G. G. Wong, J. S. Witek, P. A. Temple, K. M. Wilkens, A. C. Leary, C. P. Lexenberg, S. S. Jones, E. L. Brown, R. M. Kay, E. C. Orr, C. Shoemaker, D. W. Golde, R. J. Kaufman, R. M. Hewick, E. A. Wang and S. C. Clark, *Science* **228**, 810 (1985).

173. N. M. Gough, J. Gough, D. Metcalf, A. Kelso, D. Grail, N. A. Nicola, A. W. Burgess and A. R. Dunn, *Nature* **309**, 763 (1984).

174. S. Nagata, M. Tsuchiya, S. Asano, Y. Kasiro, T. Yamazaki, O. Yamamoto, Y. Hirata, N. Kubota, M. Oheda, H. Nomura and M. Ono, *Nature* **319**, 415 (1986).

175. G. E. Nedwin, S. L. Naylor, A. Y. Sakaguchi, D. Smith, J. Jarrett-Nedwin, D. Pennica, D. V. Goeddel and P. W. Gray, *NARes* **13**, 6361 (1985).

176. T. Shirai, H. Yamaguhi, H. Ito, C. W. Todd and R. B. Wallace, *Nature* **313**, 803 (1985).

177. P. W. Gray, B. B. Aggarwal, C. V. Benton, T. S. Bringman, W. J. Henzel, J. A. Jarrett, D. W. Leung, B. Moffat, P. Ng, L. P. Svedersky, M. A. Palladino and G. E. Nedwin, *Nature* **312**, 721 (1984).

178. F. van Straaten, R. Muller, T. Curran, C. van Beveren and I. M. Verma, *PNAS* **80**, 3183 (1983).

179. C. van Beveren, F. van Straaten, T. Curran, R. Muller and I. M. Verma, *Cell* **32**, 1241 (1983).

180. W. W. Colby, E. Y. Chen, D. H. Smith and A. D. Levinson, *Nature* **301**, 722 (1983).

181. G. Selten, H. T. Cuypers, W. Boelens, E. Robanus-Maandag, J. Verbeek, J. Domen, C. van Beveren and A. Berns, *Cell* **46**, 603 (1986).

182. R. Zakut-Houri, S. Hazum, D. Givol and A. Telerman, *Gene* **54**, 105 (1987).

183. B. Majello, L. C. Kenyon and R. Dalla-Favera, *PNAS* **83**, 9636 (1986).

184. K. V. Visvanathan and S. Goodbourn, *EMBO J.* **8**, 1129 (1989).

185. R. Sen and D. Baltimore, *Cell* **46**, 705 (1986).

186. R. Sen and D. Baltimore, *Cell* **47**, 921 (1986).

187. M. Lenardo, J. W. Pierce and D. Baltimore, *Science* **236**, 1573 (1987).
188. G. Nabel and D. Baltimore, *Nature* **326**, 711 (1987).
189. B. Nelsen, L. Hellman and R. Sen, *MCBiol* **8**, 3526 (1988).
190. J. W. Pierce, M. Lenardo and D. Baltimore, *PNAS* **85**, 1482 (1988).
191. P. A. Baeuerle and D. Baltimore, *Cell* **53**, 211 (1988).
192. P. A. Baeuerle and D. Baltimore, *Science* **242**, 540 (1988).
193. A. G. Saltzman and R. Weinman, *FASEB J.* **3**, 1723 (1989).
194. U. Nir, B. Cohen, L. Chen and M. Revel, *NARes* **12**, 6979 (1984).
195. J. D. Mosca and P. M. Pitha, *MCBiol* **6**, 2279 (1986).
196. R. Reeves, T. S. Elton, M. S. Nissen, D. Lehn and K. R. Johnson, *PNAS* **84**, 6535 (1987).
197. S. Efrat and R. Kaempfer, *PNAS* **81**, 2601 (1984).
198. G. D. Schuler and M. D. Cole, *Cell* **55**, 1115 (1988).
199. T. J. Ernst, A. R. Ritchie, G. D. Demetri and J. D. Griffin, *JBC* **264**, 5700 (1989).
200. G. Brewer and J. Ross, *MCBiol* **8**, 1697 (1988).
201. R. Pei and K. Calame, *MCBiol* **8**, 2860 (1988).
202. G. C. Pendergast and M. D. Cole, *MCBiol* **9**, 124 (1989).
203. K. S. Kabnick and D. E. Housman, *MCBiol* **8**, 3244 (1988).
204. W. M. F. Lee, C. Lin and T. Curran, *MCBiol* **8**, 5521 (1988).
205. J. Ross, *Sci. Am.* **260**, 48 (1989).
206. G. Brawerman, *Cell* **57**, 9 (1989).
207. W. M. Marzluff and N. B. Pandey, *Trends Biochem. Sci. (Pers. Ed.)* **13**, 49 (1988).
208. T. Hunt, *Nature* **334**, 567 (1988).
209. D. W. Cleveland, *Trends Biochem. Sci. (Pers. Ed.)* **13**, 339 (1988).
210. N. S. Magnuson, A. G. Spies, M. S. Nissen, C. D. Buck, A. D. Weinberg, P. J. Barr, J. A. Magnuson and R. Reeves, *Vet. Immunol. Immunopathol.* **17**, 183 (1987).
211. M. Piechaczyk, J.-M. Blanchard, A. Bonnieu, P. Fort, N. Mechti, J. Rech, M. Cuny, L. Marty, F. Ferre, B. Lebleu and P. Jeanteur, *Gene* **72**, 287 (1988).
212. M. J. Clements, *Cell* **49**, 157 (1987).
213. A. S. Krayev, T. V. Markusheva, D. A. Kramerov, A. P. Ryskov, K. G. Skryabin, A. A. Bayev and G. P. Georgiev, *NARes* **10**, 7461 (1982).
214. D. A. Kramerov, I. V. Lekakh, O. P. Samarina and A. P. Ryskov, *NARes* **10**, 7477 (1982).
215. F. Meijlink, T. Curran, A. D. Miller and I. M. Verma, *PNAS* **82**, 4987 (1985).
216. I. M. Verma and W. R. Graham, *Adv. Cancer Res.* **49**, 29 (1987).
217. I. M. Verma and P. Sassone-Corsi, *Cell* **51**, 513 (1987).
218. P. Sassone-Corsi and I. M. Verma, *Nature* **236**, 507 (1987).
219. H. T. Cuypers, G. Selten, W. Quint, M. Zijlstra, E. Robanus-Maandag, W. Boelens, P. van Wezenbeek, C. Melief and A. Berns, *Cell* **37**, 141 (1984).
220. G. Selten, H. T. Cuypers, W. Boelens, E. Robanus-Maandag, J. Verbeek, J. Domen, C. van Beveren and A. Berns, *Cell* **45**, 603 (1986).
221. M. van Lohuizen, S. Verbeek, P. Krimpenfort, J. Domen, C. Saris, T. Radaszkiewicz and A. Berns, *Cell* **56**, 673 (1989).
222. R. Zakut-Houri, S. Hazum, D. Givol and A. Telerman, *Gene* **54**, 105 (1987).
223. L. Nagarajan, E. Louie, Y. Tsujimoto, A. Ar-Rushdi, K. Huebner and C. M. Croce, *PNAS* **83**, 2556 (1986).
224. A. Telerman, R. Amson, R. Zakut-Houri and D. Givol, *McBiol* **8**, 1498 (1988).
225. V. Duprez, G. Lonoir and D. Dautry-Varsat, *PNAS* **82**, 6932 (1985).
226. S. J. Chen, N. J. Holbrook, K. F. Mitchell, C. A. Vallone, J. S. Greengard, G. R. Crabtree and Y. Lin, *PNAS* **82**, 7284 (1985).
227. K. A. Smith, *Immunobiology* **161**, 157 (1982).

Index

A

Abscisic acid, seed development and, 177, 178
Adenosine deaminase, retroviral-mediated gene transfer and, 113, 114, 118–121
Amino acid biosynthesis in *Saccharomyces cerevisiae, see Saccharomyces cerevisiae*
Amylases, seed germination and, 181, 182

B

Barley, seed development and, 171, 172
Basal expression, *Saccharomyces cerevisiae* and, 203
Brain, Na,K-ATPase and, 63

C

Cardiac glycoside binding site, Na,K-ATPase and, 53–58
Cations, Na,K-ATPase and, 72–74
Cell-specific regulation, Na,K-ATPase and, 61–63
Cellular oncogenes, 241–244, 275, 276
  posttranscriptional regulation, 267
  mRNA decay, 273–275
  mRNA stability, 267–273
  RNA polymerase II, 253
  promoter region, 253–257
  transcription, 257–262
  sequential gene expression, 246–251
  transient gene expression, 244–246, 252
Chloramphenicol, prokaryotic translational initiation and, 22–25
Chromosomal location, Na,K-ATPase and, 80, 81
cis-Acting regulatory elements, *Sac-*

charomyces cerevisiae and
  binding sites, 204–211
  TATA box, 211–213
β-Conglycinin, seed development and, 167–169
Cruciforms, *Escherichia coli* promoter DNA and, 149–153
Cytokine genes, 241–244, 275, 276
  lymphokines, 251, 252
  posttranscriptional regulation, 267
  mRNA decay, 273–275
  mRNA stability, 267–273
  RNA polymerase II, 253
  sequential gene expression, 246–251
  transcription, 262–267
  transient gene expression, 244–246, 252

D

Dessication, seed development and, 178
Dihydrofolate reductase, retroviral-mediated gene transfer and, 111, 112
Dimerization, *Saccharomyces cerevisiae* and, 214–218
DNA
  Escherichia coli promoter, *see Escherichia coli* promoter DNA
  loops, 155, 156
  Saccharomyces cerevisiae and, 214–218

E

Enzymes, *Saccharomyces cerevisiae* and, 196, 197
Escherichia coli promoter DNA, 137, 138, 157–159
  kinetic analysis, 142–144

283